P9-AQN-538

St. Olaf College

JUN 20 1996

Science Library

Series on New Frontiers in Advanced Physics
ISTITUTO PER LA RICERCA DI BASE
Castello Principe Pignatelli
86075 Monteroduni (IS), Molise, Italy

New Frontiers in Gravitation

Edited by

Gennadi A. Sardanashvily

Department of Theoretical Physics
Moscow State Univerasity

117234 Moscow , Russia

HADRONIC PRESS

QC
1784
.N4
.996

Copyright © 1996 by Hadronic Press, Inc.
35246 US 19 North # 115, Palm Harbor, FL 34684 USA

All rights reserved.
No part of this book may be reproduced, stored in a retrieval system
or transmitted in any form or by any means
without the written permission
of the copyright owner.

U. S. Library of Congress
Cataloging–in–Publication data:

Sardanashvily, Gennadi A.

New Frontiers in Gravitation

Bibliography

Series of New Frontiers in Advanced Physics
of the Istituto per la Ricerca di Base
Monteroduni (IS), Italy

Additional data supplied on request

ISBN 0–911767–96–7

34 752964

NEW FRONTIERS IN GRAVITATION
G. A. Sardanashvily, Editor

TABLE OF CONTENTS

PREFACE

Born eighty years ago, gravitation theory still holds up under extensive theoretical and experimental scrutiny with the understanding that a number of aspects remain yet to be resolved. As it occurs for Einstein's general relativity, a number of other gravitational theories also satisfy all known tests of post–Newtonian and post–post–Newtonian gravity. Moreover, Newton's gravitation law has been verified repeatedly in a number of authoritative laboratories, while the hypothesis of the "fifth" fundamental force remains under discussion.

Twenty years ago, generalizations and modifications of Einstein's gravitation theory were motivated mainly by efforts to overcome the intrinsic difficulties of this theory, such as: the problem of gravitational energy, description of gravitational singularities, the notion of reference frames, quantization of gravity, representation of antimatter, etc.

At present, the targets of quantizing gravity and its unification with other fundamental forces dominate gravitation research. However, we face the problem that gravity stands apart from other interactions in many ways. For instance, different gauge models of gravity have been suggested, but none of them is generally accepted as a viable possibility of unification. The geometry of space-time also seems to be far from the simplicity of the pseudo-Riemannian geometry of general relativity.

Moreover, the physical nature of the Minkowski space-time remains elusive, particularly for interior problems within physical media. Under these circumstances, a variety of theoretical and mathematical approaches to gravitation theory have been developed. At the same time, there is the tendency of unification of mathematical machinery applied to current gravitational models as well as models of high energy physics in which the geometric and topological methods play a prominent role.

This volume presents a collection of original refereed articles devoted to a wide range of problems at the frontiers of current knowledge of gravitation theories and related areas of field theory and mathematics.

Gennady A. Sardanashvily
Moscow State University

Gennadi A. Sardanashvily, Editor
New Frontiers in Gravitation
Hadronic Press, Palm Harbor, FL 34682-1577, U.S.A.
ISBN 0–911767–96–7, 1996, Pages 1–3

FRACTALS, DIFFERENCE EQUATIONS AND COSMOLOGICAL MODELS

P.N.Antonyuk

Moscow State University of Technology
Department of Fundamental Sciences

The discrete space-time hypothesis [1] may be applied to cosmology by means of the discrete equations of mathematical physics, i.e. so-called difference equations. These equations are analogous to the differential equations but there are principal distinctions between their properties. We want to discuss here some moments of possible application of difference equations to modern cosmology.

Newton's statement on the usefulness of solving differential equations may be extended to difference equations as well. The mathematical framework of difference equations makes it possible to study discrete problems as opposed to continuous problems studied by differential equations. Up to now the application of difference equations has been limited generally by computational techniques. Over the recent years interest was aroused in nonlinear difference equations. It seems possible to apply difference equations to the description of a number of physical processes, e.g., evolution of matter. Difference equations provide a new way for finding universal dimensionless constants apparently connected with fundamental physical constants. Investigation of discrete properties of matter in micro- and macroworld requires the using of these equations.

The construction of the Univers evolution models is mathematical simulation of a supercomplicated dynamical system. The traditional application of differential equations is not sufficient and therefore difference equations must be used. These equations seem to suggest great opportunities for the creation of evolution models in the nearest future. The models which describe fractal structure of matter, chaotic phenomena, phase transition bifurcations, singularities etc. For example, we can present the discrete analogs of Friedmann-type models of the homogeneous isotropic Universe for some equation of state $P = h(p)$ by following two difference equations:

$$a_{n+1} = f(a_n, p_n),$$
$$p_{n+1} = g(a_n, p_n),$$

where a_n is scale factor and p_n is matter density at time moment t_n, P is pressure and f, g, h are given functions. The value $(t_{n+1} - t_n)$ is time quantum, e.g. Planck's time. Among the all possible solutions of these equations one can find some which form different strange attractors, e.g. Hénon attractor. In this case one has a quasistationary model with irregular parameter values. If one takes two ordinary differential equations one can't get nontrivial chaotic solutions because Poincaré-Bendixson theory prohibits its.

The mathematical instrument of evolution models can be expressed by two term sequences:

Differential equations–Smooth manifolds–Lie groups and so on;
Difference equations–Manifolds of points–Discrete groups and so on.

Our interest for the difference equations is based on some new possibilities these equations give us. By means of the difference equation theory one can generate a great number of different fractal sets such as Julia sets, Mandelbrot set, Newton basin etc. On the opposite side these equations allow us to understand and use so-called von Neumann's cellular automata, e.g., Conway's game of life.

The Universe hierarchical models of Lambert, Fournier d'Albe and Charlier are connected, in our opinion, with the fractal spatial distribution of matter. It is therefore essential that we must create a wide class of fractal formation algorithms to apply it to these cosmological models. We can't obtain given algorithms without difference equations.

The finite differences had also found an application in [8].

References

1. Ambarzumian V.A., Ivanenko D.D. *Zeitschrift für Physik.* 1930.- Bd. 64.- S. 563-567.

2. Antonyuk P.N. The Univers.- 1969. (Unpublished paper).

3. Stanyukovich K.P.,Antonyuk P.N. Difference equations and cosmology *11th Intern.Conf.on General Relativity and Gravitation: Abstracts.-* Folkets Hus, Stockholm, Sweden, July 6-12, 1986.- Vol. 1, P. 336.

4. Stanyukovich K.P., Antonyuk P.N. Univers evolution: difference equations and Galois fields *12th Intern.Conf.on General Relativity and Gravitation: Abstracts.-* Boulder, Colorado, USA, July 2-8, 1989.- Vol. 2, P. 354.

5. Antonyuk P.N., Stanyukovich K.P. Logistic difference equation. Period doublings and Fermat numbers *Doklady Akademii Nauk SSSR* - 1990.- Vol. 313, N 6.- P. 1289-1292.

6. Antonyuk P.N. Logistic equation for quantum statistics *Second All-Union Seminar "Problems of Engin. and Phys.": Abstracts.* - Moscow State University of Technology, 1992.- P. 102.

7. Antonyuk P.N. Difference equations and Univers evolution models *13th Intern.Conf.on General Relativity and Gravitation: Abstracts.* - Huerta Grande, Cordoba, Argentina, June 28 - July 4, 1992.- P. 126.

8. Ivanenko D.D., Galiulin R.V., Antonyuk P.N. Crystal-type model of the Universe *Astronomical Circular* - 1992.- N 1553.- P. 1-2.

Gennadi A. Sardanashvily, Editor
New Frontiers in Gravitation
Hadronic Press, Palm Harbor, FL 34682-1577, U.S.A.
ISBN 0–911767–96–7, 1996, Pages 5–44

ANTIGRAVITATING BUBBLES

Andro Barnaveli and Merab Gogberashvili

Institute of Physics of the Georgian Academy of Sciences
Tamarashvili str. 6, Tbilisi 380077, Republic of Georgia

Abstract

We investigate the gravitational behavior of spherical domain walls (bubbles) arising during the phase transitions in the early Universe. In the thin-wall approximation we show the existence of the new solution of Einstein equations with negative gravitational mass of bubbles and the reversed direction of time flow on the shell. This walls exhibit gravitational repulsion just as the planar walls are assumed to do. The equilibrium radius and critical mass of such objects are found for realistic models.

1   Introduction.

Topological structures such as domain walls, strings and monopoles could be produced at phase transitions in the Universe as it cooled [7, 13, 17, 37, 48, 49]. Within the context of general relativity they are assumed to be an unusual sources of gravity. Cosmic strings do not produce any gravitational force on the surrounding matter locally, while global monopoles, global strings and planar domain walls are repulsive [7, 10, 24, 25, 28, 39, 47, 48, 49].

We shall consider domain walls, produced through the breakdown of discrete symmetry. Their stress-energy is composed of surface density σ and strong tension p in two spatial directions with the magnitude [48, 49]

$$\sigma = -p = const. \tag{1}$$

This state equation corresponds to de Sitter expansion in the wall-plane and the borders of the wall run away with the horizon. We can speak about the gravitational field of the wall only in normal direction to the wall. If one assumes that for such objects it is possible to use Newtonian approximation with the mass described by Tolman's formula [45]

$$M = \int (T_0^0 - T_1^1 - T_2^2 - T_3^3) \cdot \sqrt{-g} dV = \int (\sigma + 2p) \cdot \sqrt{-g} dV = -\int \sigma \cdot \sqrt{-g} dV \tag{2}$$

as it is usually assumed [48, 49], then that tension acts as a repulsive source of gravity and the planar domain wall has a negative gravitational mass and exhibits repulsive gravitational field [10, 28, 39, 48, 49].

It is natural to think that the same behavior (gravitational repulsion) must occur for the spherical domain walls (bubbles), since it is assumed that they are described by the same state equations (1) (e.g. see [10, 28, 39]), different aspects of bubble-dynamics was investigated also in papers [1, 2, 3, 4, 5, 8, 9, 10, 11, 12, 14, 18, 21, 26, 34, 37, 38, 39, 40, 43, 46]). On the other hand, according to Birkhoff's theorem, the empty space, surrounding any spherical body (including bubbles), is described by Schwarzschild metric. This metric contains parameter m (corresponding to the mass of gravitating body) which is described through the integral over energy density of the body

$$m = \int T_0^0 \cdot \sqrt{-g} dV + const. \tag{3}$$

While for planar domain walls (which stretch the horizon) the negative gravitational mass (2) can be admittable, for bubbles the negativeness of mass (3) from the first glance looks surprising since T_0^0 is positively defined everywhere. Thus independently on the state equation (1) the mass (3) usually is considered to be positive [36, 41, 45].

However there can be no contradiction since in the case of spherical domain walls (in difference to isolated matter for which the condition of energodominance is valid) it is impossible to surround the full source by any boundary inside the horizon (just as it is for planar domain walls). The domain wall is only the "part" of scalar field solution which fills the whole Universe up to horizon and which has nonzero vacuum expectation value (VEV) even in infinity. The result is that the quantity $\int T_{\mu\nu} \cdot dS^\nu$ is not a 4-vector of energy-momentum and one can not define the energy simply as $\int T_{00} \cdot dxdydz$ [44]. For example, the energy density of expanding spherical domain wall remains constant (see (1)) despite increasing of its surface i.e. this object "takes" the energy from vacuum, while the energy of vacuum depends on VEV of scalar field in the whole space including infinity. This means that for the case of topological objects we can not neglect the boundary terms at infinity since the scalar field forming the wall does not vanish there. The same situation is for global monopoles which also can exhibit the gravitational repulsion [24].

The other solution of the negative mass problem can be the fact that the domain walls are not described by the state equation (1). One must take into account the flux out from the volume of integration or some external forces stabilizing the domain wall. As a result the state equation can have a principally different form and both the spherical and planar walls can be gravitationally attractive.

The other possible reason of disagreement may be that planar domain walls can be described by the state equation (1) while the bubbles can not.

In this paper we argue that if nevertheless one assumes that spherical domain walls are described by the state equation (1) (as it is usually considered, see e.g. [10, 28, 39]), then they must have a negative gravitational mass and must be repulsive [6].

To start with, one has to note that Schwarzschild parameter m in formula (3) contains arbitrary integration constant which must be fixed from the boundary conditions [36, 41, 45]. For the ordinary matter the boundary conditions both in the center of the body and at the infinity lead to zero value of this constant. For the topological objects surface singularities in gravitational quantities allow us to use only one boundary condition dependently on the region we are interested. When investigating the outer gravitational field one has to use the boundary condition at a large distance, where the gravitational potential must be expressed by Newton's formula. Fixing the constant from this condition it is easy to see that the mass of topological objects is determined by Tolman's formula (2) (on the other hand when investigating field inside the object one must take $m = 0$, because otherwise the metric will have a singularity at the center $r = 0$). Thus the constant in formula (3) takes into account the pressure (which can not be negligible for topological objects) and so the results from formulae (2) and (3) coincide. For the bubbles this formulae give negative value of m and these objects appear to be repulsive (as the planar walls do). This leads us to conclusion that the space around such physically admitable objects as spherical domain walls are can be described by Schwarzschild solution with negative parameter m [6].

Here we would like to emphasize that though Tolman's formula is valid only for static objects, nevertheless even for the expanding (or collapsing) spherical domain walls the expression for active gravitational mass of the bubble (obtained, for example, in the thin-wall formalism, see sections 7 and 9) must contain the term corresponding to the gravitational energy (2) and in static Newton's limit (when the velocity of bubble expansion tends to zero) this expression must coincide with Tolman's formula.

Since the exact solution of Einstein's equations for thick bubbles is unknown, bubble dynamics usually is analyzed in the thin-wall formalism [15, 19, 29, 32, 41]. The above-mentioned problem emerged there too. In this formalism it also was obtained that active gravitational mass of the spherical domain wall is positive, i.e. its gravitational field is attractive [10, 28, 39]. The disagreements in gravitational properties of planar and spherical domain walls were explained by instability of the latter [28], or by existence of positive energy source stabilizing the bubble [39].

We shall investigate the bubble dynamics in the thin-wall formalism and show that the space outside the bubble can be described by Schwarzschild solution with negative mass-parameter i.e. spherical domain walls are repulsive. We shall see that this solution requires the reversal of time flow on the wall-surface. Note that the solutions of Einstein equations where in different space-regions time flows in opposite directions are well known. For example in Reissner-Nordstrom metric in the region between the upper and Cauchy radii the time coordinate changes its direction to the opposite.

Gravitational repulsion of bubbles can solve different paradoxes (for example the blueshift instead of redshift) appearing in models with large pressure [22].

It is worth to mention another contradicting example — a planar domain wall stretched by a static cosmic string hoop [28]. Such system must repel a test particle placed next to the domain wall (the domain wall is repulsive, while cosmic string does not act gravitationally [48, 49]), whereas for a distant observer it must behave as a bubble, i.e. according to [10, 28, 39] it must be gravitationally attractive. This paradox can be solved only if bubbles are repulsive.

The time flow reversal can explain also the problems mentioned in [12]. Consider the finite region of false vacuum with nonzero energy density (and thus with negative pressure) separated by a domain wall from an infinite region of true vacuum with zero energy density. In this case an observer placed into the false-vacuum region (described by de Sitter metric) would expect to see inflation and thus increasing of bubble radius. At the same time an outer observer on the true-vacuum side (described by Schwarzschild metric) would discover that the pressure forces are inward and bubble must collapse, thus he would not see an increase of the radius of curvature. This problem was explained by assumption, that false-vacuum region does not move out into true-vacuum region and this two areas expand separately [12]. However, if we take into account the time reversal in the region with the strong pressure and the negative mass (i.e. the false vacuum inside the bubble) this paradox can be explained in the frames of the standard scenario of phase transitions, when the false-vacuum region expand into true vacuum region.

In the next section we describe some features of domain walls.

The section 3 is dedicared to review of the thin-wall formalism. The motion equations of thin shells are given.

In section 4 we consider the surface stress-energy tensors for thin shells.

In section 5 we write the motion equations for spherical shells.

In section 6 the sign ambiguity of motion equations is discussed. It is shown the possibility of existence of a new solution of Einstein equations for bubbles (Schwarzschild solution with negative mass) in a thin-wall formalism. The negative value of the bubble mass in the motion equations leads to the time flow reversal on the bubble.

In sec. 7 the simplest examples of spherical dust and domain walls in vacuum are considered. It is shown that gravitational fields around this objects are described by Schwarzschild metric with the opposite signs of mass parameter.

In sec. 8 some unusual properties of repulsive spheres are mentioned. The embedding of Schwarzschild metric with different signs of mass parameter in 6-dimensional space-time is investigated.

In sec. 9 the dynamic of repulsive bubbles in general case of charged bubbles and nonzero vacuum energy density is discussed. The equilibrium radius and critical mass of static bubbles are found for different symmetry violation scales.

In sec. 10 the problem of stability is considered.

2   The domain wall.

A first-order phase transitions which take place in the most of cosmological models proceed through the nucleation of the new phase bubbles (see e.g. [13, 26, 37]). Such processes take place at the very beginning of the phase transition. At the final stage of transition the old phase fragments which are left up to that moment also take the spherical form (for example due to surface tension effects or dissipation). The surface of phase separation in the case of the first-order phase transition is represented by the so-called domain wall. Such objects are created when the vacuum manifold for the order parameter or scalar field φ driving the symmetry breaking has a discrete symmetry [48, 49]. At the time of transition there can be both infinite and closed surface walls.

To model the essential features of a domain wall, we will consider a scalar field with the Lagrangian ·

$$L = \frac{1}{2} g^{\mu\nu} \partial_\mu \varphi \partial_\nu \varphi - V(\varphi),$$

where $V(\varphi)$ has two minima at nonzero φ . Here the greek indices take the values 0,1,2,3 and the metric has the signature $(+,-,-,-)$. The example of such potential with discrete symmetry $\varphi \to -\varphi$ is

$$V(\varphi) = -\frac{M_G^2}{2} \varphi^2 + \frac{\lambda}{4} \varphi^4,$$

M_G^2/λ representing the symmetry breaking scale and λ — the self coupling constant.

In the case of a flat wall in Minkowski space the equations of motion

$$\partial_\mu \partial_\nu \varphi - \frac{\partial V(\varphi)}{\partial \varphi} = 0$$

admit the classical "domain wall" or "membrane" solution, depending on one coordinate:

$$\varphi(x) = \frac{M_G}{\sqrt{\lambda}} \cdot \tanh\left[\frac{M_G}{\sqrt{2}}(x - x_0)\right],$$

where x is the normal direction to the wall and x_0 is the wall position.

In this case the VEV of scalar field $<\varphi> \to \pm <\varphi_0> = \pm M_G/\sqrt{\lambda}$ on either side of the wall and thus there is defined the wall surface Σ — the three dimensional surface on which $\varphi = 0$.

The energy-momentum tensor

$$T_{\mu\nu} = \partial_\mu\varphi \cdot \partial_\nu\varphi - g_{\mu\nu}L$$

for this solution takes the form :

$$T_{00} = \left(\frac{\partial\varphi}{\partial x}\right)^2 = \frac{M_G^4}{2\lambda} \cdot \cosh^{-4}\left[\frac{M_G}{2}(x - x_0)\right] ;$$

$$T_{xx} = 0;$$

$$T_{yy} = T_{zz} = -T_{00}. \tag{4}$$

From the first equation of (4) it is easy to see, that the thickness and energy per unit area of this wall are respectively:

$$\Delta \sim \frac{1}{M_G};$$

$$\sigma = \int\limits_{-\infty}^{+\infty} dx T_{00} \sim \frac{M_G^3}{\lambda}.$$

From the third equation of (4) one can see that the wall solution has a high pressure along the wall, which plays an essential role in gravitational behavior of such objects (see Tolmans formula (2)).

3   Thin wall approximation.

In the limit of vanishing thickness of the domain wall it can be considered as an infinitely thin three-dimensional hypersurface Σ with the energy-momentum tensor T_ν^μ having, in general, singularities on it. This hypersurface divides the Riemannian manifold $^{(4)}V$ into two parts V^+ and V^-. Each of them contains Σ as a part of its boundary.

We intend to apply the Einstein equations

$$G_{\mu\nu} = R_{\mu\nu} - \frac{1}{2} \cdot g_{\mu\nu} R = 8\pi G \cdot T_{\mu\nu} \qquad (5)$$

to such thin boundaries of phase separation and investigate their dynamics and gravitational behavior using the thin-wall approximation. In (5) $R_{\mu\nu}$ is the Ricci tensor, expressed in terms of Christoffel connections $\Gamma^{\lambda}_{\mu\nu}$ in the usual way:

$$R_{\mu\nu} = \partial_{[\rho} \Gamma^{\rho}_{\mu]\nu} + \Gamma^{\sigma}_{\rho[\sigma} \Gamma^{\rho}_{\mu]\nu}$$

(here the square brackets denote the antisymmetrization) and

$$\Gamma^{\lambda}_{\mu\nu} = \frac{1}{2} \cdot g^{\lambda\sigma} (\partial_{\nu} g_{\sigma\mu} + \partial_{\mu} g_{\sigma\nu} - \partial_{\sigma} g_{\mu\nu}),$$

$G = M_{Pl}^{-2}$ is the gravitational constant, $M_{Pl} = 1,2 \cdot 10^{19} GeV$ is the Planck mass, ∂_{μ} is usual derivative. (One must realize, that when speaking about a thin shell we always keep in mind that the thickness of the shell must not be smaller then $1/M_{Pl}$, provided gravity is described just by the classical Einstein equations).

We shall restrict ourselves to the case of time-like hypersurfaces Σ with the energy-momentum tensor having singularities no stronger, then those given by δ-functions. Then the first derivatives of $g_{\mu\nu}$ are discontinuous on Σ, while metric itself is still continuous on Σ. Gravitational formalism for such boundaries is considered in details in papers [10, 15, 19, 29, 32, 41].

Let $\{y^{\mu}\}^{+}$ ($\{y^{\mu}\}^{-}$) be an arbitrary coordinate system in V^{+} (V^{-}) region, and $\{\xi^{i}\}$ be an arbitrary coordinate system on Σ (here the latin indices run through 0,1,2). The coordinate charts $\{y^{\mu}\}^{+}$ and $\{y^{\mu}\}^{-}$ need not join smoothly on Σ.

Let us assume, that equation of hypersurface Σ in the chosen coordinates y^{μ} has the form

$$F(y^{\mu}) = 0 \qquad (6)$$

(Since all equations in the regions V^+ and V^- differ only by the indices "+" and "−", we, for simplicity, will not write them separately if not necessary).

We can introduce the new function

$$n(y^\mu) = \varepsilon \frac{F(y^\mu)}{\sqrt{g_{\lambda\nu}\partial^\lambda F \cdot \partial^\nu F}} \qquad (7)$$

which describes the surface Σ. Here the sign function ε depends on the orientation of the (1+2)-surface Σ. If a displacement vector dy^μ lies on the hypersurface $n = const$, then

$$dn = \partial_\mu n \cdot dy^\mu = 0,$$

∂_μ being the usual derivative. Therefore a vector

$$N_\mu \equiv \partial_\mu n|_\Sigma \qquad (8)$$

is the unit normal vector to the hypersurface Σ :

$$N_\mu N^\mu = -1$$

(recall that we consider the timelike Σ).

We can also introduce the unit vectors, tangential to Σ :

$$e_i^\mu = \frac{\partial y^\mu}{\partial \xi^i}.$$

The tetrad field (N^μ, e_i^μ) is thereby defined on Σ .

For our further calculations it is convenient to split the field equations into their components orthogonal and tangential to the wall surface Σ [10, 15, 19, 29, 32, 41].

For this purpose the interval, which in y^μ chart has the form

$$ds^2 = g_{\mu\nu}dy^\mu dy^\nu$$

($g_{\mu\nu}$ is the metric tensor, which determines the geometry in V region), can be written in Gaussian normal coordinates in the form

$$ds^2 = -dn^2 + \gamma_{ij}(\xi^k, n)d\xi^i d\xi^j. \tag{9}$$

From (6) and (7) it is clear, that $n = 0$ is the equation of hypersurface Σ and thus the interval

$$ds^2 = \gamma_{ij}(\xi^k)d\xi^i d\xi^j$$

determines the 3-geometry on Σ.

Any vector and tensor naturally is splitted into its components orthogonal and tangential to Σ :

$$A^\nu = A^n N^\nu + A^i e_i^\nu,$$

$$Q^{\mu\nu} = Q^{nn} N^\mu N^\nu + Q^{ni} e_i^\mu N^\nu + Q^{jn} N^\mu e_j^\nu + Q^{ij} e_i^\mu e_j^\nu.$$

Using the Gaussian coordinates the Einstein equations (5) also can be decomposed into scalar, 3-vector and 3-tensor parts in respect to the coordinate transformations on Hypersurface Σ :

$$G_n^n = -\frac{1}{2} \cdot \left({}^{(3)}R + (K_i^i)^2 - K_i^l K_i^l \right) = 8\pi G \cdot T_n^n;$$

$$G_i^n = D_m K_i^m - D_i K_l^l = 8\pi G \cdot T_i^n;$$

$$G_j^i = {}^{(3)} G_j^i - N^\mu D_\mu(K_j^i - \delta_j^i K_l^l) + K_l^l K_j^i -$$

$$\frac{1}{2} \cdot \delta_j^i \left((K_l^l)^2 + K_m^l K_l^m \right) = 8\pi G \cdot T_j^i. \tag{10}$$

Here the D_μ denotes covariant differentiation with respect of the connection in V, while D_i denotes 3-dimensional covariant differentiation with respect to the connection on Σ , ${}^{(3)}R$ is three dimensional scalar curvature, ${}^{(3)}G_j^i$ is three dimensional Einstein tensor and K_j^i is the extrinsic curvature tensor of the hypersurface Σ , which is defined in the following way:

$$K_{ij} = -e_i^\mu e_j^\nu D_\nu N_\mu. \tag{11}$$

In the equations (10) we have used the well-known Gauss-Kodazzi equations [10, 15, 19, 29, 32, 41].

Note, that in the Gaussian coordinates (9) the tensor of extrinsic curvature (11) acquires the simple form:

$$K_{ij} = -\Gamma_{ij}^n = -\frac{1}{2} \cdot \partial_n \gamma_{ij}. \tag{12}$$

Since the 3-geometry on the surface Σ is, by assumption, well defined, the components of Christoffel symbols (in the intrinsic coordinates ξ^i), not containing indices n are regular. Components with two or three indices n are equal to zero, while with one n — are discontinuous and have the step-function behavior when crossing Σ. However $g_{\mu\nu}$ is assumed to be regular on Σ, and $g_{\mu\nu}^+$ and $g_{\mu\nu}^-$ have to match continuously on the shell. Three-curvature tensor $^{(3)}R_{ij}$ of hypersurface Σ also does not contain singularities and is expressed in terms of 3-metric tensor γ_{ij} in the usual way just as $R_{\mu\nu}$ is expressed by $g_{\mu\nu}$.

Integrating the (ij) component of equation (10) in the normal direction by the proper distance dn through Σ we can get the so-called Lanczos equation (see [10, 15, 19, 29, 32, 41]).

$$\left[K_j^i\right] - \delta_j^i \left[K_l^l\right] = 8\pi G \cdot S_j^i, \tag{13}$$

where

$$\left[K_j^i\right] \equiv lim_{\epsilon \to 0}\left(K_j^i(n = +\epsilon) - K_j^i(n = -\epsilon)\right)$$

is the discontinuity of the outer curvature tensor and

$$S_j^i = lim_{\epsilon \to 0} \int_{-\epsilon}^{+\epsilon} T_j^i dn$$

is the intrinsic surface energy tensor on the Σ.

Noting (12), writing the (nn) and (ni) components of Einstein equations in the regions V^+ and V^- and subtracting the corresponding equations for the V^+ region from those for the V^- region one yields (using (13)):

$$D_j S_i^j + [T_i^n] = 0$$
$$\{K_j^i\} S_i^j + [T_n^n] = 0, \tag{14}$$

where $\{K_j^i\} = \frac{1}{2} \cdot lim_{\epsilon \to 0} \left(K_j^i(n = +\epsilon) + K_j^i(n = -\epsilon) \right)$.

Now to describe completely the gravitational behavior and dynamics of bubbles one needs to investigate the outer curvature and energy-momentum tensors of these objects, insert these quantities into motion equations (13) and (14) and solve them.

4   The surface stress-energy tensor.

We shall restrict ourselves to a pure vacuum case, i.e. when there are no particles at the either sides off the shell.

An observer, which moves with an element of the shell finds that the momentum of the matter all the time lies on the surface of the shell i.e.

$$T_{\mu\nu} \cdot N^\mu = 0$$

on Σ and

$$T_{\mu\nu} = 0$$

outside Σ. Thus in the intrinsic coordinates

$$T_n^m = T_n^i = 0 \tag{15}$$

and the surface energy-momentum tensor for an observer on Σ is represented by the tensor S_j^i.

It is easy to see that with the condition (15) the motion equations (14) are satisfied automatically (they become identities) and one is left only with Lanczos equations (13).

Now let us suppose, that the surface energy-momentum tensor has the structure of an ideal fluid

$$S^{ij} = (\sigma + p)u^i u^j - p\gamma^{ij}, \tag{16}$$

where u^i is the 3-velocity of an element of hypersurface Σ, while σ and p are the surface energy density (energy per unit area) and surface tension respectively.

The energy-momentum conservation in the intrinsic coordinates implies that equation

$$D_i S^{ij} = 0 \tag{17}$$

expresses the energy-momentum balance of matter on the shell. For tensor (16) this conservation equation becomes

$$u^j \cdot D_i \left[(\sigma + p)u^i \right] + (\sigma + p)u^i D_i u^j - \gamma^{ij} \cdot D_i p = 0. \tag{18}$$

Multiplying (18) by u_j we yield

$$D_i \left[(\sigma + p)u^i \right] - u^i \cdot D_i p = 0. \tag{19}$$

Feeding the last relation back into (18) we obtain

$$(\gamma^{ij} - u^i u^j) \cdot D_i p - (\sigma + p)u^i D_i u^j = 0. \tag{20}$$

The conservation equations (19) and (20) are easily solved in two cases.
(a). For the dust wall

$$p = 0$$

and we have

$$D_i(\sigma u^i) = 0,$$

that states that the total amount of dust is conserved.

(b). For the domain wall

$$p = -\sigma$$

and from (19) it follows immediately that

$$\sigma = const.$$

This two examples are considered in section 7 in spherically symmetrical case.

5   The geometry of spherical vacuum shells.

Here we consider the bubbles of spherical form. For the spherical shells the Lanczos equations (13) (the only nontrivial equation of motion for the vacuum case) takes the form (see [10]):

$$\left[K_2^2\right] = 4\pi G S_0^0,$$
$$\left[K_0^0\right] + \left[K_2^2\right] = 8\pi G S_2^2. \tag{21}$$

For the spherical shell the most convenient choice for the outer region coordinates y^μ is the ordinary spherical coordinate system. The symmetry features of the problem allows us to choose the coordinates ϑ and φ to be continuous across Σ, i.e.

$$\vartheta^+ = \vartheta^- = \vartheta;$$
$$\varphi^+ = \varphi^- = \varphi.$$

The metric off the shell in the $V^\pm$ regions must be the solution of spherically symmetrical Einstein equations. According to Birkhoff's theorem such metric has the form [36, 41, 45]

$$(ds^\pm)^2 = f^\pm \cdot (dt^\pm)^2 - \frac{1}{f^\pm} \cdot (dr^\pm)^2 - (r^\pm)^2 \cdot d\Omega^2, \qquad (22)$$

where

$$d\Omega^2 = d\vartheta^2 + \sin^2 \vartheta \cdot d\varphi^2.$$

For the intrinsic coordinates ξ^i of the shell we shall use the proper time τ and the spherical angles ϑ, φ. Then the metric on (1+2)-surface Σ, induced both by exterior $(ds^+)^2$ and interior $(ds^-)^2$ metrics (22), can be expressed as

$$ds^2 = d\tau^2 - R^2(\tau)d\Omega^2, \qquad (23)$$

where $R(\tau)$ is the shell radius.

Generally speaking, the time and radial coordinates are not continuous on the shell, but some restrictions on these coordinates is obtained from the junction of metrics (22), (23):

$$(ds^+)^2 = (ds^-)^2 = ds^2_{|\Sigma}. \qquad (24)$$

The radius of the shell $R(\tau)$ can be described in the coordinate invariant way, so the (24) gives only two conditions. Identification of the two-spheres $(r, t = const)$ on Σ yields

$$r^+ = r^- = R(\tau)_{|\Sigma}, \qquad (25)$$

while the time coordinate can be discontinuous on the shell: $(t^+ \neq t^-)_{|\Sigma}$. Comparison of timelike lines $(\varphi, \vartheta = const)$ gives

$$d\tau^2 = f^+ \cdot (dt^+)^2 - \frac{1}{f^+} \cdot dR^2 = f^- \cdot (dt^-)^2 - \frac{1}{f^-} \cdot dR^2. \qquad (26)$$

From these relations it is easy to find that

$$\left(f^{\pm}\dot{t}^{\pm}\right)^2 = f^{\pm} + \dot{R}^2,$$

$$\frac{1}{f^{\pm}} \cdot \left(\frac{dR}{dt^{\pm}}\right)^2 = f^{\pm} - \frac{1}{(\dot{t}^{\pm})^2} = \frac{f^{\pm} \cdot \dot{R}^2}{f^{\pm} + \dot{R}^2}, \tag{27}$$

where the overdot denotes the derivation with respect of proper time τ. Thus, after the procedure of junction (24), there remains only one unknown function $R(\tau)$ which must obey the Einstein equations on the shell. It means that from the two equations of motion (21) only one is independent. We shall choose and solve the first one (then the second one will be satisfied automatically). Now we have to find the outer curvature tensor.

It is easy to see, that equation (25) is the equation of motion of the shell (compare with (6)):

$$F = r - R(\tau) = 0.$$

Noting, that

$$dF/dt = -dR/dt;$$

$$dF/dr = 1$$

and using equations (22),(27) we can compute the outer normal to Σ (see (7) and (8)):

$$N_0 = -\left(\frac{dR}{dt}\right) \cdot N_1,$$

$$N_1 = \varepsilon \cdot |\dot{t}|,$$

$$N_2 = N_3 = 0.$$

Here ε is a sign function, which depends on the direction of an outer normal N_μ, i.e. on the orientation of $(1+2)$-surface Σ:

$$\varepsilon = sign\left(\dot{t}, \frac{\partial r}{\partial q}\right),$$

where q is any coordinate increasing along the direction from the bubble-center.

Using formulae (11) one can find the components of extrinsic curvature tensor:

$$K_0^0 = K_2^2 + \frac{R}{\dot{R}} \cdot \dot{K}_2^2,$$

$$K_2^2 = -\varepsilon\frac{|f\dot{t}|}{R}. \tag{28}$$

Note that the first equation of (27) admits both signs for $f\dot{t}$. The sign of ε is equivalent to tha sign of $f\dot{t}$, thus instead of the second equation (28) one can write

$$K_2^2 = -\frac{f\dot{t}}{R}. \tag{29}$$

Using (27) one can yield from (28):

$$(K_\pm)_0^0 = -\varepsilon_\pm\frac{\ddot{R} + \frac{1}{2} \cdot (f^\pm)'}{\sqrt{f^\pm + \dot{R}^2}},$$

$$(K_\pm)_2^2 = -\frac{\varepsilon_\pm}{R} \cdot \sqrt{f^\pm + \dot{R}^2}, \tag{30}$$

where f' denotes the derivation by R.

Thus we have shown that the dynamics of spherically symmetrical shell is completely described by the first equation (21)

$$K_+ - K_- = 4\pi G\sigma, \tag{31}$$

where $\sigma = S_0^0$ is the energy density of the shell and K is the only independent component K_2^2 of the extrinsic curvature tensor described by (29) or (30).

The fact that the first equation of (27) admits both signs for $\dot{f}\dot{t}$ leads to the new class of solutions of Einstein equations for bubbles with outer $\varepsilon_+ = -1$. This was missed in earlier works (for example [10]), where it was considered that for bubbles, lying above the Schwarzschild horizon, in outer space always $\varepsilon_+ = 1$. The correct sign must be chosen from boundary conditions. We shall discuss this subject below.

6   The sign ambiguity of extrinsic curvature.

Investigating the dynamics of vacuum spherical shells by means of the motion equation (31) one has to be careful when choosing the sign of ε and thus of $\dot{f}\dot{t}$. For the given the inner and the outer metrics $(ds^\pm)^2$ the $\varepsilon_\pm$ determines the global geometry, i.e. how the inner geometry is stuck with the outer one. In some cases the junction is impossible.

As we have mentioned above, the sign of ε depends on the direction of an outer normal N_μ, i.e. on the orientation of (1+2)-surface Σ:

$$\varepsilon = sign\left(\dot{t}, \frac{\partial r}{\partial q}\right), \tag{32}$$

where q is any coordinate increasing along the direction from the bubble-center.

Generally speaking, the sign of ε may change at the shell motion, for example, when the shell passes the horizon. If the initial conditions allow the shell to collapse, then in the case $\varepsilon_+ > 0$ the shell forms the black hole, while in the case $\varepsilon_+ < 0$ — the warmhole.

In paper [10] the classification of possible geometries for different signs of ε_+ and ε_- was done. However in this paper the dependence of the sign-function (32) on the mutual orientation of time coordinates on and off the shell, i.e. on the sign of $\dot{t}$ was overlooked. The bubble is the (1+2)-surface embedded in the 4-dimensional space-time $^{(4)}V$ and not only the 2-sphere as it appears if we do not consider the direction of time coordinate. Thus we get the more general classification of bubble geometries compared to those presented in previous papers.

Generally speaking, we have four different cases of equation (31), depending on the signature of $\varepsilon_\pm$ or $(f\dot{t})^\pm$ and, therefore, on the signature of $K_\pm$. The sign of ε must be chosen from the motion equation (31) and the boundary conditions mentioned in the Introduction. One has to take into account the positiveness of the surface energy density σ and the fact that there must not be the contradiction between the Newton's limit of Einstein equations (31) and Tolman's formula (2).

Let us discuss this problem and examine the signatures of ε or $f\dot{t}$.

a) The signature of $f^\pm$ $(\dot{t}_\pm > 0)$.

Let us assume for a while that $\dot{t}_\pm > 0$. The the signature of $f\dot{t}$ depends on the sign of f. The general form of f for the spherically symmetrical source is

$$ f = 1 - \frac{2Gm}{r} + \frac{Ge^2}{r^2} - G\Lambda r^2, \tag{33} $$

where m is the mass of the source, e is its charge, $\Lambda = (8\pi/3) \cdot \rho$ and ρ is the vacuum energy density. In the simplest case

$$ e = \Lambda = 0 $$

and

$$ f_+ = 1 - \frac{2Gm}{R}; $$
$$ f_- = 1. \tag{34} $$

The signature of f_+ is positive if the radius of the shell lies above the Schwarzschild horizon, i.e. when $R > 2m$ and is negative beyond it. So, $f\dot{t}$ changes its signature, when the radius of shell passes the horizon. The standart metric (33) has an unphysical singularity at the horizon caused by a poor choice of the coordinate system. To be more correct in correspondence between the signature of K and the radius of shell, one can use another coordinate system, for example the isotropic coordinates (see [12]), which have no singularities at the horizon. In ref. [12] it was investigated (in Kruscal-Szekares coordinates) the case when the value $f\dot{t}$ becomes negative for the bubbles crossing the horizon, the systematical catalog of possible solutions of the equation of motion was obtained and was shown, that two signatures of f correspond to the two different, but equally acceptable trajectories of shell.

b). The signature of $\dot{t}_{\pm}$ ($f^{\pm} > 0$).

Here we shall examine the mostly interesting case of macroscopic bubbles we shall assume, that the shell always lies outside the horizon and thus the unusual features of the space geometry are avoided. In this case $f^{\pm} > 0$ and the signature of $f\dot{t}$ is determined by the sign of $\dot{t}$.

Note that the example, when time flows in opposite directions is the case of Reissner-Nordstrom metric, when in the region between the upper and Cauchy radii the time coordinate changes its direction to the opposite. In this case (in difference to the ours) the metric covers the whole space-time ($r > 0$) and such feature was easy to notice. The problem of sign ambiguity entered due to taking a square root in equation (27). Similar situation is in Dirac theory when one has states with negative energy that correspond to antiparticles.

We shall choose the positive direction for the 2-spheres in the way that the radii increase in the direction of the outer normal. Then orientation of Σ is determined by the direction of time flow on the shell and

$$\varepsilon = sign\dot{t} \qquad (35)$$

It is clear, that the signature of $\dot{t}_{\pm}$ depends on the direction of time flowing in $V^{\pm}$ regions and on the shell. It is natural to assume, that in $V^{\pm}$ regions time flows in the same direction i.e.

$$sign(t_+) = sign(t_-) \tag{36}$$

while the direction of intrinsic time τ has to be found from the equation of motion. From (35) and (36) it is clear that $\varepsilon_+ = \varepsilon_- \equiv \varepsilon = 1$ when $t_\pm$ and τ flow in the same direction and $\varepsilon = -1$ in the opposite case. Assumption (36) leaves only two cases of equation (31):

$$\sqrt{f_+ + \dot{R}^2} - \sqrt{f_- + \dot{R}^2} = \pm 4\pi\sigma GR \tag{37}$$

which depend on the values of $f_\pm$.

If $f_- > f_+$, than $|K_+| < |K_-|$ and we have to take the lower sign $(-)$ in (37), because the energy density of the shell is positive (see (31)). According to (29) and (36) this means that $\dot{t}_\pm > 0$ and thus the time off and on the shell flows in the same direction.

Similarly if $f_- < f_+$ we have $\dot{t}_\pm < 0$, that means that the time on the shall flows in the opposite direction to the time in $V^\pm$ regions.

Note, that for the simplest case (34) the signature of t is connected with the sign of constant m, which is the integration constant of solution of Einstein equations in V^+ region. This constant is fixed by matching of f_+ to the solution of Einstein equations on the shell in the same coordinates. In the Newton approximation

$$f_+ = 1 - 2G \cdot \int \left(T_0^0 - \frac{1}{2} \cdot T \right) \cdot \frac{1}{R} \cdot dV.$$

The value and the signature of m is determined by this formula and it can be positive as well as negative dependently on boundary conditions. In the next section we shall see that the correct choice of sign in (37) cancels the contradictions between Tolman's formula and Newton's limit of (37).

7 Different kinds of shells

Here we shall consider two cases of macroscopic bubbles and show how one has to choose the different signs of $\dot{t}$.

a. The dust walls in vacuum.

As we have mentioned above, for the shell of dust

$$p = 0 \tag{38}$$

and the surface energy tensor of layer (16) is equal to

$$S^{ij} = \sigma u^i u^j.$$

Conservation law (19) now has the form

$$D_i(\sigma u^i) = 0 \tag{39}$$

stating, that the total amount of dust is conserved. For the spherical shells in the intrinsic coordinates ξ^i with the interval (23) we have

$$u^0 = 1;$$
$$u^1 = u^2 = 0.$$

Therefore

$$D_i u^i = \Gamma^i_{0i} = \frac{2\dot{R}}{R}.$$

So that equation (39) reduces simply to

$$\dot{\sigma} + 2\sigma \dot{R}/R = 0.$$

This equation is easily solved and yields

$$\sigma = \frac{const}{R^2}. \tag{40}$$

To fix the constant in (40) one can use the Tolman's formula for the proper mass of the shell in the state of rest (see (2)). For the ideal fluid

$$M = 8\pi \cdot \int \left[\sigma - \frac{1}{2} \cdot (\sigma - 2p)\right] \cdot \delta(r - R) \cdot r^2 dr = 4\pi R^2 \sigma = 4\pi \cdot const. \quad (41)$$

Using (38) and (40) for the *const* from (41) we obtain

$$const = \frac{M}{4\pi}.$$

In the simplest case of uncharged shells of dust in vacuum when the metric is given by the formulae (34) the motion equation (37) takes the form

$$\sqrt{1 - 2Gm/R + \dot{R}^2} - \sqrt{1 + \dot{R}^2} = \pm 4\pi\sigma GR = \pm G\frac{M}{R}. \quad (42)$$

We can rewrite (42) in the form

$$m = \mp M \cdot \sqrt{1 + \dot{R}^2} - G\frac{M^2}{2R}. \quad (43)$$

The term $-GM^2/2R$ represents the gravitational interaction energy according to the Newton's law, and $M \cdot \sqrt{1 + \dot{R}^2}$ represents the internal mass of the shell (the root is the analog of the Lorentz factor and is equal to 1 in equilibrium, when $\dot{R} = 0$).

From this relation it is easy to find that one has to choose in (42) the *lower* sign "−" corresponding to $\dot{ft} > 0$ ($\varepsilon = 1$). Certainly, in this case $m > 0$, $f_+ < f_-$ and the condition of surface energy density positiveness is satisfied. Besides, it is easy to see that with this choice of sign the static Newton's limit of (43) coinsides with Tolman's formula (41) (though Tolman's formula is valid only for static states, which, as we'll see, do not occur in this simplest model, the term corresponding to gravitational energy of the shell must enter the expression for the shell mass with the correct sign. Then in static Newton's limit ($\dot{R} = 0$; $G = 0$) the mass of the shell will be described by Tolman's formula).

Note that if one would choose the *upper* sign "+" in (42) then he should receive the contradiction between the static Newtons limit of (43) and Tolman's formula (41).

Now let us show that in this simplest model there is no equilibrium state for the dust shell. The conditions

$$\dot{R} = 0, \quad \ddot{R} = 0 \tag{44}$$

must be satisfied for the spherical shell to be in equilibrium state. The first of them leads from (43) to the equation

$$m = M - G\frac{M^2}{2R}.$$

Taking $d/d\tau$ of (43) we obtain

$$\ddot{R} = \frac{1}{M^2} \cdot \left(m + G\frac{M^2}{2R} \right) \cdot \frac{dm}{dR},$$

so the second condition (44) gives the stipulation

$$\frac{dm}{dR} = 0. \tag{45}$$

Using (43) and (45) one can see, that the radius of stability of the shell $R_{stab} \to \infty$, i.e. there is no equilibrium configuration for the dust wall in vacuum.

b. Domain wall in vacuum.

In the case of domain wall one has the picture opposite to the previous case. For the domain wall

$$p = \sigma$$

and the surface energy tensor of layer (16) is

$$S^{ij} = \sigma\gamma^{ij}.$$

From the conservation law (19)

$$D_i\sigma = 0$$

we obtain

$$\sigma = const.$$

From the Tolman's formula (2) we have:

$$M = 8\pi \cdot \int \left[\sigma - \frac{1}{2} \cdot (\sigma - 2p)\right] \cdot \delta(r - R) \cdot r^2 dr = -4\pi\sigma R^2. \quad (46)$$

One can see that the proper mass of layer is negative, if the energy density of domain wall σ is positive.

Considering again the simplest case (34) one obtains the motion equation

$$\sqrt{1 - \frac{2Gm}{R} + \dot{R}^2} - \sqrt{1 + \dot{R}^2} = \pm 4\pi\sigma GR = \mp G\frac{M}{R}, \quad (47)$$

where M is described by (46).

Again let us rewrite (47) in the form

$$m = \pm M \cdot \sqrt{1 + \dot{R}^2} - G\frac{M^2}{2R}. \quad (48)$$

This formula as well as (43) corresponds to the energy balance equation and must contain the Newton's gravitational energy of the shell.

In opposite to dust-wall case, now one has to choose in (47) the *upper* sign "−" corresponding to $f_+ < 0$ ($\varepsilon = -1$). Certainly, in this case $m < 0$, $f_+ > 1$ and the surface energy density positiveness condition is satisfied. Besides, for this choice of sign the static Newton's limit of (48) coinsides with Tolman's formula (46).

We emphasize once more that though Tolman's formula is valid only for static states, the term corresponding to gravitational energy of bubble must enter the expression for the bubble mass with the correct sign. Then in static Newton' limit the mass of the bubble will be described by Tolman's formula.

One can see, that when one chooses the upper sign in (47) then

$$m = - \left(4\pi\sigma R^2 \sqrt{1 + \dot{R}^2} + 8\pi^2\sigma^2 G R^3 \right).$$

In this expression the mass is negative and we can believe, that distant observer will be repelled by the domain wall.

If one considers the equation (47) with different sign in the right side (see [10, 28, 39]), one will obtain the positive value for mass

$$m = \kappa R^2 \sqrt{1 + \dot{R}^2} - \frac{G\kappa^2 R^3}{2}.$$

This expression contains the rest mass (46) with the wrong sign (the first term with $\dot{R} = 0$) and contradicts with Tolman's formula (46). Thus Tolman's formula helps us to choose the correct sign in a motion equation (47).

Thus the correct choice of the sign in the motion equation (47) leads to the new solution of Einstein equations for bubbles (Schwarzschild solution with negative mass) which shows that spherical domain walls are repulsive. This fact requires a further investigation of bubble-dynamics and their creation in cosmological models.

8   Schwarzschild space with negative mass.

Let us investigate the properties of Schwarzschild metric

$$ds^2 = \left(1 - \frac{b}{r} \right) \cdot dt^2 - \frac{1}{1 - b/r} \cdot dr^2 - r^2 \cdot (d\theta^2 + \sin^2\theta \cdot d\varphi^2) \qquad (49)$$

in the case, when constant b (which is related to the active gravitational mass of the source), can be negative.

First of all, for such spaces $g_{00} > 1$ and the velocity of light exceeds its velocity measured in Minkowski space. However this fact does not cause appearance of takhions.

For the metric (49) the nonzero components of curvature tensor are

$$R_{trtr} = \frac{b}{r^3},$$

$$R_{t\theta t\theta} = \frac{R_{t\varphi t\varphi}}{\sin^2 \theta} = -\frac{b(r-b)}{2r^2},$$

$$R_{r\theta r\theta} = \frac{R_{r\varphi r\varphi}}{\sin^2 \theta} = -\frac{b}{2(r-b)},$$

$$R_{\theta\varphi\theta\varphi} = -br \cdot \sin^2 \theta.$$

In this case the complex invariants of gravitational field have the form

$$I_1 = \frac{1}{48} \cdot R_{\alpha\beta\gamma\delta} \cdot \left(R^{\alpha\beta\gamma\delta} - \frac{i}{2} \cdot \varepsilon^{\alpha\beta\mu\nu} \cdot R_{\mu\nu}^{\gamma\delta} \right) = \left(\frac{b}{2r^3} \right)^2,$$

$$I_2 = \frac{1}{96} \cdot R_{\alpha\beta\mu\nu} R^{\mu\nu\rho\sigma} \cdot \left(R_{\sigma\rho}^{\alpha\beta} - \frac{i}{2} \cdot \varepsilon_{\sigma\rho\lambda\kappa} \cdot R^{\lambda\kappa\alpha\beta} \right) = - \left(\frac{b}{2r^3} \right)^3.$$

One can see, that for the negative b the second invariant changes its sign. The result of this fact is that the 3-space $(t = const)$ Gauss curvature for the plains, normal to radius also changes its sign:

$$k = \frac{P_{\theta\varphi\theta\varphi}}{\gamma_{\theta\theta} \cdot \gamma_{\varphi\varphi}} = -P_r^r = \frac{b}{r^3}. \tag{50}$$

Here $P_{\theta\varphi\theta\varphi}$, P_r^r, $\gamma_{\theta\theta}$, $\gamma_{\varphi\varphi}$ are 3-curvatures and 3-metric tensors of space (49) in the case $t = const$. Equation (50) means, that for the different signs of b this subspaces belong to the different types of surfaces. To show this let us embed metric (49) into Euclidean space with more then 4 dimensions.

An embedding of the linear element (49) in 5 dimensions is impossible (see [20, 42]). Embedding of (49) with positive b in 6 dimensions with signature 2+4

$$ds^2 = dz_1^2 + dz_2^2 - dz_3^2 - dz_4^2 - dz_5^2 - dz_6^2$$

is given by

$$z_1 = \left(1 - \frac{b}{r}\right) \cdot \cos t,$$

$$z_2 = \left(1 - \frac{b}{r}\right) \cdot \sin t,$$

$$z_3 = \int \left(\frac{b(b + 4r^3)}{4r^3(r - b)}\right)^{1/2} \cdot dr,$$

$$z_4 = r \cdot \cos \theta,$$

$$z_5 = r \cdot \sin \theta \cdot \cos \varphi,$$

$$z_6 = r \cdot \sin \theta \cdot \sin \varphi. \tag{51}$$

It is possible to eliminate the coordinates

$$z_1^2 + z_2^2 = 1 - \frac{b}{r},$$

$$z_3 = \int \left(\frac{b(b + 4r^3)}{4r^3(r - b)}\right)^{1/2} \cdot dr,$$

$$z_4^2 + z_5^2 + z_6^2 = r^2.$$

We note, that this surface in $z_1 z_2$ plane is the 1-sphere, in the $z_4 z_5 z_6$ is the 2-sphere and z_3 is space-like. Time-like coordinates z_1 and z_2 are periodic functions of t so that embedding (51) identifies distinct points of the original manifold. This suggests replacing the trigonometrical functions by the hyperbolic functions and embedding of (49) for the positive b is possible for the signature 1+5:

$$ds^2 = dz_1^2 - dz_2^2 - dz_3^2 - dz_4^2 - dz_5^2 - dz_6^2,$$

where

$$z_1 = \left(1 - \frac{b}{r}\right) \cdot \sinh t,$$

$$z_2 = \left(1 - \frac{b}{r}\right) \cdot \cosh t,$$

$$z_3 = \int \left(\frac{b(4r^3 - b)}{4r^3(r - b)}\right)^{1/2} \cdot dr,$$

$$z_4 = r \cdot \cos\theta,$$

$$z_5 = r \cdot \sin\theta \cdot \cos\varphi,$$

$$z_6 = r \cdot \sin\theta \cdot \sin\varphi. \tag{52}$$

We note that in $z_1 z_2$ plane this surface now is hyperbola

$$z_2^2 - z_1^2 = \left(1 - \frac{b}{r}\right).$$

For the negative mass

$$b < 0$$

we can see from (51) and (52), that coordinate z_3 became complex and embedding (51) now takes place in the space with signature 3+3

$$ds^2 = dz_1^2 + dz_2^2 + dz_3^2 - dz_4^2 - dz_5^2 - dz_6^2$$

where

$$z_1 = \left(1 - \frac{b}{r}\right) \cdot \cos t,$$

$$z_2 = \left(1 - \frac{b}{r}\right) \cdot \sin t,$$

$$z_3 = \int \left(\frac{b(b - 4r^3)}{4r^3(r - b)} \right)^{1/2} \cdot dr,$$

$$z_4 = r \cdot \cos\theta,$$

$$z_5 = r \cdot \sin\theta \cdot \cos\varphi,$$

$$z_6 = r \cdot \sin\theta \cdot \sin\varphi.$$

Now the coordinate z_3 became time-like. Embedding (52) is possible for the signature 2+4

$$ds^2 = -dz_1^2 + dz_2^2 + dz_3^2 - dz_4^2 - dz_5^2 - dz_6^2$$

where

$$z_1 = \left(1 - \frac{b}{r} \right) \cdot \sinh t,$$

$$z_2 = \left(1 - \frac{b}{r} \right) \cdot \cosh t,$$

$$z_3 = \int \left(\frac{b(b - 4r^3)}{4r^3(r - b)} \right)^{1/2} \cdot dr,$$

$$z_4 = r \cdot \cos\theta,$$

$$z_5 = r \cdot \sin\theta \cdot \cos\varphi,$$

$$z_6 = r \cdot \sin\theta \cdot \sin\varphi.$$

In this case the coordinate z_1 is space-like and we can not identify the surface in $z_1 z_2 z_3$ space. $z_4 z_5 z_6$ surface is the 2-sphere $r = R$ in all the cases and is identified in our work with the surface of domain bubble.

To conclud this section we can say that the space (49) with $b < 0$ can be embedded into a 6-dimensional space with signature (2+4) or (3+3), while the usual Schwarzschild space ($b > 0$) — into the space with signature (1+5) or (2+4) respectively.

9 The model.

After we have formulated our idea [6] how to avoid the disagreements mentioned at the beginning of this paper let us investigate a more general case of a spherically symmetrical charged bubble in vacuum, when the metric outside the bubble is

$$f_+ = 1 - \frac{2Gm}{r} + \frac{Ge^2}{r^2} - G\Lambda_+ r^2,$$

while inside —

$$f_- = 1 - G\Lambda_- r^2,$$

where $\Lambda_\pm \equiv \frac{8\pi}{3} \cdot \rho$, ρ being the vacuum energy density in $V^\pm$ regions, and e is the charge on the shell.

Now the motion equation (31) takes the form

$$\sqrt{\dot{R}^2 + 1 - \Lambda_+ GR^2 - \frac{2Gm}{R} + \frac{Ge^2}{R}} - \sqrt{\dot{R}^2 + 1 - \Lambda_- GR^2} = \pm G\kappa R, \quad (53)$$

where

$$\kappa \equiv 4\pi\sigma.$$

Finding m from this equation we yield:

$$m = \frac{\Lambda_- - \Lambda_+}{2} \cdot R^3 - \frac{G\kappa^2}{2} \cdot R^3 + \frac{e^2}{2R} \mp \kappa R^2 \cdot \sqrt{\dot{R}^2 + 1 - \Lambda_- GR^2} \quad (54)$$

It is easy to understand the meaning of the terms in (54). The first term is the volume energy of the bubble (a difference between the old and new vacuum energy densities). The second term represents an energy of gravitational self-interaction of the shell (the surface-surface binding energy). The third term is the electrostatic energy lying in the three-space outside the bubble. The last term contains the kinetic energy of the shell and surface-volume binding energy. As we have mentioned above, we have to choose the upper sign in equations (53) and (54) to avoid the disagreements with Tolman's formula (46).

To examine dynamics of the bubble let us rewrite the equation (54) in the following way:

$$\dot{R}^2 - \left[\frac{1}{\kappa^2} \cdot \left(-\frac{m}{R^2} - \frac{a}{2} \cdot R + \frac{e^2}{2R^3}\right)^2 + \Lambda_- G R^2\right] = -1, \qquad (55)$$

where $a \equiv \Lambda_+ - \Lambda_- + G\kappa^2$. It is worth to note that in this equation the sign ambiguity disappears due to squaring. Introducing new dimensionless variables

$$z \equiv \frac{R}{(-2m)^{1/3}} \cdot (a^2 + 4\kappa^2\Lambda_- G)^{1/6},$$

$$\tau' \equiv \frac{\tau}{2\kappa} \cdot (a^2 + 4\kappa^2\Lambda_- G)^{1/2} \qquad (56)$$

and dimensionless parameters

$$A \equiv a \cdot (a^2 + 4\kappa^2\Lambda_- G)^{-1/2},$$

$$E \equiv -\frac{4\kappa^2}{(-2m)^{2/3}} \cdot (a^2 + 4\kappa^2\Lambda_- G)^{-2/3},$$

$$Q^2 \equiv \frac{e^2}{(-2m)^{4/3}} \cdot (a^2 + 4\kappa^2\Lambda_- G)^{1/6},$$

we can represent the motion equation (55) as

$$\left(\frac{dz}{d\tau'}\right)^2 + U(z) = E,$$

which is identical to that of the point like particle with energy E, moving in one dimension under the influence of the potential

$$U(z) = -\left[z^2 - \frac{2A}{z}\cdot\left(1+\frac{Q^2}{z}\right) + \frac{1}{z^4}\cdot\left(1+\frac{Q^2}{z}\right)^2\right], \tag{57}$$

For real trajectories U must be negative since $E < 0$. Such potentials (but for the case of uncharged shells ($Q = 0$) with $m > 0$) were discussed in [4, 12].

In the equilibrium state $\dot{z}|_{z=z_0} = 0$, where z_0 is the equilibrium point, $U(z_0) = E$ and one can find the critical mass of the bubble:

$$m_0 = -\frac{4\kappa^3}{(a^2 + 4\kappa^2 G\Lambda_-)\cdot U_0^{3/2}} \tag{58}$$

where $U = |U(z_0)| > 0$. From (56) for the equilibrium radius we have

$$R_0 = \frac{2\kappa z_0}{U_0^{1/2}\cdot(a^2 + 4\kappa^2 G\Lambda_-)^{1/2}}. \tag{59}$$

From this formula it is easy to notice that for the de Sitter spaces ($\Lambda > 0$) the radius is maximal, when a is minimal. So to get the macroscopic bubbles it is worth to set $\Lambda_+ = \Lambda_- = \Lambda$. In this case the domain wall separates the phases with the same vacuum energy. Then $a \sim G^2\kappa^4$ which is negligible compared to the second term in brackets. The charge enters the formulae (58), (59) only through U_0 and has very small influence on the values m_0 and R_0. So we can set $Q = 0$. With this assumptions one finds that U reaches its maximum $U_0 \sim 1$ at the point $z_0 \sim 1$. This implies that

$$m_0 \sim -\frac{\kappa}{G\Lambda}, R_0 \sim \frac{1}{\sqrt{G\Lambda}}.$$

Considering a scenario for domain wall production in models with spontaneous breaking of some gauge symmetry group, it is easy to see that $\Lambda \sim \alpha^{-1}M_G^4$, $\kappa \sim \alpha^{-1}M_G^3$ and the thickness of the wall $d \sim \frac{1}{M_G}$, where M_G is the symmetry breaking scale and $\alpha \sim 10^{-2}$ is the coupling constant [10, 48, 49].

For the different scales of particle physics we yield:

a). The Electro-Weak scale: $M_G \sim 10^2 GeV$. Then $\Lambda \sim 10^{10} GeV^4$, $\kappa \sim 10^8 GeV^3$ and $R_0 \sim 10^{14} GeV^{-1}$, $m_0 \sim -10^{36} GeV$. The radius of such bubble is about 1 cm, and its negative mass is about million tons.

b). The scale of family symmetry [16]: $M_G \sim 10^4 \div 10^{10} GeV$. Then $\Lambda \sim 10^{18} \div 10^{42} GeV^4$, $\kappa \sim 10^{14} \div 10^{32} GeV^3$ and $R_0 \sim 10^{10} \div 10^{-2} GeV^{-1} \sim 10^{-4} \div 10^{-16} cm$, $m_0 \sim -(10^{34} \div 10^{28}) GeV \sim -(10^{10} \div 10^4) g$.

c). The scale of Grand Unification: $M_G \sim 10^{15} GeV$. Then $\Lambda \sim 10^{62} GeV^4$, $\kappa \sim 10^{47} GeV^3$ and thus $R_0 \sim 10^{-12} GeV^{-1}$, $m_0 \sim -10^{23} GeV \sim 0, 1g$. This is a very small radius and there arises the question of the validity of the thin-wall approximation $(d \sim 10^{-15} GeV^{-1})$.

We see that in all the cases the mass of the bubble is negative and it exhibits a strong gravitational repulsion.

10 The problem of stability.

Unfortunately this equilibrium state seems to be unstable. Potential (57) has the single maximum. In contrary to the case with positive m [10], the charge does not stabilize the bubble. Perhaps one could find the stable equilibrium states of bubble with negative mass in some nonvacuum models or in models with rotating bubble.

In [23] it is suggested that the inclusion of a nonvanishing angular momentum might stabilize the shell. The surface energy-momentum density tensor of a charged rotating shell is given by [30, 38]

$$T^i_j = -\sigma u^i u_j + \delta^i_j \sigma, \qquad i,j = 0, 2, 3 \qquad (60)$$

It consists of a mixture of two perfect fluids. The first term can be interpreted as "dust" particles with negative energy density. The second one represents a domain wall. The negative mass "dust" increases the repulsive character of the bubble and can keep it static. Exterior for of a spinning charged shell is the Kerr-Newman metric. Our simple analysis based on spherical symmetrical equations is not valid in this case and model (60) requires further investigations.

If the problem of stability will be solved there will be an interesting possibility of creation of the static singular shell of macroscopic size and with repulsive gravitational field. Radius and repulsive features of such objects depend on the scale of symmetry violation and can be varied slowly by changing the forces stabilizing the bubble.

Acknowledgment .

The research described in this publication was made possible in part by Grant MXL000 from the International Science Foundation.

References

[1] A.Aurilia, R.Balbinot, E.Spallucci. "Quantum bubble dynamics in the presence of gravity". Phys.Lett. vol.262 B, No.2,3, p.222, (1991).

[2] A.Aurilia, G.Denardo, F.Legovini, E.Spallucci. "An effective action functional for the inflationary cosmology". Phys.Lett. vol.147 B, No.4,5, p.258-262, (1984).

[3] A.Aurilia, G.Denardo, F.Legovini, E.Spallucci. "Vacuum tension effects on the evolution of domain walls in the early universe". Nucl.Phys. vol.B252, No.3, p.523-537, (1985).

[4] A.Aurilia, R.Kissack, R.Mann, E.Spallucci. "Relativistic bubble dynamics: from cosmic inflation to hadronic bags". Phys.Rev. vol.D35, No.10, p.2961-2975, (1987).

[5] A.Aurilia, M.Palmer, E.Spallucci. "Evolution of bubbles in a vacuum". Preprint SLAC-PUB-4697 Rev (1989) .

[6] A.Barnaveli, M.Gogberashvili. "Gravitational repulsion of spherical domain walls". General Relativ. and Gravit., Vol.26, p.1117, (1994)
A.Barnaveli, M.Gogberashvili. "Gravitationaly repulsive domain wall bubbles". Teoret. i Mat.Fizika., Vol.100, No.2, p.303-311, (1994)
A.Barnaveli, M.Gogberashvili. in: Proc. Int. Seminar. *"Quarks-94"* (World Scientific, Singapoore, 1994).

[7] R.Basu, A.Guth, A.Vilenkin. "Quantum creation of topological defects during inflation". Preprint TUTP-91-3. (1991).

[8] V.A.Berezin, V.A.Kuzmin, I.I.Tkachev. "Thin-wall Vacuum Domain Evolution". Phys.Lett. vol.120 B, No.1-3, p.91-96, (1983).

[9] V.A.Berezin, V.A.Kuzmin, I.I.Tkachev. "New vacuum formation in the universe". Phys.Lett. vol.130 B, No.1,2, p.23, (1983).

[10] V.A.Berezin, V.A.Kuzmin, I.I.Tkachev. "Dynamics of bubbles in general relativity". Phys.Rev. vol.D36, No.10, p.2919-2944, (1987).

[11] V.A.Berezin, V.A.Kuzmin, I.I.Tkachev. "O(3)-invariant tunneling in General Relativity". Preprint NBI-HE-87-85, (1987).

[12] S.K.Blau, E.I.Guendelman, A.H.Guth. "Dynamics of false-vacuum bubbles". Phys.Rev. vol.D35, No.6, p.1747-1766, (1987).

[13] G.Börner. *The Early Universe* (Springer, Berlin, 1988).

[14] W.Z.Chao. "Gravitational effects in bubble collisions". Phys. Rev. vol.D28, No.8, p.1898-1906, (1983).

[15] J.Chase. "Gravitational Instability and Collapse of Charged Fluid Shells". Nuovo Cim. vol.67 B, No.2, p.136-152, (1970).

[16] J.Chkareuli. "Flavoured cosmic strings and monopoles". Phys.Lett., **vol. B 272**, No.3,4, p.207-212, (1991).

[17] Y.Cho, P.Freund. "Gravitating 't Hooft monopoles". Phys.Rev. vol.D12, No.6, p.1588-1589, (1975).

[18] S.Coleman. Phys.Rev. D15 (1977) 2922 ;
S.Coleman, F. De Luccia. Phys. Rev. D21 (1980) 3305.

[19] V.De La Cruz, W.Israel. "Gravitational Bounce". Nuovo Cim. vol.51 A, No.3, p.744-760, (1967).

[20] C.Fronsdal, "Completion and Embedding of the Schwarzschild solution". Phys.Rev., Vol. 116, No 3, p. 778-781, (1959).

[21] R.Gregory, D.Haws, D.Garfinkle. "Dynamics of domain walls and strings". Phys.Rev. vol.D42, No.2, p.343-348, (1990).

[22] O.Grøn. "Repulsive gravitation and electron models". Phys.Rev. vol.D31, No.8, p.2129-2131, (1985).

[23] P.Gnadig, Z.Kunszt, P.Hasenfratz, J.Kuti. Ann.Phys.(N.Y.), Vol.116 (1978) 380.

[24] D.Harrari, C.Lousto. "Repulsion from global monopoles". Phys.Rev. vol.D42, p.2626, (1990).

[25] D.Harrari, P.Sikivie. Phys. Rev. D37, (1988) 3438.

[26] P.Huet, K.Kajantie, R.Leigh, B.Liu, L.McLerran. "Hydrodynamic stability analysis of burning bubbles in electroweak theory and QCD". Preprint SLAC-PUB-5943, SCIPP-92/56 (1992).

[27] J.Ipser. "Repulsive and attractive planar walls in general relativity". Phys.Rev. vol.D30, No.12, p.2452-2456, (1984).

[28] J.Ipser, P.Sikivie. "Gravitationally Repulsive Domain Wall". Phys.Rev. vol.D30, No.4, p.712-719, (1984).

[29] W.Israel. "Singular Hypersurfaces and Thin Shells in General Relativity". Nuovo Cim. vol.44 B, No.1, p.1-14, (1966).

[30] W.Israel, Phys.Rev., **D 2** (1970) 641.

[31] J.Karriga, A.Vilenkin. "Perturbations on domain walls and strings: a covariant theory". Preprint TUTP-91-6. (1991).

[32] K.Kuchar. "Charged Shells in General Relativity and Their Gravitational Collapse". Chech.J.Phys. vol.B18, p.435-463, (1968).

[33] H.Kodama, M.Sasaki, K.Sato. "Abundance of primordial holes produced by cosmological first-order phase transitions". Progr.Theor.Phys. vol.68, No.6, p.1979-1998, (1982).

[34] P.Laguna-Castillo, R.A.Matzner. "Inflation and bubbles in general relativity". Phys.Rev. vol.D34, No.10, p.2913-2935, (1986).

[35] K.Lake "Equation of motion for bubble boundaries". Phys.Rev. vol. D29, No.8, p.1861-1862, (1984).

[36] L.D.Landau, E.M.Lifshitz. *The Classical Theory of Fields* (Pergamon, Oxford, 1975).

[37] A.D.Linde. Phys.Lett. B70 (1977) 306; Nucl.Phys. B216 (1988) 421; *Particle Physics and Inflationary Cosmology* (Harwood, 1990).

[38] C.Lopez. "Extended model of electron in general relativity". Phys.Rev. vol.D30, No.2, p.313-316, (1984).

[39] C.A.Lopez. "Dynamics of charged bubbles in general relativity and models of particles". Phys.Rev. vol.D38, No.12, p.3662- 3666, (1988).

[40] K.Maeda, K.Sato, M.Sasaki, H.Kodama. "Creation of Schwarzschild-De Sitter wormholes by a cosmological first-order phase transition". Phys.Lett. vol.108 B, No.2, p.98-102, (1982).

[41] C.W.Misner, K.S.Thorne, J.A.Wheeler. *Gravitation* (W.H.Freeman and Co., San Francisco, 1973).

[42] J.Rosen. "Embedding of various relativistic Riemannian spaces in pseudo-Euclidean spaces". Rev.Mod.Phys. vol.37, No.1, p.204- 214, (1965).

[43] K.Sato, H.Kodama, M.Sasaki, K.Maeda. "Multi-production of universes by first-order phase transition of a vacuum". Phys.Lett. vol.108 B, No.2, p.103, (1982).

[44] A.A.Sokolov, D.D.Ivanenko. *Classical Field Theory* (Moscow, 1948)

[45] R.Tolman. *Relativity, Thermodynamics and Cosmology* (At the Clarendon Press, Oxford, 1969).

[46] N.Turok. "Electroweak detonation bubbles". Preprint PUTP-91-1273 (1991).

[47] T.Vachaspati. "Gravity of cosmic loops". Phys.Rev. Vol. D35, No.6, p.1767, (1987).

[48] A.Vilenkin. "Cosmic strings and domain walls". Phys.Reports vol.D121, p.263-314, (1985).

[49] A.Vilenkin. "Gravitational field of vacuum domain walls and strings". Phys.Rev. vol.D23, No.4, p.852-857, (1981).

[50] Ya.B.Zeldovich, M.Yu.Khlopov. "On the concentration of relic magnetic monopoles in the universe". Phys.Lett. vol.79 B, No.3, p.239-241, (1978).

Gennadi A. Sardanashvily, Editor
New Frontiers in Gravitation
Hadronic Press, Palm Harbor, FL 34682-1577, U.S.A.
ISBN 0–911767–96–7, 1996, Pages 45–63

A POSSIBLE SOLUTION TO
THE PROBLEM OF EXTRA DIMENSIONS

U. Bleyer, M. Rainer

Gravitationsprojekt, Universität Potsdam
An der Sternwarte 16
D-14482 Potsdam, Germany

and A. Zhuk

Fachbereich Physik, Freie Universität Berlin
Arnimallee 14
D-14195 Berlin, Germany [1]

Abstract

We consider a multidimensional universe with the topology $M = \mathbb{R} \times M_1 \times \cdots \times M_n$, where the M_i $(i > 1)$ are d_i-dimensional Ricci flat spaces. Exploiting a conformal equivalence between minimal coupling models and conformal coupling models, we get exact solutions for such an universe filled by a conformally coupled scalar field. One of the solutions can be used to describe trapped unobservable extra dimensions.

[1]Permanent address: Department of Physics, University of Odessa, 2 Petra Velikogo, Odessa 270100, Ukraine

1 Introduction

Recently models of multidimensional universes $M = \mathbb{R} \times M_1 \times \cdots \times M_n$, where M_i, $(i = 1, \ldots, n)$ are Einstein spaces, have received increasing interest [1]. The geometry might be minimally coupled to a homogeneous scalar field Φ with a potential $U(\Phi)$. The class of multidimensional cosmological models (MCM) is rich enough to study the relation and the imprint of internal compactified extra dimensions (like in Kaluza-Klein models [2, 3]) on the external space-time. Therein, exactly solvable classical and quantum models were found by [4]. Some of these exact solutions describe the compactification of the internal dimensions up to the actual time. Accordingly, all MCM can be divided into two different classes: The first class consists of models where from the very beginning the internal dimensions are assumed to be static with a scale of Planck length $L_{Pl} \sim 10^{-33}$ cm [5, 6]. The other class consists of models where the internal dimensions, like external space-time, evolve dynamically. Thereby however, the internal spaces contract for several orders of magnitude relatively to the external one [5, 7].

In [4]-[7] a minimally coupled scalar field as a matter source was considered. More in particular, in [8] a generalized Kasner solution was found, with minimally coupled scalar field and all spaces M_i being Ricci flat. Maeda [9] (see also [10]) has shown the equivalence of a minimally coupled model to a model with arbitrary coupled scalar field. In 4 dimensions, this was used by Page [11] to get new solutions with conformally coupled scalar field from some known solutions with minimally coupled scalar field. This idea can be exploited also, more generally, for arbitrary dimensions and coupling constants [12]. In the present paper, from the multidimensional solution of [8], we obtain a new solution with conformally coupled scalar field. This new solution bears the possibility to solve the problem of extra dimensions. Rubakov and Shaposhnikov [13] and others [14]-[16] consider non-gravitational fields as dynamical variables which are trapped by a potential well (domain wall), which is narrow along corresponding internal dimensions and extended flatly in 4-dimensional space-time. In [17] also dynamical variables of gravity are trapped by a potential. We propose that some gravitational degrees of freedom may be trapped in a classically forbidden region and, hence, be invisible. In general the scale factors of all factor spaces M_i are dynamical variables of the MCM. Here we obtain solutions where the internal spaces are still trapped invisibly, while external 3-space is already born. The factor spaces (external or internal) are born in a quantum tunnelling process from "nothing" [18]-[22], i.e. from a non-real (e.g. imaginary) section in complex geometry. The birth of different factor spaces may happen at different times. Some of them may remain confined forever in a non-classical section. In complex geometry the extra dimensions also correspond to resolutions of simple singularities in a $3+1$-dimensional space-time, in which their real parts evolve as string tubes [23]. In the following, we explore these ideas in the example of a new solution.

2   Classical Multidimensional Universes

We consider a universe described by a (Pseudo-) Riemannian manifold

$$M = \mathbb{R} \times M_1 \times \ldots \times M_n,$$

with first fundamental form

$$g \equiv ds^2 = -e^{2\gamma} dt \otimes dt + \sum_{i=1}^{n} a_i^2 \, ds_i^2, \tag{2.1}$$

where $a_i = e^{\beta^i}$ is the scale factor of the d_i-dimensional space M_i. In the following we assume M_i to be an Einstein space, i.e. its first fundamental form

$$ds_i^2 = g_{kl}^{(i)} \, dx_{(i)}^k \otimes dx_{(i)}^l \tag{2.2}$$

satisfies the equations

$$R_{kl}^{(i)} = \lambda_i g_{kl}^{(i)}, \tag{2.3}$$

and hence

$$R^{(i)} = \lambda_i d_i. \tag{2.4}$$

For the metric (2.1) the Ricci scalar curvature of M is

$$R = e^{-2\gamma} \left\{ \left[\sum_{i=1}^{n} (d_i \dot{\beta}^i) \right]^2 + \sum_{i=1}^{n} d_i [(\dot{\beta}^i)^2 - 2\dot{\gamma}\dot{\beta}^i + 2\ddot{\beta}^i] \right\} + \sum_{i=1}^{n} R^{(i)} e^{-2\beta^i}. \tag{2.5}$$

Let us now consider a variation principle with the action

$$S = S_{EH} + S_{GH} + S_M, \tag{2.6}$$

where

$$S_{EH} = \frac{1}{2\kappa^2} \int_M \sqrt{|g|} R \, dx$$

is the Einstein-Hilbert action,

$$S_{GH} = \frac{1}{\kappa^2} \int_{\partial M} \sqrt{|h|} K \, dy$$

is the Gibbons-Hawking boundary term [24], where K is the trace of the second fundamental form, which just cancels second time derivatives in the equation of motion, and

$$S_M = \int_M \sqrt{|g|} [-\frac{1}{2} g^{ik} \partial_i \Phi \partial_j \Phi - U(\Phi)] \, dx$$

is a matter term. Here, and in the following, Φ is a homogeneous minimally coupled scalar field. In the case of minimal coupling, we denote the lapse function by $e^{\hat{\gamma}^i}$, and the other scale factors by $\hat{a}_i \equiv e^{\hat{\beta}^i}$. Then we define the metric on minisuperspace, given in the coordinates $\hat{\beta}^i$ and Φ. We set

$$G_{ij} := d_i \delta_{ij} - d_i d_j \tag{2.7}$$

and define the minisuperspace metric as

$$G = G_{ij} d\hat{\beta}^i \otimes d\hat{\beta}^j + \kappa^2 d\Phi \otimes d\Phi. \tag{2.8}$$

Furthermore we define

$$N := e^{\hat{\gamma} - \sum_{i=1}^{n} d_i \hat{\beta}^i} \tag{2.9}$$

and a minisuperspace potential $V = V(\hat{\beta}^i, \Phi)$ via

$$V := -\frac{\mu}{2} \sum_{i=1}^{n} R^{(i)} e^{-2\hat{\beta}^i + \hat{\gamma} + \sum_{j=1}^{n} d_j \hat{\beta}^j} + \mu \kappa^2 U(\Phi) e^{\hat{\gamma} + \sum_{j=1}^{n} d_j \hat{\beta}^j}, \tag{2.10}$$

where

$$\mu := \kappa^{-2} \prod_{i=1}^{n} \sqrt{|\det g^{(i)}|}. \tag{2.11}$$

Then the variational principle of (2.6) is equivalent to a Lagrangian variational principle in minisuperspace,

$$S = \int L dt, \quad \text{where} \quad L = N\{\frac{\mu}{2} N^{-2} (G_{ij} \dot{\hat{\beta}}^i \dot{\hat{\beta}}^j + \kappa^2 \dot{\Phi}^2) - V\}. \tag{2.12}$$

Here μ is the mass of a classical particle in minisuperspace. Note that μ^2 is proportional to the volumes of spaces M_i.

Next let us compare different choices of time τ in Eq. (2.1). The time gauge is determined by the function γ. There exist few natural time gauges (compare also [12]). In the following we need only:

i) The *synchronous time gauge*

$$\gamma \equiv 0, \tag{2.13}$$

for which t in Eq. (2.1) is the proper time t_s of the universe. The clocks of geodesically comoved observers go synchronous to that time.

ii) The *harmonic time gauge*

$$\gamma \equiv \gamma_h := \sum_{i=1}^{n} d_i \hat{\beta}^i \tag{2.14}$$

yields the time $t \equiv t_h$, given by

$$dt_h = \left(\prod_{i=1}^{n} a_i^{d_i} \right)^{-1} dt_s \tag{2.15}$$

In this gauge the time is a harmonic function, i.e. $\Delta[g]t = 0$, and $N \equiv 1$. The latter is especially convenient when we work in minisuperspace.

In the harmonic time gauge the equations of motion from Eq. (2.12) yield

$$\mu G_{ij} \ddot{\beta}^j = -\frac{\partial V}{\partial \beta^i} \qquad \ddot{\Phi} + \frac{\partial U}{\partial \Phi} e^{2\gamma} = 0 \tag{2.16}$$

plus the energy constraint

$$\frac{\mu}{2}(G_{ij}\dot{\beta}^i\dot{\beta}^j + \kappa^2\dot{\Phi}^2) + V = 0. \tag{2.17}$$

3 Conformally Related Models

Let us follow [9] and consider an action of the kind

$$S = \int d^D x \sqrt{|g|}(F(\phi, R) - \frac{\epsilon}{2}(\nabla\phi)^2). \tag{3.1}$$

With

$$\omega := \frac{1}{D-2}\ln(2\kappa^2|\frac{\partial F}{\partial R}|) + A, \tag{3.2}$$

where $D = 1 + \sum_{i=1}^n d_i$ and A is an arbitrary constant, $g_{\mu\nu}$ is conformally transformed to the minimal metric

$$\hat{g}_{\mu\nu} = e^{2\omega}g_{\mu\nu}. \tag{3.3}$$

Especially let us consider in the following actions, which are linear in R. With

$$F(\phi, R) = f(\phi)R - V(\phi). \tag{3.4}$$

the action is

$$S = \int d^D x \sqrt{|g|}(f(\phi)R - V(\phi) - \frac{\epsilon}{2}(\nabla\phi)^2). \tag{3.5}$$

In this case

$$\omega = \frac{1}{D-2}\ln(2\kappa^2|f(\phi)|) + A \tag{3.6}$$

The scalar field in the minimal model is

$$\Phi = \kappa^{-1} \int d\phi \{ \frac{\epsilon(D-2)f(\phi) + 2(D-1)(f'(\phi))^2}{2(D-2)f^2(\phi)} \}^{1/2} =$$

$$= (2\kappa)^{-1} \int d\phi \{ \frac{2\epsilon f(\phi) + \xi_c^{-1}(f'(\phi))^2}{f^2(\phi)} \}^{1/2}, \qquad (3.7)$$

where

$$\xi_c := \frac{D-2}{4(D-1)} \qquad (3.8)$$

is the conformal coupling constant.

For the following we define $\mathrm{sign}x$ to be ± 1 for $x \geq 0$ resp. $x < 0$. Then with the new minimally coupled potential

$$U(\Phi) = (\mathrm{sign}f(\phi)) \, [2\kappa^2 |f(\phi)|]^{-D/D-2} V(\phi) \qquad (3.9)$$

the corresponding minimal action is

$$S = \mathrm{sign}f \int d^D x \sqrt{|\hat{g}|} \left(-\frac{1}{2}[(\hat{\nabla}\Phi)^2 - \frac{1}{\kappa^2}\hat{R}] - U(\Phi) \right). \qquad (3.10)$$

Example 1:

$$f(\phi) = \frac{1}{2}\xi\phi^2, \qquad (3.11)$$

$$V(\phi) = -\lambda\phi^{\frac{2D}{D-2}}. \qquad (3.12)$$

Substituting this into Eq. (3.9) the corresponding minimal potential U is constant,

$$U(\Phi) = (\mathrm{sign}\xi) \, |\xi\kappa^2|^{-D/D-2} \lambda. \qquad (3.13)$$

It becomes zero precisely for $\lambda = 0$, i.e. when V is zero. With

$$f'(\phi) = \xi\phi \qquad (3.14)$$

we obtain

$$\Phi = \kappa^{-1} \int d\phi \left\{ \frac{(\frac{\epsilon}{\xi} + \frac{1}{\xi_c})\phi^2}{\phi^4} \right\}^{\frac{1}{2}} = \left(\kappa\sqrt{\xi}\right)^{-1} \sqrt{\frac{1}{\xi_c} + \frac{\epsilon}{\xi}} \int d\phi \frac{1}{|\phi|}$$

$$= \kappa^{-1} \sqrt{\frac{1}{\xi_c} + \frac{\epsilon}{\xi}} \ln |\phi| + k \tag{3.15}$$

for $-\frac{\xi}{\epsilon} \geq \xi_c$, where k is a constant of integration. Note that for

$$\frac{\xi}{\epsilon} = -\xi_c, \tag{3.16}$$

e.g. for $\epsilon = -1$ and conformal coupling, we have

$$\Phi = k. \tag{3.17}$$

Thus here the conformal coupling theory is equivalent to a theory without scalar field. For $-\frac{\xi}{\epsilon} < \xi_c$ the field Φ would become complex and, for imaginary k, purely imaginary. In any case, the integration constant k may be a function of the coupling ξ and the dimension D.

Example 2:

$$f(\phi) = \frac{1}{2}(1 - \xi\phi^2), \tag{3.18}$$

$$V(\phi) = \Lambda. \tag{3.19}$$

Then the constant potential V has its minimal correspondence in a non constant U, given by

$$U(\Phi) = \pm\Lambda|\kappa^2(1 - \xi\phi^2)|^{-D/D-2} \tag{3.20}$$

respectively for $\phi^2 < \xi^{-1}$ or $\phi^2 > \xi^{-1}$.

Let us set in the following

$$\epsilon = 1. \tag{3.21}$$

Then with

$$f'(\phi) = -\xi\phi \tag{3.22}$$

we obtain

$$\Phi = \kappa^{-1} \int d\phi \{ \frac{1 + c\xi\phi^2}{(1 - \xi\phi^2)^2} \}^{1/2}, \tag{3.23}$$

where

$$c := \frac{\xi}{\xi_c} - 1. \tag{3.24}$$

For $\xi = 0$ it is $\Phi = \kappa^{-1}\phi + k$, i.e. the coupling remains minimal. To solved this integral for $\xi \neq 0$, we substitute $u := \xi\phi^2$. To assure a solution of (3.23) to be real, let us assume $\xi \geq \xi_c$ which yields $c \geq 0$. Then we obtain

$$\Phi = \frac{\text{sign}(\phi)}{2\kappa\sqrt{\xi}} \int \frac{\sqrt{u^{-1}+c}}{|1-u|} du + k_{\lessgtr}$$

$$= \frac{\text{sign}((1-u)\phi)}{2\kappa\sqrt{\xi}}[-\sqrt{c}\ln(2\sqrt{c}\sqrt{1+cu}\sqrt{u}+2cu+1)+$$

$$\sqrt{1+c}\ln(\frac{2\sqrt{1+c}\sqrt{1+cu}\sqrt{u}+2cu+1+u}{|1-u|})] + k_{\lessgtr}$$

$$= \frac{\text{sign}((1-\xi\phi^2)\phi)}{2\kappa\sqrt{\xi}}\{-\sqrt{c}\ln(2\sqrt{c}\sqrt{1+c\xi\,\phi^2}\sqrt{\xi}|\phi|+2c\xi\,\phi^2+1)$$

$$+\sqrt{1+c}\ln(\frac{2\sqrt{1+c}\sqrt{1+c\xi\,\phi^2}\sqrt{\xi}|\phi|+2c\xi\,\phi^2+1+\xi\,\phi^2}{|1-\xi\phi^2|})\} + k_{\lessgtr}$$

$$= \frac{\text{sign}((1-\xi\phi^2)\phi)}{2\kappa\sqrt{\xi}}\ln\frac{[2\sqrt{1+c}\sqrt{1+c\xi\phi^2}\sqrt{\xi}|\phi|+(2c+1)\xi\,\phi^2+1]^{\sqrt{1+c}}}{[2\sqrt{c}\sqrt{1+c\xi\phi^2}\sqrt{\xi}|\phi|+2c\xi\,\phi^2+1]^{\sqrt{c}}\cdot|1-\xi\phi^2|^{\sqrt{1+c}}}$$

$$+ k_{\lessgtr}. \tag{3.25}$$

The integration constants $k_{\lessgtr}$ for $\phi^2 < \xi^{-1}$ and $\phi^2 > \xi^{-1}$ respectively may be arbitrary functions of ξ and the dimension D. The singularities of the transformation $\phi \to \Phi$ are located at $\phi^2 = \xi^{-1}$.

If the coupling is conformal $\xi = \xi_c$, i.e. $c = 0$, the expressions (3.25) simplify to

$$\kappa\Phi = \frac{1}{\sqrt{\xi_c}}[(\text{artanh}\sqrt{\xi_c}\phi) + c_<] \tag{3.26}$$

for $\phi^2 < \xi_c^{-1}$ and to

$$\kappa\Phi = \frac{1}{\sqrt{\xi_c}}[(\text{arcoth}\sqrt{\xi_c}\phi) + c_>] \tag{3.27}$$

for $\phi^2 > \xi_c^{-1}$, with redefined constants of integration $c_<$. In the following we restrict to this case of conformal coupling. The inverse formulas expressing the conformal field ϕ in terms of the minimal field Φ are

$$\phi = \frac{1}{\sqrt{\xi_c}} \left[\tanh(\sqrt{\xi_c} \kappa \Phi - c_<) \right] \tag{3.28}$$

with $\phi^2 < \xi_c^{-1}$ and

$$\phi = \frac{1}{\sqrt{\xi_c}} \left[(\coth(\sqrt{\xi_c} \kappa \Phi - c_>) \right] \tag{3.29}$$

with $\phi^2 > \xi_c^{-1}$ respectively.

The conformal factor is according to Eqs. (3.6) and (3.18) given by

$$\omega = \frac{1}{D-2} \ln(\kappa^2 |1 - \xi_c \phi^2|) + A. \tag{3.30}$$

4 Trapped Internal Dimensions

In the following we want to compare the solutions of the minimal model to those of the corresponding conformal model. We specify the geometry for the minimal model to be of MCM type (2.1), with all M_i Ricci flat (when necessary, assumed to be compact), hence $R^{(i)} = 0$ for $i = 1, \ldots, n$. The minimally coupled scalar field is assumed to have zero potential $U \equiv 0$. In the harmonic time gauge (2.14) with harmonic time

$$\tau \equiv t_h^{(m)}, \tag{4.1}$$

we demand this model to be a solution for Eq. (2.16) with vanishing $R^{(i)}$ and $U(\Phi)$. We set $\hat{\beta}^{n+1} := \kappa \Phi$ and obtain as solution a multidimensional (Kasner like) universe, given by

$$\hat{\beta}^i = b^i \tau + c^i \text{ and } \hat{\gamma} = \sum_{i=1}^{n} d_i \hat{\beta}^i = (\sum_{i=1}^{n} d_i b^i)\tau + (\sum_{i=1}^{n} d_i c^i), \tag{4.2}$$

with $i = 1, \ldots, n+1$, where with $V \equiv 0$ the constraint Eq. (2.17) simply reads

$$G_{ij}b^i b^j + (b^{n+1})^2 = 0. \tag{4.3}$$

With Eq. (3.30) the scaling powers of the universe given by Eqs. (4.2) with $i = 1, \ldots, n$ transform to corresponding scale factors of the conformal universe

$$\beta^i = \hat\beta^i - \omega$$
$$= b^i \tau + \frac{1}{2-D} \ln|1 - \xi_c(\phi)^2| + c^i + \frac{2}{2-D} \ln \kappa - A \tag{4.4}$$

and

$$\gamma = \sum_{i=1}^{n} d_i \hat\beta^i - \omega$$
$$= \left(\sum_i d_i b^i\right)\tau + \frac{1}{2-D}\ln|1 - \xi_c(\phi)^2| + \left(\sum_i d_i c^i\right) + \frac{2}{2-D}\ln\kappa - A. \tag{4.5}$$

It should be clear that the variable τ, when harmonic in the minimal model, in the conformal model cannot be expected to be harmonic either, i.e. in general

$$\tau \neq t_h^{(c)}. \tag{4.6}$$

Actually from

$$\gamma = \sum_{i=1}^{n} d_i \beta^i = \sum_{i=1}^{n} d_i \hat\beta^i - \omega(D-1)$$

we see that $\tau = t_h^{(c)}$ only for $D = 2$ (but we have $D > 2$!).

Let us take for simplicity

$$A = \frac{2}{2-D} \ln \kappa, \tag{4.7}$$

which yields the lapse function

$$e^\gamma = e^{(\sum_i d_i b^i)\tau + (\sum_i d_i c^i)}|1 - \xi_c(\phi)^2|^{\frac{1}{2-D}} \tag{4.8}$$

and for $i = 1, \ldots, n$ the scale factors

$$e^{\beta^i} = e^{b^i \tau + c^i} |1 - \xi_c(\phi)^2|^{\frac{1}{2-D}}. \tag{4.9}$$

Let us further set for simplicity

$$c_< = c_> = \sqrt{\xi_c} c^{n+1}. \tag{4.10}$$

By Eqs. (3.28) or (3.29), the minimally coupled scalar field

$$\kappa \Phi(\tau) = b^{n+1} \tau + c^{n+1}, \tag{4.11}$$

substituted into Eqs. (4.8) and (4.9), yields

$$e^\gamma = e^{(\sum_i d_i b^i)\tau + (\sum_i d_i c^i)} \cosh^{\frac{2}{D-2}} \left(\sqrt{\xi_c} b^{n+1} \tau \right) \tag{4.12}$$

resp.

$$e^\gamma = e^{(\sum_i d_i b^i)\tau + (\sum_i d_i c^i)} |\sinh^{\frac{2}{D-2}} \left(\sqrt{\xi_c} b^{n+1} \tau \right)| \tag{4.13}$$

and, with $i = 1, \ldots, n$, non-singular scale factors

$$e^{\beta^i} = e^{b^i \tau + c^i} \cosh^{\frac{2}{D-2}} \left(\sqrt{\xi_c} b^{n+1} \tau \right) \tag{4.14}$$

resp. singular scale factors

$$e^{\beta^i} = e^{b^i \tau + c^i} |\sinh^{\frac{2}{D-2}} \left(\sqrt{\xi_c} b^{n+1} \tau \right)| \tag{4.15}$$

for the conformal model. The scale factor singularity of the minimal cou-pling model for $\tau \to -\infty$ vanishes in the conformal model of Eqs. (4.12) and (4.14) for a scalar field ϕ bounded according to (3.28). For $D = 4$ this result had already been indicated by [25].

On the other hand in the conformal model of Eqs. (4.13) and (4.15), with ϕ according to (3.29), though the scale factor singularity of the minimal model for $\tau \to -\infty$ has also disappeared, instead there is another new scale factor singularity at finite (harmonic) time $\tau = 0$.

Let us consider a special case of the non-singular solution with $\phi^2 < \xi_c^{-1}$, where we assume the internal spaces to be static in the minimal model, i.e. $b^i = 0$ for $i = 2, \ldots, n$. Then in the conformal model, the internal spaces are no longer static. Their scale factors (4.14) with $i > 2$ have a minimum at $\tau = 0$. From Eq. (4.3) with $G_{11} = d_1(1 - d_1)$ we find

$$(b^{n+1})^2 = d_1(d_1 - 1)(b^1)^2. \tag{4.16}$$

With real b_1 then also

$$b^{n+1} = \pm\sqrt{d_1(d_1 - 1)}b^1 \tag{4.17}$$

is real and by Eq. (4.14) the scale a_1 of M_1 has a minimum at

$$\tau_0 = (\sqrt{\xi_c}b^{n+1})^{-1}\mathrm{artanh}\left(\frac{(2 - D)}{2\sqrt{\xi_c}}\frac{b^1}{b^{n+1}}\right), \tag{4.18}$$

with $\tau_0 > 0$ for $b^1 < 0$ and $\tau_0 < 0$ for $b^1 > 0$.

Let M_1 be the external space with $b^1 > 0$ and hence $\tau_0 < 0$. Let us start with an Euclidean region of complex geometry given by scale factors

$$a_k = e^{-ib^k\tau + \tilde{c}^k}|\sin(\sqrt{\xi_c}b^{n+1}\tau)|^{\frac{2}{D-2}}.$$

Then we can perform an analytic continuation to the Lorentzian region with $\tau \to i\tau + \pi/(2\sqrt{\xi_c}b^{n+1})$, and we require $c^k = \tilde{c}^k - i\pi b^k/(2\sqrt{\xi_c}b^{n+1})$ to be the real constants of the real geometry.

The quantum creation (via tunnelling) of different factor spaces takes place at different values of τ (see Fig. 1). First the factor space M_1 comes into real existence and after an time interval $\Delta\tau = |\tau_0|$ the internal factor spaces $M_2, \ldots, M_n$ appear in the Lorentzian region. Since $\Delta\tau$ may be arbitrarily large, there is in principle an alternative explanation of the unobservable extra dimensions, independent from concepts of compactification and shrinking to a fundamental length. Similar to the spirit of the idea that internal dimensions might be hidden due to a potential barrier ([13]-[17]), they may have been up to now still in the Euclidean region and hence unobservable. This view is also compatible with their interpretation as complex resolutions of simple singularities in external space [23].

Now let us perform a transition from Lorentzian time τ to Euclidean time $-i\tau$. Then with a simultaneous transition from b^k to ib^k for $k = 1, \ldots, n$ the geometry remains real, since $\hat{\beta}^k = b^k\tau + c^k$ is unchanged. The analogue of Eq. (4.17) for the Euclidean region then becomes

$$b^{n+1} = \pm i\sqrt{d_1(d_1 - 1)}b^1. \tag{4.19}$$

This solution corresponds to a classical (instanton) wormhole. The sizes of the wormhole throats in the factor spaces $M_2, \ldots, M_n$ coincide with the sizes of static spaces in the minimal model, i.e. $\hat{a}_2(0), \ldots, \hat{a}_n(0)$ respectively.

With Eq. (4.17) replaced by (4.19), the Eq. (4.18) remains unchanged in the transition to the Euclidean region, and the minimum of the scale a_1 (unchanged geometry !) now corresponds to the throat of the wormhole in the factor space M_1.

If one wants to compare the synchronous time pictures of the minimal and the conformal solution, one has to calculate them for both metrics. In the minimal model we have

$$dt_s^{(m)} = e^{\hat{\gamma}}d\tau = e^{(\sum_i d_i b^i)\tau + (\sum_i d_i c^i)}d\tau, \tag{4.20}$$

which can be integrated to

$$t_s^{(m)} = (\sum_i d_i b^i)^{-1}e^{\hat{\gamma}} + t_0. \tag{4.21}$$

The latter can be inverted to

$$\tau = (\sum_i d_i b^i)^{-1}\left\{[\ln(\sum_i d_i b^i)(t_s^{(m)} - t_0)] - (\sum_i d_i c^i)\right\}. \tag{4.22}$$

Setting

$$B := \sum_{i=1}^{n} d_i b^i \text{ and } C := \sum_{i=1}^{n} d_i c^i, \tag{4.23}$$

this yields the scale factors

$$\hat{a}_s{}^i = (t_s^{(m)} - t_0)^{b^i/B} e^{\frac{b_i}{B}(\ln B - C) + c_i} \tag{4.24}$$

and the scalar field

$$\kappa\Phi = \frac{b^{n+1}}{B}\{[\ln B(t_s^{(m)} - t_0)] - C\} + c^{n+1}. \tag{4.25}$$

Let us define for $i = 1, \ldots, n+1$ the numbers

$$\alpha^i := \frac{b^i}{B}. \tag{4.26}$$

With (4.23) they satisfy

$$\sum_{i=1}^{n} d_i \alpha^i = 1, \tag{4.27}$$

and by Eq. (4.3) also

$$\alpha^{n+1} = \sqrt{1 - \sum_{i=1}^{n} d_i(\alpha^i)^2}. \tag{4.28}$$

Eqs. (4.24) shows, that the solution (4.2) is really a generalized Kasner universe with exponents α^i satisfying generalized Kasner conditions (4.27) and (4.28).

In the conformal model the synchronous time is given as

$$t_s^{(c)} = \int e^\gamma d\tau = \int \cosh^{\frac{2}{D-2}}(\sqrt{\xi_c} b^{n+1} \tau) e^{B\tau + C} d\tau \tag{4.29}$$

resp.

$$t_s^{(c)} = \int e^\gamma d\tau = \int \sinh^{\frac{2}{D-2}}(\sqrt{\xi_c} b^{n+1} \tau) e^{B\tau + C} d\tau. \tag{4.30}$$

5 Conclusion

In the first part of this paper, we reexamine the conformal equivalence between a model with minimal coupling and one with non-minimal coupling in the MCM case. The domains of equivalence are separated by certain critical values of the scalar field ϕ. Furthermore the coupling constant ξ of the coupling between ϕ and R is critical at both, the minimal value $\xi = 0$ and the conformal value $\xi_c = \frac{D-2}{4(D-1)}$. In different noncritical regions of ξ a solution of the model behaves qualitatively very different.

In the second part, we applied the conformal equivalence transformation to the multidimensional generalized Kasner universe with minimally coupled scalar field. So we obtained a new exact solution of a universe with Ricci flat factor spaces and conformally coupled scalar field. It has two qualitatively different regions of equivalence: In the first it is singular w.r.t. scale factors, in the other it is regular. For both, static internal spaces in the minimally coupling model become dynamical in the conformal coupling model. For the regular solution, scale factors are highly asymmetric in time. They have minima at different values harmonic time τ. These may naturally considered as the different times of birth of the factor spaces, where they emerge from the classically forbidden region. Hence the extra dimensions of the internal factor spaces may be still trapped, while external space is already born by quantum tunnelling. In particular it is also possible that some internal spaces never leave the classically forbidden region. Analytic continuation of this solution to the Euclidean region (while pertaining geometry and scalar field real), yields a classical wormhole (instanton).

Acknowledgements

This work was supported by WIP grant 016659 (U.B.), in part by DAAD and by DFG grant 436 UKR - 17/7/93 (A. Z.) and DFG grant Bl 365/1-1

(M.R.). A. Z. also thanks Prof. Kleinert and the Freie Universität Berlin as well as the members of the Gravitationsprojekt at Universität Potsdam for their hospitality.

References

[1] V. D. Ivashchuk, V. N. Melnikov, A. I. Zhuk, Nuovo Cim. B **104**, 575 (1989),

[2] U. Bleyer, D.-E. Liebscher and A. G. Polnarev, Nuovo Cim. B **106**, 107 (1991).

[3] U. Bleyer, D.-E. Liebscher and A. G. Polnarev, *Kaluza-Klein Models*, Proc. Vth Seminar on Quantum Gravity, Moscow 1990, World Scientific (1991).

[4] V. D. Ivashchuk Phys. Lett. A **170**, 16 (1992). A. I. Zhuk, Class. Quant. Grav. **9**, 2029 (1992); Sov J. Nucl. Phys. **55**, 149 (1992); Phys. Rev. D **45**, 1192 (1992).

[5] U. Bleyer and A. Zhuk, *Multidimensional Integrable Cosmological Models with Positive External Space Curvature; Multidimensional Integrable Cosmological Models with Negative External Space Curvature.* Gravitation and Cosmology **1** (1995), in press.

[6] U. Bleyer and A. Zhuk, Class. Quant. Grav. **11**, 1 (1994).

[7] U. Bleyer and A. Zhuk, Nucl. Phys. B **429**, 177 (1994).

[8] U. Bleyer and A. Zhuk, *Kasner-like and Inflation-like Solutions in Multidimensional Cosmology, in preparation.*

[9] K. Maeda, Phys. Rev. D **39**, 3159 (1989).

[10] B. C. Xanthapoulos and Th. E. Dialynas, J. Math. Phys. **33**. 1463 (1992).

[11] D. N. Page, J. Math. Phys. **32**, 3427 (1991).

[12] M. Rainer, *Conformal Coupling and Invariance in Arbitrary Dimensions*, Int. J. Mod. Phys. D (1994), in press.

[13] V. A. Rubakov, M. E. Shaposhnikov, Phys. Lett. B **125**, 136 (1983).

[14] M. Visser, Phys. Lett. B **159**, 22 (1985).

[15] E. J. Squires, Phys. Lett. B **167**, 286 (1986).

[16] M. D. Maia and V. Silveira, Phys. Rev. D **48**, 954 (1993).

[17] L. Amendola, E. W. Kolb, M. L. Litterio and F. Occhionero, Phys. Rev. D **42**, 1944 (1990).

[18] E. P. Tryon, Nature **246**, 396 (1973).

[19] P. I. Fomin, Doklady A.N.UkrSSR **9**, 831 (1975).

[20] Ya. B. Zeldovich, Pis'ma Astron. Zh. (Sov. Astron. Lett.) **7**, 579 (1981).

[21] L. P. Grishchuk, Ya. B. Zeldovich, Proc. IInd Sem. on Quantum Gravity, Moscow (1982).

[22] A. Vilenkin, Phys. Lett. B **117**, 25 (1982); Phys. Rev. D **27**, 2848 (1983).

[23] M. Rainer, *Projective Geometry for Relativistic Quantum Physics*, Proc. 23rd Ann. Iranian Math. Conf. (Baktaran, 1992); J. Math. Phys. **35**, 646 (1994).

[24] G. W. Gibbons and S. W. Hawking, Phys. Rev. D **15**, 2752 (1977).

[25] D. V. Gal'tsov and B. C. Xanthopoulos, J. Math. Phys. **33**, 273 (1992).

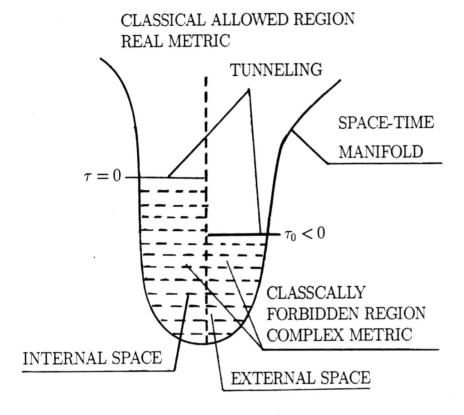

Fig. 1: Quantum birth with compact Ricci flat spaces and birth time $\tau_0 \leq 0$ of external Lorentzian space M_1. The birth of internal factor spaces $M_2, \ldots, M_n$ is delayed by the interval $\Delta\tau = |\tau_0|$. For $\Delta\tau \to \infty$ the internal spaces remain for ever in the (unobservable) classically forbidden region.

Gennadi A. Sardanashvily, Editor
New Frontiers in Gravitation
Hadronic Press, Palm Harbor, FL 34682-1577, U.S.A.
ISBN 0–911767–96–7, 1996, Pages 65–92

ON THE STRUCTURE OF THE EINSTEIN-YANG-MILLS EQUATIONS

N. Egidi and G. Giachetta

Dipartimento di Matematica e Fisica
Università di Camerino, 62032 Camerino, Italia

Abstract

We study the Einstein-Yang-Mills equations in the framework of the geometrical theory of partial differential equations. We prove that the Einstein-Yang-Mills differential operator is involutive and formally integrable. To this end a key role is played by the gauge-invariance and general covariance properties of the field equations. The existence of local solutions for the Einstein-Yang-Mills equations in the analytic context is proved.

1. Introduction

Let $P \rightarrow M$ be a principal fibre bundle over an oriented base manifold M. The Einstein-Yang-Mills (EYM) equations are

$$G(g) + \lambda g = T(g, A),$$
$$\nabla^A * F(A) = 0. \tag{1}$$

The solutions of this system of partial differential equations (pde's) are metrics g on M of fixed signature and principal connections A on P. Here G is the Einstein tensor, F is the gauge curvature tensor, T is the energy-momentum tensor of the Yang-Mills field, $*$ is the Hodge operator and $\lambda \in \mathbf{R}$.

These equations are the subject of our study in this paper. Essentially, we show that the EYM equations are involutive, and hence formally integrable. These results are important not only on their own but also because allow us to establish the existence of local solutions of the equations (1) in the analytic context. This is the main result of the paper.

We use the formal theory of overdetermined systems of pde's in the form given by Goldschmidt [1]. In precedent papers [2], [3] the pure Yang-Mills equations and the Yang-Mills-Higgs equations were studied using the same approach and similar theorems were shown to hold. Some years ago other authors had applied the formal theory of pde's to establish existence theorems for the Einstein equations [4] and to find metrics with prescribed Ricci curvature [5].

The organization of the paper is as follows.

In section 2 we briefly summarize the main facts about the jet formalism. In particular we define a system of pde's in jet bundle terms. We recall an important theorem of Malgrange [6] which guarantees, under some regularity conditions, the existence of analytic solutions of pde's. We state a well-known theorem of Goldschimdt [7] which furnishes a criterion for the formal integrability. The notion of involutive system of pde's is also given.

In section 3 we turn our attention to the EYM equations. Unfortunately, in this case a direct check of the Malgrange's conditions is not simple. We overcome this difficulty by showing that the EYM equations form an involutive system and are formally integrable. To this end a key role is played by the gauge-invariance and general covariance properties of the equations. For example, the divergenceless of the Einstein tensor, the charge conservation identity and an other differential identity involving the divergence of the energy-momentum tensor, are interpreted as conditions of surjectivity of a certain map. This surjectivity is one of the conditions required in the above mentioned theorem of Goldschmidt.

Section 4 is devoted to the proof of some results that we use in section 3.

2. The jet formalism and the formal theory of pde's

Throughout the paper all manifolds and maps will be smooth (C^∞). Manifolds will always be paracompact, Hausdorff topological spaces.

If M is a differentiable manifold we denote by TM and T^*M its tangent and cotangent bundles, respectively, and by $\otimes^p T^*M$, $\vee_p T^*M$ and $\wedge^p T^*M$, with $p \geq 0$, the p-th tensor, symmetric and exterior product of T^*M, respectively.

We identify $\vee_p T^*M$ and $\wedge^p T^*M$ with subbundles of $\otimes^p T^*M$ by defining

$$\alpha_1 \vee \cdots \vee \alpha_p = \sum_{\sigma \in S_p} \alpha_{\sigma(1)} \otimes \ldots \otimes \alpha_{\sigma(p)}$$

and

$$\alpha_1 \wedge \ldots \wedge \alpha_p = \sum_{\sigma \in S_p} \text{sgn}\sigma \, \alpha_{\sigma(1)} \otimes \ldots \otimes \alpha_{\sigma(p)},$$

for all $\alpha_1, \ldots, \alpha_p \in T^*M$, where S_p is the group of permutations of $\{1, \ldots, p\}$ and $\text{sgn}\sigma$ is the sign of $\sigma \in S_p$.

If $\varphi \in \wedge^p T^*M$ and $\vartheta \in \wedge^q T^*M$, we define the wedge product $\varphi \wedge \vartheta \in \wedge^{p+q} T^*M$ by

$$\varphi \wedge \vartheta(X_1, \ldots, X_{p+q}) =$$

$$\frac{1}{p!q!} \sum_{\sigma \in S_{p+q}} \text{sgn}\sigma \, \varphi(X_{\sigma(1)}, \ldots, X_{\sigma(p)}) \vartheta(X_{\sigma(p+1)}, \ldots, X_{\sigma(p+q)}),$$

for all $X_1, \ldots, X_{p+q} \in TM$.

2.1. Pde's in jet bundle terms. A standard reference for material on jet formalism is [8].

Let $\pi : E \to M$ be a fibered manifold (i.e. a surjective submersion), with

$$m = \dim M \quad \text{and} \quad m + l = \dim E.$$

The standard chart of E is denoted by (x^λ, y^i), with $1 \leq \lambda \leq m$ and $1 \leq i \leq l$.

Let $J^k E$ be the k-th order jet prolongation of π, with $k \geq 0$ ($J^0 E = E$). This is naturally a fibered manifold $\pi^k : J^k E \to M$ and a fiber bundle $\pi^k_h : J^k E \to J^h E$, respectively, with $0 \leq h \leq k$. The standard chart of $J^k E$ is denoted by (x^λ, y^i_B), with $0 \leq |B| \leq k$, where $B = (B_1, \ldots, B_m)$ is a multi-index and $|B| = B_1 + \cdots + B_m$. We put

$$O = (0, \ldots, 0), \qquad B + \lambda = (B_1, \ldots, B_\lambda + 1, \ldots, B_m),$$
$$y^i = y^i_O, \quad y^i_\lambda = y^i_{O+\lambda}, \quad y^i_{\lambda\mu} = y^i_{O+\lambda+\mu}, \ldots. \tag{2}$$

If $s : M \to E$ is a (local) section then $j^k s : M \to J^k E$ is its k-th order prolongation, whose coordinate expression is

$$(x^\lambda, y^i_B) \circ j^k s = (x^\lambda, \partial_B s^i),$$

where

$$s^i = y^i \circ s \qquad \text{and} \qquad \partial_B s^i = \partial_1^{B_1} \ldots \partial_m^{B_m} s^i.$$

We always put $j^k_x s \equiv j^k s(x)$, for all x in the domain where s is defined, and $\partial_\lambda \equiv \partial/\partial x^\lambda$.

We have a basic affine structure on jet manifolds; namely $\pi^k_{k-1} : J^k E \to J^{k-1} E$ is an affine bundle, for $k \geq 1$, whose vector bundle is the pull-back bundle $J^{k-1} E \underset{E}{\times} \vee_k T^* M \otimes VE$.

If $\pi : E \to M$ is a vector bundle then one can easily see that $\pi^k : J^k E \to M$ is also a vector bundle. Moreover, there is a morphism of vector bundles (over M)

$$\epsilon : \vee_k T^* M \otimes E \to J^k E$$

defined by

$$\epsilon((df_1 \vee \cdots \vee df_k \otimes s)(x)) = j^k_x((\prod_{j=1}^{k} f_j)s), \qquad (3)$$

where $f_1, \ldots, f_k$ are real-valued functions on M vanishing at $x \in M$ and $s : M \to E$ is a section. From (3) one can easily check that the sequence

$$0 \longrightarrow \vee_k T^* M \otimes E \xrightarrow{\epsilon} J^k E \xrightarrow{\pi^k_{k-1}} J^{k-1} E \longrightarrow 0$$

is exact, for all $k \geq 1$.

A pde of order k on E is defined to be a fibered submanifold $R^k \to M$ of $\pi^k : J^k E \to M$. A solution of R^k is a (local) section $s : M \to E$ such that its k-th order prolongation $j^k s$ is a section of $\pi^k : R^k \to M$.

A less general definition of pde is the following. Let $\pi' : E' \to M$ be another fibered manifold and let $\phi : J^k E \to E'$ be a morphism of fibered manifolds over M. Given a section $s' : M \to E'$, we define

$$R^k = \text{Ker}_{s'} \phi = \{p \in J^k E : \phi(p) = s' \circ \pi^k(p)\} \qquad (4)$$

and assume that

$$s'(M) \subset \text{Im}(\phi) \quad \text{and} \quad \phi \text{ has locally constant rank.} \qquad (5)$$

Then one can show that R^k is a fibered submanifold of $J^k E \to M$ and a pde of order k [7].

Note that these two definitions are locally equivalent.

In what follows we shall be interested in a particular class of pde's. Let $\pi : E \to M$ and $\pi' : E' \to M$ be a fibered manifold and a vector bundle, respectively. Let $\phi : J^k E \to E'$ be a morphism of fibered manifolds. We say that ϕ is *quasi-linear* if there exists a morphism of vector bundles

$$\sigma(\phi) : \mathsf{V}_k T^* M \otimes VE \to E' \tag{6}$$

over $J^{k-1}E$ such that

$$\phi(p + (\pi^k_{k-1}(p), u)) = \phi(p) + \sigma(\phi)(\pi^k_{k-1}(p), u),$$

for every $p \in J^k E$ and $u \in \mathsf{V}_k T^* M \otimes VE$ over the same point of E. In other words ϕ is quasi-linear if it is an affine morphism with respect to the affine structure of $J^k E$ over $J^{k-1}E$. The map $\sigma(\phi)$, uniquely determined by ϕ, is called the *symbol* of ϕ and the pde defined in (4), (5) is called *quasi-linear*.

As it is easily seen, if ϕ is quasi-linear and $\sigma(\phi)$ is an epimorphism then ϕ is a surjective submersion. Hence (5) is satisfied and

$$\pi^k_{k-1}(R^k) = J^{k-1}E. \tag{7}$$

Usually one denotes by $G^k \subset R^k \underset{E}{\times} \mathsf{V}_k\, T^* M \otimes VE$ the pull-back over R^k of the kernel of $\sigma(\phi)$. Sometimes G^k itself is called the *symbol* of ϕ. Of course G^k has a structure of vector bundle over R^k only under some regularity conditions of $\sigma(\phi)$.

We now introduce a basic concept of the theory of pde's, namely that of prolongation. Let $\phi : J^k E \to E'$ and $s' : M \to E'$ be as in (5). The *h-th order prolongation* of ϕ ($h \geq 0$) is the morphism

$$p_h(\phi) : J^{k+h} E \to J^h E'$$

over M defined by

$$p_h(\phi)(j_x^{k+h}s) = j_x^h(\phi \circ j^k s), \tag{8}$$

for every $x \in M$ and for every section $s : M \to E$ ($p_0(\phi) = \phi$). The subset

$$R^{k+h} = \mathrm{Ker}_{j^h s'}p_h(\phi) \subset J^{k+h}E \tag{9}$$

is called the *h-th order prolongation* of the pde R^k.

It can be shown [9] that this definition depends only on R^k and not on the morphism ϕ used to define it. Obviously the canonical projection $\pi_{k+h}^{k+h+1} : J^{k+h+1}E \to J^{k+h}E$ restricts to a map $\pi_{k+h}^{k+h+1} : R^{k+h+1} \to R^{k+h}$, for every $h \geq 0$.

One can easily check that if ϕ is quasi-linear then so is its prolongation of any order. The uniquely determined morphism of vector bundles

$$\sigma_h(\phi) : \mathsf{V}_{k+h}T^*M \otimes VE \to \mathsf{V}_h T^*M \otimes E' \tag{9bis}$$

over $J^{k-1}E$ is called the *h-th order prolongation* of the symbol $\sigma(\phi)$. It is defined by the composition

$$\mathsf{V}_{k+h}T^*M \otimes VE \overset{i}{\hookrightarrow} \mathsf{V}_h T^*M \otimes \mathsf{V}_k T^*M \otimes VE \overset{\sigma(\phi)}{\to} \mathsf{V}_h T^*M \otimes E', \tag{9tres}$$

where i denotes the canonical inclusion.

The pull-back over R^k of the kernel of $\sigma_h(\phi)$ is denoted by $G^{k+h} \subset R^k \underset{E}{\times} \mathsf{V}_{k+h} T^*M \otimes VE$. Even if G^k is a vector bundle G^{k+h} may fail to be a vector bundle.

2.2. Involutive pde's. If M is a real-analytic manifold, E and E' are real-analytic fibered manifolds over M, $\phi : J^k E \to E'$ is a real-analytic morphism and $s' : M \to E'$ is a real-analytic section, then the pde defined in (4), (5) is said to be an *analytic* pde.

Given an analytic pde R^k of order k, we are interested in finding its convergent power series solutions in a neighborhood of any given point $x \in M$. We call a point of R^{k+h} a formal solution of R^k of order $k + h$ and a point of $R^\infty = \text{proj} \lim R^{k+h}$ a formal solution.

Of course, in the construction of analytic solutions of R^k a preliminary step is to check whether a formal solution of order $\geq k$ can be prolonged to a formal solution. A sufficient condition is obviously that

$$\text{the map} \quad \pi^{k+h+1}_{k+h} : R^{k+h+1} \to R^{k+h} \quad \text{is surjective, for all } h \geq 0. \quad (10)$$

The following important theorem [6] guarantees the existence of power series solutions for analytic pde's satisfying (10).

Theorem 2.1. *Let R^k be an analytic pde of order k. Let $x \in M$ and $h \geq 0$. If $\pi^{k+n+1}_{k+n} : R^{k+n+1}_x \to R^{k+n}_x$ is surjective for all $n \geq h$, then for every point $p \in R^{k+h}_x$ there exists an analytic solution $s : U \subset M \to E$ over a neighborhood U of x such that $j^{k+h}_x s = p$.*

In general a direct check of (10) is not simple. However, there are criteria which allow us to verify the surjectivity of the maps (10) in a finite number of steps. One of these criteria is the formal integrability of the pde. We say that R^k is *formal integrable* if the maps (10) are surjective submersions.

The following theorem is due to Goldschimdt [7] and gives sufficient conditions for the formal integrability. Combined with Theorem 2.1, it leads to the existence of analytic solutions of analytic quasi-linear pde's.

Theorem 2.2. Let $\phi : J^k E \to E'$ be a quasi-linear morphism and let R^k be the pde defined in (4), (5). If

(i) G^{k+1} is a vector bundle over R^k,

(ii) $\pi_k^{k+1} : R^{k+1} \to R^k$ is surjective,

(iii) G^k is 2-acyclic

then R^k is formally integrable.

The condition (iii) refers to the vanishing of some of the Spencer's cohomology groups $H^{k-j,j}(G^k)$. One can show [10] that this condition may be replaced by a stronger one, namely

(iii') for all $p \in R^k$ there exists a quasi-regular basis of $T_{\pi^k(p)}M$ for G^k at p.

This means the following. Let $x \in M$ and let (X_λ), with $1 \le \lambda \le m$, be a basis of $T_x M$. If (θ^λ) is the basis of $T^* M$ dual to (X_λ), then we denote by $\vee_{k,j} T_x^* M$ the subspace of $\vee_k T_x^* M$ spanned by $\theta^{\mu_1} \vee \cdots \vee \theta^{\mu_k}$, with $j + 1 \le \mu_1 \le \cdots \le \mu_k \le m$. For every $p \in R^k$ one defines

$$(G^k)_{p,j} = (G^k)_p \cap \vee_{k,j} T_x^* M \otimes (VE)_e,$$

where $x = \pi^k(p)$ and $e = \pi_0^k(p)$. One says that (X_λ) is a *quasi-regular* basis for G^k at p if

$$\dim(G^{k+1})_p = \dim(G^k)_p + \sum_{j=1}^{m-1} \dim(G^k)_{p,j}. \tag{11}$$

The condition (iii') corresponds to the *involutivity* of the symbol G^k of R^k. A pde R^k is said to be *involutive* if it is formally integrable and its symbol G^k is involutive.

3. The EYM equations

3.1. Geometric setup of the EYM pde's. Let $P \to M$ be a principal fibe r bundle over an m-dimensional manifold M, with n-dimensional structure Lie group G [11]. We denote by $C \to M$ the affine bundle of principal connections on P. Its associated vector bundle is $T^*M \otimes V_G P \to M$, where the quotient bun dle $V_G P = VP/G \to M$ is the vector bundle of right invariant vertical vector fields on P. The standard chart of C is denoted by (x^λ, a_λ^r). If $A : M \to C$ is a principal connection then we write

$$(x^\lambda, a_\lambda^r) \circ A = (x^\lambda, A_\lambda^r),$$

where A_λ^r are local functions on M. As is well known a principal connecti on A induces a linear connection ∇^A in the vector bundle $V_G P \to M$. Its connection parameters are

$$\nabla^A e_q = c_{pq}^r A_\lambda^p \, dx^\lambda \otimes e_r, \tag{12}$$

where (e_p), with $1 \leq p \leq n$, is a basis of the Lie algebra LG of G and c_{pq}^r are the right structure constants of G [12].

Let $L \subset V_2 T^*M \to M$ be the bundle of metrics on M of fixed signatur e [13]. The standard chart of L is denoted by $(x^\lambda, g_{\lambda\mu})$. For every metr ic $g : M \to L$ let ∇^g be the corresponding Levi-Civita connection. Its connection parameters are the Christoffel symbols, i.e.

$$\Gamma^\alpha_{\lambda\mu} = \frac{1}{2}\mathbf{g}^{\alpha\beta}(\partial_\lambda \mathbf{g}_{\beta\mu} + \partial_\mu \mathbf{g}_{\beta\lambda} - \partial_\beta \mathbf{g}_{\lambda\mu}), \tag{13}$$

with

$$(x^\lambda, g_{\lambda\mu}) \circ g = (x^\lambda, \mathbf{g}_{\lambda\mu}).$$

We recall that for every tensor field $u \in T^r_s(M)$,

$$u = u^{\lambda_1...\lambda_r}_{\mu_1...\mu_s} \partial_{\lambda_1} \otimes ... \otimes \partial_{\lambda_r} \otimes dx^{\mu_1} \otimes ... \otimes dx^{\mu_s},$$

its covariant derivative $\nabla^g u \in T^r_{s+1}(M)$ is defined locally by

$$\nabla^g_\nu u^{\lambda_1...\lambda_r}_{\mu_1...\mu_s} = \partial_\nu u^{\lambda_1...\lambda_r}_{\mu_1...\mu_s} + \Gamma^{\lambda_1}_{\nu\rho} u^{\rho\lambda_2...\lambda_r}_{\mu_1...\mu_s} + \cdots - \Gamma^\rho_{\nu\mu_1} u^{\lambda_1...\lambda_r}_{\rho\mu_2...\mu_s} - \cdots \tag{14}$$

If $u \in T^1_1(M)$ we denote by $\mathrm{div}^g u$ the 1-form

$$(\mathrm{div}^g u)_\mu = \nabla^g_\lambda u^\lambda_\mu. \tag{15}$$

Given a principal connection $A : M \to C$, we can define a covariant derivative $\nabla^{g,A} u$ of $V_G P$-valued tensor fields $u \in T^r_s(M; V_G P)$. If

$$u = u^{\lambda_1...\lambda_r p}_{\mu_1...\mu_s} \partial_{\lambda_1} \otimes ... \otimes \partial_{\lambda_r} \otimes dx^{\mu_1} \otimes ... \otimes dx^{\mu_s} \otimes e_p$$

then $\nabla^{g,A} u \in T^r_{s+1}(M; V_G P)$ is given locally by

$$\nabla^{g,A}_\nu u^{\lambda_1...\lambda_r p}_{\mu_1...\mu_s} = \nabla^g_\nu u^{\lambda_1...\lambda_r p}_{\mu_1...\mu_s} + c^p_{tq} A^t_\nu u^{\lambda_1...\lambda_r q}_{\mu_1...\mu_s}. \tag{16}$$

Since we are concerned with the interaction between gravitational and gauge fiel ds, our configuration bundle is the fibered product bundle $Q =$

$L \times_M C \to M$. There are two basic objects related to the configuration bundle Q, namely the *gauge curvature* operator

$$F : J^1C \to \overset{2}{\wedge} T^*M \otimes V_G P,$$

$$F = \frac{1}{2} F_{\lambda\mu}{}^r \, dx^\lambda \wedge dx^\mu \otimes e_r, \quad F_{\lambda\mu}{}^r = a_{\lambda,\mu}{}^r - a_{\mu,\lambda}{}^r + c_{pq}^r a_\lambda^p a_\mu^q \tag{17}$$

and the *Ricci* operator

$$R : J^2L \to V_2 T^*M,$$

$$R = \frac{1}{2} R_{\mu\nu} \, dx^\mu \vee dx^\nu, \quad R_{\mu\nu} = \partial_\alpha \Gamma^\alpha_{\mu\nu} - \partial_\mu \Gamma^\alpha_{\alpha\nu} + \Gamma^\alpha_{\alpha\beta}\Gamma^\beta_{\mu\nu} - \Gamma^\alpha_{\mu\beta}\Gamma^\beta_{\alpha\nu}. \tag{18}$$

Note that R is quasi-linear; its symbol

$$\sigma(R) : V_2 T^*M \otimes V_2 T^*M \to V_2 T^*M$$

over L (note that $VL = L \times_M V_2 T^*M$) is defined by

$$\sigma(R)(g, \alpha \vee \beta \otimes \gamma \vee \delta) = \frac{1}{2}[-2g(\alpha,\beta)\gamma \vee \delta - 2g(\gamma,\delta)\alpha \vee \beta$$
$$+ g(\beta,\delta)\alpha \vee \gamma + g(\alpha,\gamma)\beta \vee \delta \tag{19}$$
$$+ g(\beta,\gamma)\alpha \vee \delta + g(\alpha,\delta)\beta \vee \gamma],$$

for every metric $g : M \to L$ and α, β, γ, $\delta \in T^*M$.

The *Einstein morphism*

$$\mathcal{E} : V_2 T^*M \to V_2 T^*M$$

is the linear morphism over L given by

$$\mathcal{E}(g, \alpha \vee \beta) = \alpha \vee \beta - g(\alpha,\beta)g, \tag{20}$$

for every $g : M \to L$ and α, $\beta \in T^*M$.

Lemma 3.1. Let $m \neq 2$. For every metric $g : M \to L$ the morphism $\mathcal{E}(g) : \mathsf{V}_2 T^* M \to \mathsf{V}_2 T^* M$ over M is an automorphism.

Proof. Denoting by $(x^\lambda, u_{\lambda\mu})$ the standard chart of $\mathsf{V}_2 T^* M$, we easily find

$$\mathcal{E}(g) : u_{\lambda\mu} \mapsto u_{\lambda\mu} - \frac{1}{2} g_{\lambda\mu} g^{\alpha\beta} u_{\alpha\beta}. \tag{21}$$

Then

$$g^{\lambda\mu}(u_{\lambda\mu} - \frac{1}{2} g_{\lambda\mu} g^{\alpha\beta} u_{\alpha\beta}) = (1 - m/2) g^{\lambda\mu} u_{\lambda\mu}$$

and hence

$$u_{\lambda\mu} - \frac{1}{2} g_{\lambda\mu} g^{\alpha\beta} u_{\alpha\beta} = 0 \Longrightarrow g^{\lambda\mu} u_{\lambda\mu} = 0 \Longrightarrow u_{\lambda\mu} = 0.$$

The *Einstein operator* can be seen as a morphism over M

$$G : J^2 L \to \mathsf{V}_2 T^* M$$

defined by

$$G = \mathcal{E} \circ R. \tag{22}$$

Clearly G is quasi-linear, the corresponding symbol being the morphism over L

$$\sigma(G) : \mathsf{V}_2 T^* M \otimes \mathsf{V}_2 T^* M \to \mathsf{V}_2 T^* M$$

given by

$$\sigma(G) = \mathcal{E} \circ \sigma(R). \tag{23}$$

Assume M to be oriented and let h be a metric in the Lie algebra of G such that the adjoint representation is orthogonal. Then the EYM equations are

$$G(g) + \lambda g = T(g, A), \tag{24a}$$

$$\nabla^A * F(A) = 0. \tag{24b}$$

Here $\lambda \in \mathbf{R}$ is a constant, $*$ is the Hodge operator on M and T is the energy-momentum tensor of the Yang-Mills field:

$$T : L \underset{M}{\times} J^1 C \to \vee_2 T^* M,$$

$$2T_{\lambda\mu} = \frac{1}{4} g_{\lambda\mu} F^{\alpha\beta}{}_r F_{\alpha\beta}{}^r + g_{\lambda\alpha} F^{\alpha\beta}{}_r F_{\beta\mu}{}^r, \tag{24}$$

where

$$F^{\lambda\mu}{}_r = h_{rs} g^{\lambda\alpha} g^{\mu\beta} F_{\alpha\beta}{}^s. \tag{25}$$

From (12) and (21) we easily see that locally the equations (3.13) read

$$R_{\lambda\mu} - \frac{1}{2} g_{\lambda\mu} g^{\alpha\beta} R_{\alpha\beta} + \lambda g_{\lambda\mu} = T_{\lambda\mu}, \tag{26a}$$

$$\nabla^A_\lambda(\sqrt{|g|} F^{\lambda\mu}{}_r) \equiv \partial_\lambda(\sqrt{|g|} F^{\lambda\mu}{}_r) - \sqrt{|g|} c^s_{qr} A^q_\lambda F^{\lambda\mu}{}_s = 0. \tag{26b}$$

3.2. Involutivity of the EYM pde's. Let us define

$$\phi : J^2 Q \to \vee_2 T^* M \oplus {}^{m-1}\wedge T^* M \otimes V^*_G P,$$

$$\phi(j^2_x g, j^2_x A) = (G(g) + \lambda g - T(g, A), \nabla^A * F(A))(x), \tag{27}$$

for every $x \in M$, $(g, A) : M \to Q$. A section $(g, A) : M \to Q$ is a solution of the EYM equations iff $\phi(j^2 g, j^2 A) = 0$. According to (4) we define

$$R^2 = \operatorname{Ker} \phi \subset J^2 Q. \tag{28}$$

As (17), (18) and (16) show, ϕ is a quasi-linear morphism and its symbol

$$\sigma(\phi) : \mathsf{V}_2 T^* M \otimes \overline{Q} \to \mathsf{V}_2 T^* M \oplus \overset{m-1}{\wedge} T^* M \otimes V_G^* P \tag{29}$$

over $J^1 Q$ is given by

$$\sigma(\phi) = \sigma(G) \oplus \sigma(\nabla * F). \tag{30}$$

Here $\overline{Q} = \mathsf{V}_2 T^* M \oplus T^* M \otimes V_G P$ is the vector bundle associated with $Q \to M$.

The linear morphism

$$\sigma(\nabla * F) : \mathsf{V}_2 T^* M \otimes T^* M \otimes V_G P \to \overset{m-1}{\wedge} T^* M \otimes V_G^* P$$

is given by the following composition

$$\mathsf{V}_2 T^* M \otimes T^* M \otimes V_G P \overset{\xi}{\longrightarrow} T^* M \otimes V_G P \overset{\eta}{\longrightarrow} \overset{m-1}{\wedge} T^* M \otimes V_G^* P, \tag{31}$$

with

$$\xi(g, \alpha \vee \beta \otimes \gamma \otimes v) = [2g(\alpha, \beta)\gamma - g(\alpha, \gamma)\beta - g(\beta, \gamma)\alpha] \otimes v, \tag{32}$$

for every $g : M \to L$, α, β, $\gamma \in T^* M$ and $v \in V_G P$, and where η is the tensor product morphism of the Hodge operator on M and the metric isomorphism of $V_G P$ induced by h.

Lemma 3.2. *If $m \geq 3$ the symbol $\sigma(\phi)$ is surjective.*

Proof. We show that both $\sigma(G)$ and $\sigma(\nabla * F)$ are surjective.

Since $\sigma(G) = \mathcal{E} \circ \sigma(R)$, owing to Lemma 3.1 we only need to show the surjectivity of $\sigma(R)$. Let (dx^λ) be an orthonormal basis of $T_x^* M$, $x \in M$, with respect to a metric $g : M \to L$, i.e.

$$g(dx^\lambda, dx^\mu) = \begin{cases} 0, & \text{if } \lambda \neq \mu \\ \pm 1, & \text{if } \lambda = \mu. \end{cases}$$

If $1 \leq \lambda$, μ, $\nu \leq m$ are different from each other, then using (19) we find

$$\sigma(R)(g, dx^\lambda \vee dx^\mu \otimes dx^\nu \vee dx^\nu) = -g^{\nu\nu} dx^\lambda \vee dx^\mu. \tag{33}$$

If $\lambda \neq \mu$ then

$$\sigma(R)(g, dx^\lambda \vee dx^\lambda \otimes dx^\mu \vee dx^\mu) = -g^{\lambda\lambda} dx^\mu \vee dx^\mu - g^{\mu\mu} dx^\lambda \vee dx^\lambda.$$

Choosing $1 \leq \alpha$, β, $\gamma \leq m$ different from each other, we easily see that

$$g^{\alpha\alpha} dx^\rho \vee dx^\rho + g^{\rho\rho} dx^\alpha \vee dx^\alpha, \quad \text{with } \rho \neq \alpha,$$
$$g^{\gamma\gamma} dx^\beta \vee dx^\beta + g^{\beta\beta} dx^\gamma \vee dx^\gamma,$$

along with (33), form a basis of $\vee_2 T_x^* M$. Hence $\sigma(R)$ is surjective.

Coming to $\sigma(\nabla * F)$, let us prove that ξ is surjective. For this, according to (32), it is sufficient to solve the equations

$$2g(\alpha, \beta)\gamma - g(\alpha, \gamma)\beta - g(\beta, \gamma)\alpha = dx^\lambda, \quad 1 \leq \lambda \leq m.$$

One can easily verify that solutions of these equations are $\gamma = g^{\mu\mu} dx^\lambda$ and $\alpha = \beta = \dfrac{1}{\sqrt{2}} dx^\mu$, with $\mu \neq \lambda$.

From Lemma 3.2 it follows that $R^2 \to M$ is a fibered submanifold of $J^2Q \to M$ and a pde (see section 2.1). Moreover

$$\pi_1^2(R^2) = J^1Q. \tag{34}$$

Now we consider the first order prolongation of ϕ, i.e.

$$p_1(\phi) : J^3Q \to J^1(\vee_2 T^*M \oplus {}^{m-1}\wedge\, T^*M \otimes V_G^*P), \tag{35}$$

$$p_1(\phi)(j_x^3 g, j_x^3 A) = (j_x^1(G(g) + \lambda g - T(g, A)), \, j_x^1(\nabla^A * F(A))).$$

From (9tres) and (30) we see that its symbol is the morphism

$$\sigma_1(\phi) : \vee_3 T^*M \otimes \overline{Q} \to T^*M \otimes (\vee_2 T^*M \oplus {}^{m-1}\wedge\, T^*M \otimes V_G^*P) \tag{36}$$

over J^1Q given by

$$\sigma_1(\phi) = \sigma_1(G) \oplus \sigma_1(\nabla * F), \tag{37}$$

where

$$\sigma_1(G) : \vee_3 T^*M \otimes \vee_2 T^*M \to T^*M \otimes \vee_2 T^*M$$

and

$$\sigma_1(\nabla * F) : \vee_3 T^*M \otimes T^*M \otimes V_G P \to T^*M \otimes {}^{m-1}\wedge\, T^*M \otimes V_G^*P$$

are the symbols of the first order prolongation of the Einstein operator G and the Yang-Mills operator $\nabla * F$, respectively.

In order to verify the conditions (i) and (ii) of Theorem 2.2 we introduce the following morphisms over J^1Q:

$$\psi_1 : J^1(\vee_2 T^*M) \to T^*M,$$

$$\psi_1(j_x^1 g, j_x^1 u) = \mathrm{div}^g \widehat{u} \tag{38}$$

and

$$\psi_2 : J^1(\overset{m-1}{\wedge} T^*M \otimes V_G^*P) \to \overset{m}{\wedge} T^*M \otimes V_G^*P, \tag{39}$$

$$\psi_2(A(x), j_x^1\theta) = (\nabla^A\theta)(x),$$

for every $x \in M$, $(g, A) : M \to Q$, $u : M \to V_2T^*M$ and $\theta : M \to \wedge^{m-1} T^*M \otimes V_G^*P$. In (38), $\hat{u} \in T_1^1(M)$ is the tensor equivalent to u obtained by using the metric g. Note that (38) and (39) are both linear morphisms. Their symbols are given by

$$\sigma(\psi_1) : T^*M \otimes V_2T^*M \to T^*M, \tag{40}$$

$$\sigma(\psi_1)(g, \alpha \otimes \beta \vee \gamma) = g(\alpha, \beta)\gamma + g(\alpha, \gamma)\beta$$

and

$$\sigma(\psi_2) : T^*M \otimes \overset{m-1}{\wedge} T^*M \otimes V_G^*P \to \overset{m}{\wedge} T^*M \otimes V_G^*P, \tag{41}$$

$$\sigma(\psi_2)(\alpha \otimes \theta) = \alpha \wedge \theta.$$

A consequence of the following Lemma is that $G^3 = \operatorname{Ker} \sigma_1(\phi)$ is a vector bundle.

Lemma 3.3. *If $m \geq 3$ then the sequence over J^1Q*

$$0 \to G^3 \to V_3T^*M \otimes \overline{Q} \xrightarrow{\sigma_1(\phi)} T^*M \otimes (V_2T^*M \oplus \overset{m-1}{\wedge} T^*M \otimes V_G^*P)$$

$$\xrightarrow{\sigma(\psi_1) \oplus \sigma(\psi_2)} T^*M \oplus \overset{m}{\wedge} T^*M \otimes V_G^*P \to 0$$

is exact.

Proof. Recalling (37), we see that the sequence decomposes in the following ones:

$$0 \to (G_1)^3 \to V_3T^*M \otimes V_2T^*M \xrightarrow{\sigma_1(G)} T^*M \otimes V_2T^*M \xrightarrow{\sigma(\psi_1)} T^*M \to 0$$

and

$$0 \to (G_2)^3 \to \vee_3 T^*M \otimes T^*M \otimes V_G P \xrightarrow{\sigma_1(\nabla * F)} T^*M \otimes \overset{m-1}{\wedge} T^*M \otimes V_G^* P$$

$$\xrightarrow{\sigma(\psi_2)} \overset{m}{\wedge} T^*M \otimes V_G^* P \to 0.$$

The exactness of the first sequence is proved by Gasqui [4]. Here we prove that the second sequence is exact.

Obviously $\sigma(\psi_2)$ is surjective. Denoting by $(x^\lambda, u_{\alpha\nu\mu,\lambda}^r)$ the standard chart of $\vee_3 T^*M \otimes T^*M \otimes V_G P$, we have

$$(x^\lambda, g_{\lambda\mu}, u_{\alpha\nu\mu,\lambda}^r) \xrightarrow{\sigma_1(\nabla * F)} \sqrt{|g|} h_{rs} g^{\lambda\alpha} g^{\mu\beta} (u_{\nu\lambda\alpha,\beta}^s - u_{\nu\lambda\beta,\alpha}^s)$$

$$\xrightarrow{\sigma(\psi_2)} \sqrt{|g|} h_{rs} g^{\lambda\alpha} g^{\mu\beta} (u_{\mu\lambda\alpha,\beta}^s - u_{\mu\lambda\beta,\alpha}^s)$$

$$= \sqrt{|g|} h_{rs} (g^{\lambda\alpha} g^{\mu\beta} u_{\mu\lambda\alpha,\beta}^s - g^{\mu\beta} g^{\lambda\alpha} u_{\lambda\mu\alpha,\beta}^s) = 0.$$

Hence $\text{Im}(\sigma_1(\nabla * F)) \subset \text{Ker}(\sigma(\psi_2))$. Recalling (9tres) and (31), instead of proving the opposite inclusion we prove the equivalent one, namely $\text{Im}(\xi \circ i) \supset \text{Ker}(\sigma(\psi_2) \circ \eta)$. Apart from $V_G P$ and $V_G^* P$, from (32) we find

$$\xi \circ i(g, \alpha \vee \alpha \vee \alpha \otimes \beta) = 6\alpha \otimes [g(\alpha, \alpha)\beta - g(\alpha, \beta)\alpha],$$

for every α, $\beta \in T^*M$ and $g : M \to L$. On the other hand, $\text{Ker}(\sigma(\psi_2) \circ \eta)$ is generated by $\mu \otimes \mu$, with $g(\mu, \mu) = 0$, and/or $\mu \otimes \rho$, with $g(\mu, \rho) = 0$, $g(\mu, \mu) \neq 0$, $g(\rho, \rho) \neq 0$, for all μ, $\rho \in T^*M$ (depending on the signature of the metric). Now the equations

$$6\alpha \otimes [g(\alpha, \alpha)\beta - g(\alpha, \beta)\alpha] = \mu \otimes \mu,$$

$$6\alpha \otimes [g(\alpha, \alpha)\beta - g(\alpha, \beta)\alpha] = \mu \otimes \rho$$

have solutions:

$$\alpha = \mu, \qquad \beta \text{ such that } -6g(\mu, \beta) = 1$$

and

$$\alpha = \mu, \qquad \beta = \frac{1}{6g(\mu, \mu)}\rho.$$

respectively. This completes the proof of the Lemma.

Lemma 3.4. *If $m \geq 3$ then the map $\pi_2^3 : R^3 \rightarrow R^2$ is surjective.*

Proof. Let $p \in R^2$ and let $(g, A) : M \rightarrow Q$ be a section such that $p = (j_x^2 g, j_x^2 A)$. Consider

$$\epsilon^{-1} \circ p_1(\phi)(j_x^3 g, j_x^3 A) \in T_x^* M \otimes (V_2 T_x^* M \oplus \overset{m-1}{\wedge} T_x^* M \otimes (V_G^* P)_x).$$

Since $p_1(\phi)$ is quasi-linear the fiber $(R^3)_p$ is not empty iff

$$\epsilon^{-1} \circ p_1(\phi)(j_x^3 g, j_x^3 A) \in \text{Im}(\sigma_1(\phi))$$

or, owing to the precedent Lemma, iff

$$\sigma(\psi_1) \oplus \sigma(\psi_2) \circ \epsilon^{-1} \circ p_1(\phi)(j_x^3 g, j_x^3 A) = 0.$$

Since (38) and (39) are both linear morphisms, this relation is equivalent to

$$\psi_1 \oplus \psi_2 \circ p_1(\phi)(j_x^3 g, j_x^3 A) = 0.$$

We have

$$\psi_1 \oplus \psi_2 \circ p_1(\phi)(j_x^3 g, j_x^3 A)$$
$$= \psi_1 \oplus \psi_2(j_x^1(G(g) + \lambda g - T(g, A)), j_x^1(\nabla^A * F(A)))$$
$$= (\text{div}^g(\widehat{G}(g) + \lambda \widehat{g} - \widehat{T}(g, A))(x), \nabla^A \nabla^A * F(A)(x)).$$

Using the Bianchi identity $\text{div}^g \widehat{G}(g) = 0$ [14], the charge conservation identity $\nabla^A \nabla^A * F(A) = 0$ [15], and the identity $\text{div}^g \widehat{g} = 0$ which holds since ∇^g is the Levi-Civita connection of g, the above relation yields

$$\psi_1 \oplus \psi_2 \circ p_1(\phi)(j_x^3 g, j_x^3 A) = (-\text{div}^g \widehat{T}(g, A)(x), 0).$$

But (see (15))

$$\nabla_\mu^g T_\nu^\mu = \nabla_\mu^A (\sqrt{|g|} F^{\mu\beta}_{\ \ r}) F_{\beta\nu}{}^r \sqrt{|g|}^{-1}. \tag{42}$$

Since the equation (26b) is identically satisfied on R^2, the result follows.

The identity (42) is a consequence of the gauge-invariance and covariance properties of the field system we are considering [12], [13]. Later on we shall give a direct proof of (42).

Finally, let us show that the condition (iii') of section 2.2 holds.

Lemma 3.5. *If $m \geq 3$ then for every $p \in R^2$ there is a quasi-regular basis of $T_{\pi^2(p)} M$ for G^2 at p.*

Proof. Let $p = (j_x^2 g, j_x^2 A)$ and let (dx^λ) be a g-orthonormal basis of $T_x^* M$. We have the following dimension counting, the proof of which will be given in the next section:

$$\dim(G^2)_{p,m-1} = m + n, \qquad (43)$$

$$\dim(G^2)_{p,j} =$$
$$\left[\frac{(m-j)(m-j+1)}{2} - 1\right]\left[\frac{m(m+1)}{2} + mn\right], \quad 1 \le j \le m - 2, \qquad (44)$$

$$\dim(G^2)_p = \left[\frac{m(m+1)}{2} - 1\right]\left[\frac{m(m+1)}{2} + mn\right], \qquad (45)$$

$$\dim(G^3)_p = \left[\binom{m+2}{3} - m\right]\left[\frac{m(m+1)}{2} + mn\right] + m + n. \qquad (46)$$

Therefore

$$\dim(G^2)_p + \sum_{j=1}^{m-1} \dim(G^2)_{p,j}$$

$$= \sum_{j=0}^{m-2}\left[\frac{(m-j)(m-j+1)}{2} - 1\right]\left[\frac{m(m+1)}{2} + mn\right] + m + n.$$

Since

$$\sum_{j=0}^{m-2} \frac{(m-j)(m-j+1)}{2} = \frac{m^3 + 3m^2 + 2m - 6}{6},$$

we find that

$$\dim(G^2)_p + \sum_{j=1}^{m-1} \dim(G^2)_{p,j} = \frac{m^3 + 3m^2 - 4m}{6}\left[\frac{m(m+1)}{2} + mn\right] + m + n$$

and this is equal to (46).

Summarizing the discussion of this section, we have shown that the EYM pde (28) is involutive. Assume now that the principal bundle $P \to$

M be real analytic. Then the EYM pde is analytic and Theorem 2.1 leads directly to the following theorem.

Theorem 3.6. *Let the principal bundle $P \to M$ be real analytic. Then for every $p \in R^2$ there is an analytic section $(g, A) : U \subset M \to Q$ over a neighborhood U of $x = \pi^2(p)$ such that (g, A) is a solution of the EYM equations and $(j_x^2 g, j_x^2 A) = p$.*

4. Appendix

Proof of (32). We have

$$2\nabla_\mu^g(g^{\lambda\mu} T_{\lambda\nu}) = 2\nabla_\mu^g(1/4\delta_\nu^\mu F^{\alpha\beta}{}_r F_{\alpha\beta}^r + F^{\mu\beta}{}_r F_{\beta\nu}{}^r).$$

Let us write explicitly the covariant derivative on the right hand side. We find

$$
\begin{aligned}
&\nabla_\mu^g(F^{\mu\beta}{}_r F_{\beta\nu}{}^r) \\
&= \partial_\mu(F^{\mu\beta}{}_r F_{\beta\nu}{}^r) + \Gamma^\mu_{\mu\rho} F^{\rho\beta}{}_r F_{\beta\nu}{}^r - \Gamma^\rho_{\mu\nu} F^{\mu\beta}{}_r F_{\beta\rho}{}^r \\
&= \partial_\mu(\sqrt{|g|} F^{\mu\beta}{}_r) F_{\beta\nu}{}^r \sqrt{|g|}^{-1} + \sqrt{|g|} F^{\mu\beta}{}_r \partial_\mu(F_{\beta\nu}{}^r \sqrt{|g|}^{-1}) + \\
&\quad \Gamma^\mu_{\mu\rho} F^{\rho\beta}{}_r F_{\beta\nu}{}^r - \Gamma^\rho_{\mu\nu} F^{\mu\beta}{}_r F_{\beta\rho}{}^r \\
&= \partial_\mu(\sqrt{|g|} F^{\mu\beta}{}_r) F_{\beta\nu}{}^r \sqrt{|g|}^{-1} + \sqrt{|g|} F^{\mu\beta}{}_r \nabla_\mu^g(F_{\beta\nu}{}^r \sqrt{|g|}^{-1}) \\
&= \nabla_\mu^A(\sqrt{|g|} F^{\mu\beta}{}_r) F_{\beta\nu}{}^r \sqrt{|g|}^{-1} + \sqrt{|g|} F^{\mu\beta}{}_s [\nabla_\mu^g(F_{\beta\nu}{}^s \sqrt{|g|}^{-1}) \\
&\quad + c_{qr}^s a_\mu^q F_{\beta\nu}{}^r \sqrt{|g|}^{-1}]
\end{aligned}
$$

and

$$\nabla^g_\mu(\delta^\mu_\nu F^{\alpha\beta}_{\ \ r}F_{\alpha\beta}^{\ \ r})$$
$$= \partial_\nu(F^{\alpha\beta}_{\ \ r}F_{\alpha\beta}^{\ \ r}) = 2\sqrt{|g|}F^{\alpha\beta}_{\ \ r}\nabla^g_\nu(F_{\alpha\beta}^{\ \ r}\sqrt{|g|}^{-1})$$
$$= 2\sqrt{|g|}F^{\alpha\beta}_{\ \ r}[\nabla^g_\nu(F_{\alpha\beta}^{\ \ r}\sqrt{|g|}^{-1}) + c^r_{qs}a^q_\nu F_{\alpha\beta}^{\ \ s}\sqrt{|g|}^{-1}],$$

where in the last equality we have used the relation

$$h_{rt}c^r_{qs} + h_{rs}c^r_{qt} = 0$$

expressing the orthogonality of the adjoint representation. Therefore

$$2\nabla^g_\mu(g^{\lambda\mu}T_{\lambda\nu})$$
$$= \sqrt{|g|}F^{\alpha\beta}_{\ \ r}[\nabla^{g,A}_\nu(F_{\alpha\beta}^{\ \ r}\sqrt{|g|}^{-1})$$
$$+ 2\nabla^{g,A}_\alpha(F_{\beta\nu}^{\ \ r}\sqrt{|g|}^{-1})] + 2\nabla^A_\mu(\sqrt{|g|}F^{\mu\beta}_{\ \ r})F_{\beta\nu}^{\ \ r}\sqrt{|g|}^{-1}$$
$$= \frac{1}{2}\sqrt{|g|}F^{\alpha\beta}_{\ \ r}\nabla^{g,A}_{[\nu}(F_{\alpha\beta]}^{\ \ r}\sqrt{|g|}^{-1}) + 2\nabla^A_\mu(\sqrt{|g|}F^{\mu\beta}_{\ \ r})F_{\beta\nu}^{\ \ r}\sqrt{|g|}^{-1},$$

where we denote $\theta_{[\lambda_1\lambda_2\lambda_3]} = \sum_{\sigma\in S_3} sgn\ \sigma\ \theta_{\lambda_{\sigma(1)}\lambda_{\sigma(2)}\lambda_{\sigma(3)}}$. Then the result follows from the Bianchi identity for the Yang-Mills fields, i.e. $\nabla^A F(A) = 0$.

Proof of (33)–(36). Let us first prove (43). By definition $(G^2)_{p,m-1} = \text{Ker}(\sigma(\phi)_{p,m-1})$, where

$$\sigma(\phi)_{p,m-1} : \vee_{2,m-1}T^*_x M \otimes \overline{Q}_x \to \vee_2 T^*_x M \oplus \overset{m-1}{\wedge} T^*_x M \otimes(V^*_G P)_x$$

is the restriction of the symbol (29) to $V_{2,m-1}T_x^*M \otimes \overline{Q}_x$. From (19) and (32) we find

$$\sigma(R)_{p,m-1}(dx^m \vee dx^m \otimes dx^\lambda \vee dx^\lambda) =$$
$$\begin{cases} 0, & \text{if } \lambda = m \\ -g^{mm}dx^\lambda \vee dx^\lambda - g^{\lambda\lambda}dx^m \vee dx^m, & \text{if } \lambda \neq m \end{cases}$$

$$\sigma(R)_{p,m-1}(dx^m \vee dx^m \otimes dx^\lambda \vee dx^\mu) =$$
$$\begin{cases} 0, & \text{if } \lambda = m \text{ or } \mu = m, \lambda \neq \mu \\ -g^{mm}dx^\lambda \vee dx^\mu, & \text{if } \lambda \neq m, \mu \neq m, \lambda \neq \mu \end{cases}$$

$$\xi_{p,m-1}(dx^m \vee dx^m \otimes dx^\lambda) = \begin{cases} 0, & \text{if } \lambda = m \\ 2g^{mm}dx^\lambda, & \text{if } \lambda \neq m. \end{cases}$$

These relations show that

$$\dim(G^2)_{p,m-1} = \dim[\text{Ker } \sigma(R)_{p,m-1}] + \dim[\text{Ker } \xi_{p,m-1}] = m + n.$$

To prove (44) let us go back to the proof of Lemma 3.2. It is easily seen that the morphism

$$\sigma(\phi)_{p,j} : V_{2,j}T_x^*M \otimes \overline{Q}_x \rightarrow V_2T_x^*M \oplus \overset{m-1}{\wedge}T_x^*M \otimes (V_G^*P)_x, \quad 1 \leq j \leq m-2$$

is surjective and hence (44) holds.

(45) and (46) are immediate consequences of Lemmas 3.2 and 3.3.

Acknowledgment

The authors wish to acknowledge the Ministero della Pubblica Istruzione, Italy, for having supported this work (national and local funds).

References

[1] H.L.Goldschmidt, Existence theorems for analytic linear partial differential equations, *Ann. of Math.* 86(1967) 246–270.

[2] G.Giachetta and L.Mangiarotti, On the formal integrability of the Yang-Mills equations, Preprint, University of Camerino, Camerino, 1994 (to appear).

[3] G.Giachetta, On the Formal Integrability of the Yang-Mills-Higgs equations, Preprint, University of Camerino, Camerino, 1994.

[4] J.Gasqui, Sur la résolubilité locale des équations d'Einstein, *Compositio Math.* 47(1982) 42–69.

[5] D.M.DeTurck, Existence of metrics with prescribed Ricci curvature: local theory, *Invent. Math.* 65(1981) 179–207.

[6] B.Malgrange, Equationes de Lie I, II, *J. Differential Geom.* 6(1972) 503–522; 7(1972) 117–141.

[7] H.L.Goldschmidt, Integrability criteria for systems of non-linear partial differential equations, *J. Differential Geom.* 1(1967) 269–307.

[8] D. Saunders, *The geometry of jet bundles* (Cambridge University Press, Cambridge, 1989).

[9] J.F.Pommaret, *Systems of partial differential equations and Lie pseudogroups* (Gordon and Breach, New York, 1978).

[10] V.W.Guillemin and S.Stenberg, An algebric model of transitive differential geometry, *Bull. Amer. Math. Soc.* 70(1964) 16–47.

[11] S.Kobayashi and K.Nomizu, *Foundations of differential geometry* vol. I (Wiley-Interscience, New York, 1963).

[12] G.Giachetta and L.Mangiarotti, Gauge-invariant and covariant operators in gauge theories, *Int. J. Theor. Phys.* 29(1990) 789–804.

[13] G.Giachetta, L.Mangiarotti and R.Vitolo, The Einstein-Yang-Mills equations, *Gen. Relat. and Gravitation* 23(1991) 641–659.

[14] C.W.Misner, K.S.Thorne and J.A. Wheeler, *Gravitation* (W.H. Freeman and Company, New York, 1973).

[15] L.Mangiarotti and M.Modugno, On the geometric structure of gauge theories, *J. Math. Phys.* 26(1985) 1373–1379.

Gennadi A. Sardanashvily, Editor
New Frontiers in Gravitation
Hadronic Press, Palm Harbor, FL 34682-1577, U.S.A.
ISBN 0–911767–96–7, 1996, Pages 93–113

GRAVITATIONAL SHOCK WAVES AND PLANKIAN SCATTERINGS

Koichi Hayashi

Department of Mathematics and Physics
Faculty of Science and Technology
Kinki University, Higashi-osaka
Osaka 577, Japan

and Toshiharu Samura

Astroparticle Physics, Department of Physics
Faculty of Science, Kobe University
Nada, Kobe 657, Japan

Abstract

The metrics of gravitational shock waves for a Schwarzschild black hole and a Reissner–Nordstrom black hole in Schwarzschild coordinates, and for a Kerr black hole in Boyer-Lindquist coordinates are derived. Then, for massive black holes the metrics are calculated. Two properties of the metrics are investigated: the shift and the refraction angle of a null geodesic in crossing the gravitational shock wave. We discuss the particle scattering problem at Planck energies as an application to particle physics. Although the physical picture is very different, our scattering amplitude is very similar to that derived from the string theory.

1 Introduction

The metrics of *stationary* black holes which are derived from the vacuum solution of Einstein's equation have been investigated for many years. But the
space–time structure of *moving* black holes have not been studied as much.
In this paper, we investigate the metric when a black hole (Schwarzschild,
Kerr and Reissner–Nordstrom) is moving at the very large velocity. Such
metrics are often called the metrics of the gravitational shock waves (GSW).
Recently, several papers have been published investigating these metrics. In
particular, the problem of the scattering of elementary particles at Planck
energies are much of interest. We also discuss about this points using our
derived metrics.

2 Schwarzschild Black Holes

We discuss the GSW metric for a *massive* Schwarzschild black hole. Throughout this section, we use the unit of $c=G=1$.

A metric of a Schwarzschild black hole in Schwarzschild coordinates is
well known. Then the metric is divided into the Minkowski metric term,
ds_M^2, and the surplus term, ΔS_S^2:

$$
\begin{aligned}
ds_S^2 &= -(1-2M/\bar{r})\,d\bar{t}^2 + (1-2M/\bar{r})^{-1}\,d\bar{r}^2 + \bar{r}^2 d\bar{\theta}^2 + \bar{r}^2 \sin^2\bar{\theta}\,d\bar{\phi}^2 \\
&= ds_M^2 + \Delta S_S^2 \,,
\end{aligned}
\tag{1}
$$

where

$$
\begin{aligned}
ds_M^2 &= -d\bar{t}^2 + d\bar{r}^2 + \bar{r}^2 d\bar{\theta}^2 + \bar{r}^2 \sin^2\bar{\theta}\,d\bar{\phi}^2 \,, \\
\Delta S_S^2 &= (2M/\bar{r})\,d\bar{t}^2 + (2M/\bar{r})/(1-2M/\bar{r})\,d\bar{r}^2 \,.
\end{aligned}
$$

We set $\bar{r}^2 = \bar{x}^2 + \bar{y}^2 + \bar{z}^2$ and M is the mass of the black hole.

This black hole is stationary in the laboratory system. Now, perform a
Lorentz transformation to the system where the black hole is moving in the

z–direction with the velocity v close to 1:

$$t = \gamma(\bar{t} + v\bar{z}) \quad , \quad z = \gamma(\bar{z} + v\bar{t}) \quad , \quad x = \bar{x} \quad , \quad y = \bar{y} \quad , \tag{2}$$

where

$$\gamma = (1 - v^2)^{-1/2} \quad .$$

As ds_M^2 of (1) is invariant for Lorentz transformations, only ΔS_S^2 is transformed according to (2).

We should notice the following point to derive the GWS metric for a massive black hole. We assume that γ factor becomes very large but finite. Then only the leading term of $O(\gamma)$ in $1/\gamma$ expansion should be considered while the mass of the black hole takes an arbitrary finite value.

ΔS_S^2 is then given by:

$$\Delta S_S^2 = 2p \left[\frac{1}{\sqrt{u^2 + \tilde{\rho}^2}} + \frac{u^2}{\sqrt{(u^2 + \tilde{\rho}^2)^3} - 2\tilde{M}(u^2 + \tilde{\rho}^2)} \right] du^2 \quad , \tag{3}$$

where we set $u = t - z, v = t + z, \rho^2 = x^2 + y^2, \tilde{\rho} = \rho/\gamma, \tilde{M} = M/\gamma$ and the energy $p = \gamma M$.

Next, we take the limit of large γ. We do not perform the limitation of $\gamma \to \infty$ directly. We calculate the limitation using the method of Loustó and Sánchez [1]. First, integrate the ΔS_S^2 by u, next, take the limit of a large γ and finally differentiate it by u. Then, note for the limit of a large γ. The GWS metrics of Aichelburg–Sexl [2] and Loustó – Sánchez are derived by taking the limit of $\gamma \to \infty$, so the mass of the black hole is zero, because the energy with a finite mass is divergent. We assume the γ factor is very large but finite. In the paper of [3], we wrote $\gamma \to \infty$. Mathematically, this expression is not exact, and it should be interpreted that the symbol ∞ means very large but finite. Similarly $\delta(u)$ is not exactly equal to the delta–function. However, physically it is appropriate to use such a treatment. In fact, it is applicable to the scattering problem at Planckian energies and to the collision problem of two black holes.

Let us now consider the large limit of γ.

$$\lim_{\gamma \to large} \Delta S_S^2 \longrightarrow$$

$$4p \left[\frac{1}{|u|} - \left[\log \rho^2 - \frac{\rho}{4M} \left(\pi - 4\sqrt{1 - \frac{4M^2}{\rho^2}} \tan^{-1} \sqrt{\frac{\rho + 2M}{\rho - 2M}} \right) \right] \delta(u) \right] du^2.$$

$$(4)$$

Introducing a new coordinate

$$dv' = dv - 4p \, du/|u| \,, \tag{5}$$

we obtain the exact GSW metric for a massive Schwarzschild black hole (dash on v' is omitted):

$$\lim_{\gamma \to large} ds_S^2 \longrightarrow -du \, dv + dx^2 + dy^2$$

$$-4p \left[\log \rho^2 - \frac{\rho}{4M} \left(\pi - 4\sqrt{1 - \frac{4M^2}{\rho^2}} \tan^{-1} \sqrt{\frac{\rho + 2M}{\rho - 2M}} \right) \right] \delta(u) \, du^2 \,.$$

$$(6)$$

When $\rho \gg 2M$, (6) is reduced to:

$$\lim_{\gamma \to large} ds_S^2 \xrightarrow{\rho \gg 2M} -du \, dv + dx^2 + dy^2$$

$$-4p \left[\log \rho^2 + 1 - \frac{\pi}{2} \frac{M}{\rho} + \frac{4}{3} \frac{M^2}{\rho^2} + O\left(\frac{M^3}{\rho^3}\right) \right] \delta(u) \, du^2. \tag{7}$$

We immediately see that (6) is reduced to the GSW metric for a massless Schwarzschild black hole (called Aichelburg–Sexl metric [2]) when $M \to 0$ and $\hat{\rho} = e\rho$ (e: the base of natural logarithm).

It is recognized that our method is general enough to include the case of GSW of a *massless* black hole. Does the finite mass have a much significance compared with the massless case? This point is the main aim of this paper.

Now we investigate the properties of the GSW metric. First we treat the general case when a test particle has chargeless and spinless. The GSW metric moving at the limit of the light velocity in the z–direction is given by:

$$\lim_{\gamma \to large} ds^2 \longrightarrow -du \, dv + dx^2 + dy^2 - A(\rho) \, \delta(u) \, du^2 \quad . \tag{8}$$

The geodesic equation can be derived from the Lagrangian.

$$\mathcal{L} = \frac{1}{2}\left[-\dot{u}\dot{v} + \dot{\rho}^2 + \rho^2\dot{\phi}^2 - A(\rho) \, \delta(u) \, \dot{u}^2\right] \quad . \tag{9}$$

where the dot denotes the derivative with respect to the affine parameter λ. From the Euler–Lagrange equation, the shift Δv of the geodesic v crossing $u = 0$ is:

$$\Delta v = -2A(\rho)|_{\rho=\rho_0} \quad , \tag{10}$$

where ρ_0 is the value of ρ when the geodesic reaches $u = 0$. The refraction angle $\Delta\phi$ to the parallel direction of z is also given by:

$$\tan(\Delta\phi) = \frac{1}{2}\frac{dA(\rho)}{d\rho}\bigg|_{\rho=\rho_0} \quad . \tag{11}$$

In the case of the GSW of a Schwarzschild black hole, the refraction angle is shown in the bold line of Fig. 1, where we put $M = 1$. It is to be noted that the refraction angle becomes 90° for $\rho = 2M$. This is natural because it corresponds to the event horizon as the event horizon for ρ–direction is invariant under the Lorentz transformation for z–direction.

3   Kerr black holes

In this section, we calculate the GSW metric for a massive Kerr black hole. We consider a Kerr metric in Boyer–Lindquist coordinates:

$$\begin{aligned}ds_K^2 &= -\left(1 - \frac{2M\bar{r}}{\Sigma}\right)d\bar{t}^2 - \frac{4M\bar{r}a\sin^2\bar{\theta}}{\Sigma}d\bar{t}\,d\bar{\phi} + \frac{\Sigma}{\Delta}d\bar{r}^2 \\ &\quad + \Sigma \, d\bar{\theta}^2 + \left(\bar{r}^2 + a^2 + \frac{2M\bar{r}a^2\sin^2\bar{\theta}}{\Sigma}\right)\sin^2\bar{\theta}\,d\bar{\phi}^2 \quad , \end{aligned} \tag{12}$$

where a is the angular momentum per mass and

$$\Delta = \bar{r}^2 - 2M\bar{r} + a^2 \ ,$$
$$\Sigma = \bar{r}^2 + a^2 \cos^2 \bar{\theta} \ .$$

Below, we consider the two types of the GSW metrics: First, for the motion parallel to the rotation axis of the Kerr black hole, and second, for the perpendicular one. The rotational axis is taken in the z–direction.

3.1   Motion Parallel to the Rotational Axis

The GSW metric can be calculated as before. The exact GSW metric for a massive Kerr black hole moving parallel to the rotational axis is given by:

$$\lim_{\gamma \to large} ds^2_{K\|} \longrightarrow -du\,dv + dx^2 + dy^2$$
$$-4p\left[\Delta g_1 + \Delta g_2 + \Delta g_3 + \Delta g_4\right]\,\delta(u)\,du^2 \ , \quad (13)$$

where

$$\Delta g_1 = \log\rho^2 + \frac{1}{2\sqrt{2}\alpha}\left[\sqrt{\alpha+1}\log\frac{\sqrt{\alpha+1}+\sqrt{2}}{\sqrt{\alpha+1}-\sqrt{2}}\right.$$
$$\left.-2\sqrt{\alpha-1}\tan^{-1}\sqrt{\frac{2}{\alpha-1}}\right] \ ,$$

$$\Delta g_2 = -\frac{2}{\beta-\zeta}\left[\sqrt{\beta}(1+\zeta)\tan^{-1}\left(1/\sqrt{\beta}\right) - \sqrt{\zeta}(1+\beta)\tan^{-1}\left(1/\sqrt{\zeta}\right)\right],$$

$$\Delta g_3 = \frac{\rho}{Ma^4}\left[\left(a^4 + 2a^2\rho^2 - 8\rho^2 M^2\right)\pi/8 - a^2 M\rho\right.$$
$$+\frac{1}{4\sqrt{M^2-a^2}}\left[\left[\eta\sqrt{\beta}-\theta/\sqrt{\beta}\right]\tan^{-1}\left(1/\sqrt{\beta}\right)\right.$$
$$\left.\left.-\left[\eta\sqrt{\zeta}-\theta/\sqrt{\zeta}\right]\tan^{-1}\left(1/\sqrt{\zeta}\right)\right]\right] \ ,$$

$$\Delta g_4 = -\frac{\pi a^2}{32\rho M} \ .$$

where

$$\alpha = \frac{\sqrt{4\rho^2 + a^2}}{a} \quad ,$$

$$\beta = \frac{\rho^2 - a^2 + 2\rho\sqrt{M^2 - a^2}}{\rho^2 + a^2 + 2M\rho} \quad ,$$

$$\zeta = \frac{\rho^2 - a^2 - 2\rho\sqrt{M^2 - a^2}}{\rho^2 + a^2 + 2M\rho} \quad ,$$

$$\eta = \left(4\rho M^2 - a^2\rho - 2a^2 M\right)\left(\rho^2 + a^2 + 2\rho M\right) \quad ,$$

$$\theta = \left(4\rho M^2 - a^2\rho + 2a^2 M\right)\left(\rho^2 + a^2 - 2\rho M\right) \quad .$$

When the limit of $a \to 0$ is taken, the GSW metric of the Schwarzschild black hole is naturally recovered.

Assuming no naked singularities, a Kerr black hole with $a = M$ is the maximally rotating black hole. This situation is most convenient to investigate the property of the rotating black hole. In the limit of $M \to a$, (13) has the form:

$$\lim_{M \to a} ds_K^2 \to -du\,dv + dx^2 + dy^2$$

$$-4\rho \left[\log \rho^2 + 1 + \frac{1}{2\sqrt{2}}\frac{1}{\alpha}\left(\sqrt{\alpha+1}\log\frac{\sqrt{\alpha+1} + \sqrt{2}}{\sqrt{\alpha+1} - \sqrt{2}}\right.\right.$$

$$-2\sqrt{\alpha-1}\tan^{-1}\sqrt{\frac{2}{\alpha-1}}\left.\right) + \frac{(3\rho^4 - 2a^2\rho^2 - 2a^4)}{a^3\sqrt{\rho^2 - a^2}}\tan^{-1}\sqrt{\frac{\rho+a}{\rho-a}}$$

$$+ \left(\frac{\rho}{8a} - \frac{3\rho^3}{4a^3} - \frac{a}{32\rho}\right)\pi - \frac{3\rho^2}{2a^2}\left.\right]\delta(u)\,du^2 \quad . \tag{14}$$

The refraction angle is represented in Fig.1 by the thin solid line. The refraction angle is $90°$ at $\rho = M$, the event horizon of the Kerr black hole.

When $\rho \gg a$, (14) becomes:

$$\lim_{M \to a} ds_K^2 \xrightarrow[\rho \gg a]{} -du\,dv + dx^2 + dy^2$$

$$-4p\left[\log\rho^2+1-\frac{\pi}{2}\frac{a}{\rho}+\left(\frac{4}{3}-\frac{4}{5}\right)\frac{a^2}{\rho^2}+O\left(\frac{a^3}{\rho^3}\right)\right]\delta\left(u\right)\,du^2\ .$$

$$(15)$$

We compare (14) with the result of Loustó and Sánchez [1]. In the case of the Kerr black hole, their metric of GWS involves only the even powers of (a/ρ), because the spin contribution couples to the kinetic momentum only through even (negative) powers of ρ. However, a represents both the spin and mass $(a \to M)$ in our case, so our metric develops all powers of (a/ρ).

We see that the case of finite mass is essentially different from the massless one.   ·

3.2   Motion Perpendicular to the Rotational Axis

The metric in a reference system moving perpendicular to the rotational axis of a Kerr black hole is calculated. We discuss that the moving direction is taken in the x–direction, and the rotational axis is set in the z–direction. We discuss only in the equatorial plane $(\theta = \pi/2,\ \dot\theta = 0)$.

The boost in the x–direction with the speed v gives:

$$t=\gamma\left(\bar{t}+v\bar{x}\right),\ x=\gamma\left(\bar{x}+v\bar{t}\right),\ y=\bar{y},\qquad(16)$$

and z is always set to zero. We put $u = t - x$ and $v = t + x$ as the null coordinates.

Carrying out a bit calculations, the exact GWS metric is obtained:

$$\lim_{\gamma\to large}ds^2_{K\perp}\ \longrightarrow\quad -du\,dv+dy^2$$

$$-4p\left[\delta g_1+\delta g_2+\delta g_3+\delta g_4\right]\delta(u)\,du^2\ ,\qquad(17)$$

where

$$\delta g_1\ =\ \log|\tilde{y}|^2-\frac{2}{\beta'-\zeta'}\left(\sqrt{\beta'}\left(1+\zeta'\right)\tan^{-1}\left(1/\sqrt{\beta'}\right)\right.$$

$$-\sqrt{\zeta'}\,(1+\beta')\tan^{-1}\left(1/\sqrt{\zeta'}\right)\ ,$$

$$\beta' = \frac{y^2 - a^2 + 2|y|\sqrt{M^2 - a^2}}{y^2 + a^2 + 2M|y|}\ ,$$

$$\zeta' = \frac{y^2 - a^2 - 2|y|\sqrt{M^2 - a^2}}{y^2 + a^2 + 2M|y|}\ ,$$

$$\delta g_2 = \frac{2|y|a^2}{M\left\{|y|\left(\sqrt{M^2 - a^2} + M\right) + a^2\right\}}\ ,$$

$$\times \left\{\frac{1}{\beta' - 1}\left[\frac{\pi}{4} - \frac{1}{\sqrt{\beta'}}\tan^{-1}\left(1/\sqrt{\beta'}\right)\right]\right.$$

$$\left.+\frac{\zeta'}{\zeta' - \beta'}\left[\frac{1}{\sqrt{\zeta'}}\tan^{-1}\left(1/\sqrt{\zeta'}\right) - \frac{1}{\sqrt{\beta'}}\tan^{-1}\left(1/\sqrt{\beta'}\right)\right]\right\}$$

$$\delta g_3 = \frac{2a}{y}$$

$$\delta g_4 = -1 - \frac{y^2}{2a\sqrt{y^2 + a^2}}\log\frac{\sqrt{y^2 + a^2} - a}{\sqrt{y^2 + a^2} + a}\ .$$

Here, the important point to be noted is that δg_3 depends on the sign of y explicitly. In other words, when the magnitudes of y's are equal with opposite signs, the shift Δv's and the refraction angles are different. As the term is derived from $g_{t\phi}dt d\phi$ of the Kerr metric, the effect of the space–time dragging would be the cause.

The properties of this case are now to be discussed. Take the limit $M \to a$; i.e. the fast rotating black hole:

$$\lim_{M \to a}\left[\lim_{\gamma \to large} ds_K^2\right] \longrightarrow -du\,dv + dy^2$$

$$-4p\left[\log|y|^2 - \frac{1}{2} + \frac{y^2 - 2a^2}{a\sqrt{y^2 - a^2}}\tan^{-1}\sqrt{\frac{|y| + a}{|y| - a}} - \frac{|y|}{4a}\pi\right.$$

$$\left.+\frac{2a}{y} - \frac{y^2}{2a\sqrt{y^2 + a^2}}\log\frac{\sqrt{y^2 + a^2} - a}{\sqrt{y^2 + a^2} + a}\right]\delta(u)\,du^2\ . \qquad (18)$$

Consider the case of $|y| >> a$, i. e. far from the hole:

$$ds^2_K \xrightarrow{|y| \gg a} - du\, dv + dy^2$$

$$-4p \left[\log |y|^2 + 1 - \frac{3\pi}{8} \left(\frac{a}{|y|} \right) + 2 \left(\frac{a}{y} \right) - \frac{4}{3} \left(\frac{a^2}{y^2} \right) + O \left(\frac{a^3}{y^3} \right) \right] \delta(u)\, du^2.$$

$$(19)$$

The refraction angle is depicted in Fig.1. The ratio of the refraction angle of the negative sign of y to that of the positive one is shown in Fig.2. This figure indicates that the refraction for $y < 0$ is larger than that for $y > 0$.

4   Reissner– Nordstrom Black Holes

In this section, we calculate the GSW for a massive Reissner–Nordstrom (RN) black hole [4]. A RN metric reads:

$$ds^2_{RN} = - \left(1 - 2M/\bar{r} + Q^2/\bar{r}^2 \right) d\bar{t}^2 + \left(1 - 2M/\bar{r} + Q^2/\bar{r}^2 \right)^{-1} d\bar{r}^2$$
$$+ \bar{r}^2 d\bar{\theta}^2 + \bar{r}^2 \sin^2 \bar{\theta} d\bar{\phi}^2,$$
$$(20)$$

where Q is the charge of the black hole. Now, take a Lorentz transformation with velocity v in the z–direction. Then the exact GSW metric is obtained for large γ:

$$\lim_{\gamma \to large} ds^2_{RN} \longrightarrow -du\, dv + dx^2 + dy^2$$
$$-4p \left[\Delta g_1 + \Delta g_2 + \Delta g_3 \right] \delta(u)\, du^2 , \qquad (21)$$

where

$$\Delta g_1 = \log \rho^2 - \frac{2}{\alpha - \beta} \left\{ \sqrt{\alpha} (1 + \beta) \tan^{-1} \left(1/\sqrt{\alpha} \right) \right. $$
$$\left. - \sqrt{\beta} (1 + \alpha) \tan^{-1} \left(1/\sqrt{\beta} \right) \right\} ,$$

$$\Delta g_2 \quad = \quad \frac{2\rho Q^2}{M\left\{\rho\left(\sqrt{M^2-Q^2}+M\right)+Q^2\right\}} \quad ,$$

$$\times \left\{ \frac{1}{\alpha-1}\left[\frac{\pi}{4}-\frac{1}{\sqrt{\alpha}}\tan^{-1}\left(1/\sqrt{\alpha}\right)\right] \right.$$

$$\left. +\frac{\beta}{\beta-\alpha}\left[\frac{1}{\sqrt{\beta}}\tan^{-1}\left(1/\sqrt{\beta}\right)-\frac{1}{\sqrt{\alpha}}\tan^{-1}\left(1/\sqrt{\alpha}\right)\right]\right\} \quad ,$$

$$\Delta g_3 \quad = \quad \frac{\pi\,Q^2}{4\rho M} \quad ,$$

and

$$\alpha \quad = \quad \frac{\rho^2-Q^2+2\rho\sqrt{M^2-Q^2}}{\rho^2+Q^2+2M\rho} \quad ,$$

$$\beta \quad = \quad \frac{\rho^2-Q^2-2\rho\sqrt{M^2-Q^2}}{\rho^2+Q^2+2M\rho} \quad .$$

We deal with the case of the extremum $(M \to Q)$ RN black hole. In this limit, (21) has the following form:

$$\lim_{M\to Q}\left[\lim_{\gamma\to large} ds^2_{RN}\right] \longrightarrow -du\,dv+dx^2+dy^2$$

$$-4p\left[\log\rho^2+\frac{1}{2}+\frac{\rho^2-2Q^2}{Q\sqrt{\rho^2-Q^2}}\tan^{-1}\sqrt{\frac{\rho+Q}{\rho-Q}}-\frac{\rho^2-Q^2}{4\rho Q}\pi\right]\delta\left(u\right)\,du^2 \quad ,$$

$$\tag{22}$$

and for $\rho \gg Q$, we expand in the negative powers of ρ:

$$\lim_{M\to Q}\left[\lim_{\gamma\to large} ds^2_{RN}\right]\xrightarrow{\rho\gg Q} -du\,dv+dx^2+dy^2$$

$$-4p\left[\log\rho^2+1-\frac{\pi}{8}\left(\frac{Q}{\rho}\right)-\frac{2}{3}\left(\frac{Q^2}{\rho^2}\right)+O\left(\frac{Q^3}{\rho^3}\right)\right]\delta\left(u\right)\,du^2. \tag{23}$$

Here, our metric is expanded in all powers of (Q/ρ) because of the contribution of the finite mass. In contrast, Loustó and Sánchez's metric of the GSW of the massless RN black hole is expanded in the odd powers of (Q/ρ).

Next, we investigate the properties of the metric. When a test particle is chargeless, the shift Δv of the geodesic v is (10) and the refraction angle is (11) as before. Natural but uninteresting.

In this section, we consider that a test particle has a charge [5]. When the metric of the stationary RN black hole is $ds^2 = g_{\mu\nu}dx^\mu \, dx^\nu$, the motion of a test particle with a charge is determined by the Lagrangian [6]:

$$\mathcal{L} = \frac{1}{2}[g_{\mu\nu}\dot{x}^\mu \, \dot{x}^\nu] + qA_\rho\dot{x}^\rho , \tag{24}$$

where q is the charge per unit mass of the test particle and A_ρ is the vector potential. The only nonvanishing component of the vector potential is:

$$A_0 = -\frac{Q}{r} . \tag{25}$$

For a large γ, the ds^2 becomes a metric of the GSW and the A_0 becomes:

$$\lim_{\gamma \to large} A_0 \longrightarrow \frac{Q}{\gamma}\log\rho^2\delta(u) . \tag{26}$$

Therefore the Lagrangian is changed into:

$$\lim_{\gamma \to large} \mathcal{L} = \frac{1}{2}\left[-\dot{u}\dot{v} + \dot{\rho}^2 + \rho^2\dot{\rho}^2 - A(\rho)\,\delta(u)\,\dot{u}^2\right] + qQ\log\rho^2\delta(u)\,\dot{u} . \tag{27}$$

We consider the case of the extremum black hole $(M \to Q)$. From the Euler-Lagrange equation, the shift Δv of the geodesic v is calculated:

$$\Delta v = -2\left[(4p - qQ)\log\rho^2 \right.$$
$$\left. +4p\left(\frac{1}{2} + \frac{\rho^2 - 2Q^2}{Q\sqrt{\rho^2 - Q^2}}\tan^{-1}\sqrt{\frac{\rho+Q}{\rho-Q}} - \frac{\rho^2 - Q^2}{4\rho Q}\pi\right)\right]\Bigg|_{\rho=\rho_0} \tag{28}$$

and the refraction angle, $\Delta\phi$, is given by:

$$\tan(\Delta\phi) = \frac{1}{2}\left[\frac{dA(\rho)}{d\rho} - \frac{4qQ}{\rho}\right]\Bigg|_{\rho=\rho_0} . \tag{29}$$

Comparing (29) with (11), it is found that the attraction (repulsion) force works for $qQ < 0$ $(qQ > 0)$.

5   Planckian Scatterings for GWS

In the last few years, many authors have considered the particle scattering at Planck energies by using the gravitational shock waves of black holes [1, 4, 7, 9, 10, 11, 13, 15]. In 1989, 't Hooft first investigated the Planckian scattering by identifying a particle moving at Planck energies with the GSW of a massless black hole [7]. After that, hot discussions of particle physics using a black hole metric are performed in the world. In particular, it is noted that the results obtained from the approach of quantum gravity for the black hole is very similar to that of string theories.

Amati et. al. derived the scattering amplitude using the eikonal approximation of the string theory at the Planck scale [8]. Also, 't Hooft [9] and Verlinde et. al. [10] independently showed the analogy of the black hole theory and the string theory. Recently, Fabbrichesi et. al. [11] attempted to deal with the problems of quantum gravity, applying the surface term of the Einstein–Hilbert action. It is also interesting to calculate the scatterings amplitude in the multi–Regge kinematics [12].

Here, we treat the case of the scattering of the massive particles using the GSW. This investigation is not a simple extension of the results of 't Hooft. Since our derived GSW metric is applied to the scattering, the mass of the particle is retained throughout. The calculation of massive particle scatterings can be realized by the GSW of the *massive* black hole. So this is the *mass* correction to the results of 't Hooft, and is not the second order correction to it. The mass correction is of the form of $Gs\ Gm^{(2)}$, whereas the second order correction is $G^2 s^2$.

We investigate further the scattering of charged particles. Jackiw et. al. [13] dealt with the high energy scatterings with electromagnetic interactions, and they showed that the scattering amplitude is identical to that derived from the eikonal approach of QED.

We discuss the scattering involving both the gravitational and electromagnetic interactions using the GSW for the RN black hole.

Below, we recover G and set $c = \hbar = 1$.

5.1 Scatterings of Non–Charged Particles

Consider the scatterings of two non–charged particles (particle (1) and particle (2)). Now, particle (2) has a mass near the Planck mass, and moves in the z–direction at Planck energies or above. On the other hand, particle (2) has a very light mass and moves slowly. We assume that the impact parameter, b, is much bigger than the gravitational radius. From above assumptions, the following relations hold:

$$Gs \gg 1, \tag{30}$$
$$E \gg M_{Planck}, \tag{31}$$
$$b \gg Gm^{(i)} . \tag{32}$$

Particle (2) is considered as a black hole at Planck scale. Then, the gravitational field is represented by the metric of the GSW. However, since we have assumed that the impact parameter is much larger than the gravitational radius, the characteristics of the black hole would not appear. It is interesting to study the near region of the black hole, but we do not treat it in this paper.

We assume particle (1) to be spinless and chargeless. Before the scattering, its wave function is given by:

$$\Psi_-^{(1)} = \exp\left(i\tilde{p}^{(1)}\tilde{x} - ip_+^{(1)}u - ip_-^{(1)}v \right) , \tag{33}$$

where $\tilde{p}$ and $\tilde{x}$ are the momentum and the coordinate perpendicular to the z–direction, respectively. We put $\bar{u} = (t - z)/2$ and $\bar{v} = (t + z)/2$.

After the scattering, the particle (1) passed through the GSW of (2). Then, the v component of the particle (1) has to be shifted to $v + \Delta v$. The shifted wave function is given by:

$$\Psi_+^{(1)} = \exp\left(i\tilde{p}^{(1)}\tilde{x} - ip_+^{(1)} [\bar{v} + \Delta\bar{v}/2] \right) . \tag{34}$$

Since the particles are spinless and chargeless, we use the shift Δv of the Schwarzschild's GSW.

$\cdot$ The change of the wave function after scattering reflects on to the scattering amplitude of the particle (1). The 4-momentum $p^{(1)} = (p^{(1)}_+, p^{(1)}_-, \tilde{p}^{(1)})$ of the particle (1) before the scattering is changed to $k = (k_+, k_-, \tilde{k})$ after the scattering. Then the scattering amplitude is given by:

$$U(s,t) \sim \delta\left(k_+ - p^{(1)}_+\right) \frac{1}{4\pi} \int d^2\tilde{x} \exp\left\{i\left(\tilde{p}^{(1)} - \tilde{k}\right)\tilde{x} - 2iGsA(\rho)\right\}$$

$$\longrightarrow \frac{1}{4\pi}\delta\left(k_+ - p^{(1)}_+\right) e^{-2iGs}$$

$$\times \int d^2\tilde{x} e^{i\left(\tilde{p}^{(1)} - \tilde{k}\right)\tilde{x}} \left(\frac{\rho}{2Gm^{(2)}}\right)^{-4iGs} \times e^{i\frac{\pi}{2}Gs\frac{2Gm^{(2)}}{\rho}}$$

$$\longrightarrow \frac{1}{4\pi}\delta\left(k_+ - p^{(1)}_+\right) e^{-2iGs} \left(2Gm^{(2)}\right)^{4iGs} \left(\frac{4}{-t}\right)^{1-2iGs} (-2iGs)$$

$$\times \sum_{n=0}^{\infty}\left[\frac{1}{(2n)!}\left(i\frac{\pi}{4}Gm^{(2)}\sqrt{-t}\right)^{2n}\frac{\Gamma(-2iGs)}{\Gamma(2iGs)}\right.$$

$$\left. - \frac{1}{(2n+1)!}\left(i\frac{\pi}{4}Gm^{(2)}\sqrt{-t}\right)^{2n+1}\frac{\Gamma\left(\frac{1}{2} - 2iGs\right)}{\Gamma\left(\frac{1}{2} + 2iGs\right)}\right] , \quad (35)$$

where s and t are the Mandelstam variables; $s = 2p^{(1)}_+ p^{(2)}_0 = -2\left(p^{(1)} \cdot p^{(2)}\right)$, and $t = -\left(k - p^{(1)}\right)^2$.

This is the general expression of the scattering amplitude of the particle (1) when the particle (2) has the finite mass $m^{(2)}$, with $Gs \gg 1$ and $Gm^{(2)}/\rho \gg 1$. This form contains many physical results. When the particle (1) has a very light mass, $m^{(1)}/\rho \ll 1$, The leading order term, which is given by the $n = 0$ of the first term, is almost equal to the scattering amplitude of the string theory [7, 8]. The next order term which is the $n = 0$ in the second term of (35) is the contribution of the mass of the particle (2) [4]. This is also alike to the amplitude of the massive particle derived from the string theory [14]. The contribution is interpreted as the exchange of two gravitons exchanges. However, two gravitons are distinguished by the coupling strength; one graviton is coupled by the strength Gs and the other by $Gm^{(2)}\sqrt{-t}$. Namely, our calculation is not the next order correction, G^2s^2, of the leading term, but the mass correction, $Gs\,Gm^{(2)}\sqrt{-t}$.

For $Gs \gg 1$, $\frac{\Gamma(-2iGs)}{\Gamma(2iGs)} \sim 1$, so that the scattering amplitude of the massive particle becomes:

$$U(s,t) \longrightarrow \frac{1}{4\pi}\delta\left(k_+ - p_+^{(1)}\right)e^{-2iGs}\left(2Gm^{(2)}\right)^{4iGs}\left(\frac{4}{-t}\right)^{1-2iGs}$$
$$\times\left(-2iGs\right)e^{-\frac{\pi}{4}Gm^{(2)}\sqrt{-t}} \,. \tag{36}$$

When $m^{(2)} \to 0$, the amplitude is idential to the results of 't Hooft.

Finally, the cross section is given by:

$$\sigma\left(\tilde{p}^{(1)} \to \tilde{k}^{(1)}\right)d^2\tilde{k}\frac{16G^2s^2}{t^2}e^{-\frac{\pi}{2}Gm^{(2)}\sqrt{-t}}d^2\tilde{k} \,. \tag{37}$$

5.2 Scatterings of Charged Particles

In this section, we discuss the scatterings of the charged particles. The charges of the particle (1) and (2) are set $e^{(1)}$ and $e^{(2)}$, respectively. We have to treat the electromagnetic interaction, simultaneously with the gravitational interaction. The approach of the calculation is the same as above. The particle (2) moving at Planck energy is identified with a Reissner–Nordstrom black hole. Then, the shift Δv at $u = 0$ becomes (10).

Here we calculate the scattering amplitude of the leading order, because the contribution of the charge of the test particle is given only by the leading term of the logarithm. The amplitude is calculated as:

$$U(s,t) = \frac{1}{2\pi}e^{(2)4i(Gs-\alpha/2)}\left(\frac{4}{-t}\right)^{1-2i(Gs-\alpha/2)}e^{2iGs}$$
$$\times\frac{\Gamma(1 - 2i(Gs - \alpha/2))}{\Gamma(2i(Gs - \alpha/2))} \,. \tag{38}$$

where we set $\alpha = e^{(1)}e^{(2)}$ according to the paper of Ref. [13].

We compare (38) with the leading order of (35) derived from the scattering of the non–charged particles. It is found that Gs of (35) is replaced by $Gs - \alpha/2$ of (38) to involve the electromagnetic interaction. This is the 't Hooft's indication using the shift of the GSW of the RN black hole.

Next, consider the case of $G \to 0$. In this case, only the electromagnetic interaction is involved and the amplitude coincides with (13) of [13], and also with the amplitude derived from the eikonal approximation of the QED. It is realized that the electromagnetic interaction is dominated below the low–energy $(Gs \ll \alpha)$ scattering, and the gravitational interaction is dominated at the high–energy $(Gs \gg \alpha)$ scattering.

Finally, we derive the scattering cross section. When $Gs - \alpha/2 \gg 1$, it is given by:

$$\sigma\left(\tilde{p}^{(1)} \to \tilde{k}^{(1)}\right) d^2\tilde{k} \xrightarrow[Gs \gg 1]{} \frac{64}{t^2}\left(G^2 s^2 - Gs\alpha + \alpha^2/2\right) d^2\tilde{k} \ . \tag{39}$$

It is interpreted that the first term denotes the one–graviton exchange term, and the third term denotes the one–photon exchange. The second term shows the interference term.

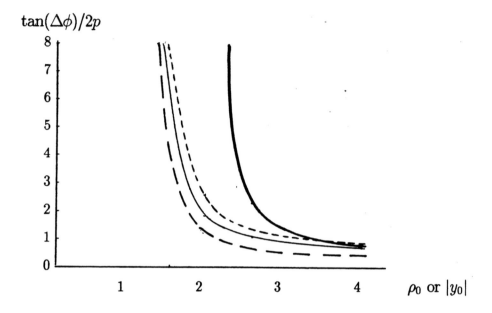

Fig.1: The refraction angle, $\Delta\phi$, crossing $u = 0$ where the light ray is injected perpendicular to the shock wave. We put $M = 1$. The bold line indicates the Schwarzschild case, and the thin solid line indicates the Kerr case moving parallel to the rotational axis, where the limit $M \rightarrow a$ is taken. The dashed line and the dotted line represent the Kerr case moving perpendicular to the axis, where the limit $M \rightarrow a$ is taken. The dashed line indicates $y > 0$, and the dotted line indicates $y < 0$.

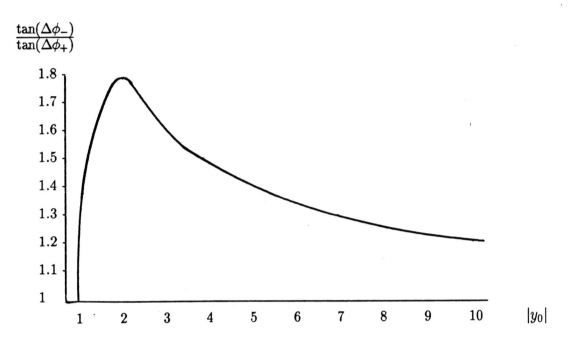

Fig.2: The ratio of the refraction angle of the negative sign of y to that of the positive sign.

Acknowledgments

We would like to gratefully thank Professor Keizo Kobayakawa at Kobe University for helpful comments. We would like to thank Professor C.O.Loustó for helpful suggestions. We are grateful to professor M. Fabbrichchsi for pointing a similarity between our amplitude and Veneziano amplitude by a private communication.

References

[1] C.O.Loustó and N.Sánchez, Phys. Lett. **B232**, 462(1989); ibid Int. J. Mod. Phys. **A5**, 915 (1990); ibid Nucl. Phys. **B355**, 231(1991); ibid Nucl. Phys. **B383**, 377 (1992); ibid preprint gr-qc/9410041.

[2] P.C.Aichelburg and R.U.Sexl, Gen. Relativ. Gravit. **2**, 303(1971).

[3] K. Hayashi and T. Samura, Phys. Rev. **D50**, 3666(1994).

[4] K. Hayashi and T. Samura, Planckian Scatterings of Massive Particles and Gravitational Shock Waves, preprint KOBE-FHD-93-05 and hep-th/9405013 (1994).

[5] K. Hayashi and T. Samura, in preparation.

[6] S Chandrasekhar, *The Mathematical Theory of Black Holes* (Clarendon Press, Oxford, 1983).

[7] G.'t Hooft, Phys. Lett. **B198**, 61(1987).

[8] D. Amati et.al., Phys. Lett. **B197**, 81(1987) .

[9] G.'t Hooft, Nucl. Phys. **B355**, 138 (1990).

[10] H. Verlinde and E. Verlinde, Nucl. Phys. **B371**, 246 (1992).

[11] M. Fabbrichesi et. al., Nucl. Phys. **B419**, 147 (1994).

[12] L. N. Lipatov, Sov. Phys. JETP**55**, 582 (1982); ibid Nucl. Phys. **B307**, 705 (1988); Nucl. Phys. **B365**, 614 (1991).

[13] J. Jackiw et. al., Phys. Lett. **B277** , 148 (1992).

[14] G. Cristofano et. al., Phys. Lett. **B246**, 45 (1990); M. Fabbrichesi et. al., Nucl. Phys. **B402**, 360 (1993).

[15] V. Ferrari and M. Martellini, Nucl. Phys. **B385**, 604 (1992).

Gennadi A. Sardanashvily, Editor
New Frontiers in Gravitation
Hadronic Press, Palm Harbor, FL 34682-1577, U.S.A.
ISBN 0–911767–96–7, 1996, Pages 115–144

NONLINEAR GAUGE FOUNDATION
OF AFFINE THEORIES
OF GRAVITY WITH FERMIONIC MATTER

J. Julve, A. Lopez–Pinto, A. Tiemblo
and R. Tresguerres

IMAFF, Consejo Superior de Investigaciones Cientficas
Serrano 123, Madrid 28006, Spain

Abstract

We present a general nonlinear approach for the gauging of the affine group, which gives an answer to several basic questions. In the first place, it clarifies the relationship between the linear translational connections and the coframes, and it also explains the gauge-theoretical origin of the degrees of freedom of the metric tensor in the standard metric-affine theories. We show that the gravitational interactions are mediated exclusively by connections, as in ordinary Yang-Mills theories, whereas the usual description of these interactions in terms of the metric corresponds to a degenerate case. Furthermore, our scheme allows to include ordinary fermionic matter in the metric–affine gauge theories of gravity without breaking the affine symmetry. We choose, at this purpose, the Lorentz group as the classification subgroup of the matter and gravitational fields.

1. Introduction

The geometrical formulation of ordinary General Relativity (GR) hiddes in some extent its dynamical character. Even retaining the fundamental idea that the structure of spacetime is determined by matter, one must emphasize that gravitation is, in the first place, an interaction. The remaining fundamental forces are described in terms of gauge theories of given groups. They are mediated by connections which play the basic role of gauge fields. In Einstein's GR instead, the interaction is determined by the metric tensor, whereas the Christoffel connections are derived objects constructed in terms of the metric. This central role played by the classical concept of distance more than by the connections could be a reason why the programme of quantizing gravity has been unsuccessful until now. In any case, the gravitational interaction appears as essentialy different from the other ones. To overcome this anomaly, it is desirable to provide the spacetime with a suitable dynamical structure which privileges the role of the connections as the fundamental intermediate fields. In other words, the first step in an unification programme is the establishment of a link between geometry –i.e. gravitation– and gauge theories. The treatment of gravity as a gauge theory of a certain spacetime group was proposed short after the introduction of the Yang-Mills theories[1].

The problem of the interpretation of the dynamical role played by the metric tensor is closely related to that of the correct treatment of the coframes. Some attempts were made to clarify the link between them and the translational connections. The main difficulty is that one cannot identify the gauge fields of the translations with the tetrads, since the latter are covectors and lack the inhomogeneous term under gauge transformations. At this respect, several authors[2] recognized that the geometrical reformulation of the dynamical gauge theory of gravity can only be realized by introducing extra nondynamical degrees of freedom in the theory. In the context of Poincar gauge theories, Grignani and Nardelli called them the *Poincar coordinates* ξ^α. These authors considered them as Higgs–type fields transforming as vectors under gauge transformations of the Poincar group. In general, as shown by Mielke et al.[3], introducing a vector–valued zero form ξ^α which transforms as a Poincar (resp. as an affine) vector, and assuming that the relationship between the tetrads and the linear translational gauge fields $\overset{(T)}{\Gamma^\alpha}$ is given by

$$\vartheta^\alpha := \overset{(T)}{\Gamma^\alpha} + D\xi^\alpha \, , \tag{1.1}$$

the right transformation properties are guaranteed.

One of the goals of this paper is to explain the origin of the *coordinates* ξ^α as coset parameters which, as we will show below, come out from the nonlinear approach to the gauge theory of spacetime groups. They turn out to be an essential element in the definition of the nonlinear translational connection. Indeed, the link between the translational gauge fields and the coframes is explained by means of a nonlinear realization of the translations. The coframes turn out to be nonlinear translational connections, with the right tensorial transformation properties[4]. We will show that the term $D\xi^\alpha$ in (1.1) is a necessary contribution arising from the nonlinear realization of spacetime gauge symmetries. The linear translational connections do not appear as independent objects of the theory. Only the particular combination (1.1) of the translational gauge fields and the coset parameters occurs, playing the role of the coframes. The coset parameters ξ^α associated to the translations are interpreted as spacetime coordinates. The whole geometrical setting arises as the result of gauging the nonlinear realization of the group in a coset space. Indeed, nonlinear group realizations allow to interpret a quotient space of the whole group space as the very spacetime manifold, as noticed by several authors[5]. The coordinate–independent formulation of the theory in terms of differential forms thus shows that the theory is independent of the coset parametrization.

In the early works of Utiyama, Sciama and Kibble[1], the role of the translations was played by general coordinate transformations. Hehl et al.[6] proposed an improved approach, based on the Poincar group actively interpreted, regarding the gauged translations as represented by parallel transport. They substituted the usual translational generators by covariant derivatives. The price one has to pay is that the translations no longer constitute an Abelian group. In our approach instead, the translational generators obey the usual commutation relations.

A further question has to do with the coupling of gravitation to fundamental particles. In the ordinary holonomic description of GR, there is no obvious place for fermions. Nevertheless, the anholonomic formulation allows to include them in a natural way if we supose that the Lorentz group acts on the anholonomic indices. The symmetry properties of the gauge and matter fields must be the same. Thus, the first candidate to play the role of the dynamical spacetime group is the Poincar group, since it is the semidirect product of the Lorentz group, and the translations needed to define the coframes. However, according to Einstein's original aim, a general relativistic theory should guarantee the undistiguishability of the states of movement of arbitrary observers. From the geometrical point of view, the most general spacetime transformations are those of the affine group. The affine tensor spaces[7] involve the vector basis $e_\alpha := e_\alpha{}^i \partial_i$, representing a coordinate–independent local frame, and its dual 1–form basis ϑ^β, i.e. the coframe, defined by the requirement that the interior product of both bases is $e_\alpha \rfloor \vartheta^\beta = \delta_\alpha^\beta$. In addition, a linear connection $\Gamma_\alpha{}^\beta$, necessary in view of the local covariance, is in order. The group transformations act on the anholonomic indices. In particular, the general linear group acts on the frame attached to the observer, rotating, shearing and dilatating it. Accordingly, the linear connections may be splitted up into an antisymmetric, a symmetric traceless and a trace contribution. In principle, these are, in the absence of matter, the dynamical degrees of freedom involved.

As pointed out before, the role of the Lorentz group as the classification group of the elementary particles oblies us to consider it as the effective dynamical group. In fact, matter fields must be placed on the linear representations of the Lorentz group. Accordingly, if we take this group to be the transformation group which acts on the frames, at the same time we are introducing the correspondig invariant Minkowski metric. Thus, a metrization of the pure affine geometry takes place. Nevertheless, this does not mean that we have to renounce to the original affine symmetry. One can realize the affine group nonlinearly in such a way that the Lorentz group plays the role of the classification subgroup, without imposing constraints which reduce the number of degrees of freedom of the original general linear connection. In fact, this is the most natural way to match geometry and matter, preserving the simultaneous validity of the spacetime groups characteristic for each one. This will be our leading idea in the following.

From various generalizations of the original gauge theory of gravity[1] which were developped in recent times[8], the metric-affine gauge theory (MAGT) proposed by Hehl et al.[9] is perhaps the most promising one. It is particularly interesting, since it provides a dynamical foundation of the geometrical theory equiped with the most general connection, namely with the general linear connection $\Gamma_\alpha{}^\beta$. Its gauge group is the affine group. There are several reasons which strongly suggest the necessity of developing such dynamical theories involving the most general post-Riemannian geometries. For instance, according to Ne'eman and Šijački[10], the adoption of the affine group as the dynamical group could solve certain renormalizability and unitarity problems in Quantum Gravity, with the help of the additional degrees of freedom contained in the linear connection.

Nevertheless, the MAGT approach is faced with several difficulties. The main one is the problem of including ordinary fermions in the general framework. The reason is well known: no half–integer linear finite representations of the affine group exist. Some suggestions were even made at this purpose, being the essential one the introduction of *manifields* proposed by Ne'eman and Šijački[10]. *Manifields* are infinite-dimensional representations of the group SL(n,R). These authors proposed such a group as the classification group for hadrons, which perhaps allows to study the corresponding phaenomenological matter Lagrangians. But the question of introducing ordinary Dirac particles in the affine gravitational scheme is not solved in this way.

Nevertheless, the inclusion of ordinary matter in the affine scheme becomes possible in the context of nonlinear realizations of symmetry groups[11]. The whole difficulty in treating spinors consistently in the framework of affine theories is related with the implicit assumption that the gauge symmetry has to be realized linearly, which is by no means evident. There is no an *a priori* reason to suppose that a given physical symmetry must be realized linearly in nature. Indeed, studying the general formulation of nonlinear realizations of spacetime symmetry groups, the linear realizations manifest themselves as a very special case. At this respect, it is worthwhile mentioning the work of Ogievetskii and Polubarinov[12], who found out a nonlinear affine transformation law for ordinary fermions, which strongly suggested to explore the possibility of a nonlinear realization of the affine group.

This group does not posses natural invariants, as required to define the action of the theory. The conventional approach to overcome this difficulty consists in distinguishing two kinds of representations describing co- and contravariant objects, transforming with Λ and Λ^{-1} respectively, where Λ is a general linear transformation. This duplication of the representation space is related with the inclusion of a metric tensor in the MAGT's, with ten additional, dynamically (i.e. gauge–theoretically) not justified degrees of freedom, playing a role similar as in the geometrical approach. We claim that a more natural solution to get invariants is to project the action of the whole affine group into a subgroup which admits such invariants. In particular we choose the Lorentz group, which has the Minkowski metric as a natural invariant. Thus, as a consecuence of the nonlinear realization, it becomes possible to construct invariants without increasing the number of degrees of freedom of the theory, since the Minkowski metric is a constant tensor. We will show below that the metric tensor of the standard MAGT's can be obtained from our approach as a degenerate case, by rearranging the hidden degrees of freedom contained in the nonlinear realization, in such a way that the general linear group becomes the classification subgroup.

From the papers of Coleman et al.[11], we have a systematical formal approach to the nonlinear realizations known in the literature as coset realizations. They start from the introduction of the equivalence classes associated with a given subgroup H of a larger group G as a space to realize the group G itself. This can be done due to the fact that the quotient space G/H is a complete partition (being its elements equivalence classes) of the group space. The *natural* nonlinear realization of a group is represented by its action on the group space itself. This approach is explicitely gauge covariant with respect to the classification subgroup.

The nonlinear coset realizations, initially proposed to treat internal symmetries, were soon extended to spacetime symmetries. In fact, several attempts were made to apply them to gravity. Isham, Salam and Strathdee[4] considered the nonlinear action of $GL(4,R)$, taking the Lorentz group as classification subgroup. Borisov and Ogievetski[13] considered a nonlinear realization of the affine group with the Lorentz group as the classification subgroup. However, they only took into account the global case, in conjunction with a simultaneous nonlinear realization of the conformal group, since they were interested in reproducing local diffeomorphisms from the closure of the algebras of both groups. They did not construct a gauge theory with degrees of freedom associated to independent connections. Stelle and West[14] investigated the nonlinear realization allowed by the spontaneous symmetry breaking of SO(3,2) down to SO(3,1). Pseudotranslations were defined from the broken generators of SO(3,2). Their parameters, i.e. the nondynamical SO(3,2) vector fields ξ^α constrained to take their values in an internal anti–de Sitter space, were identified as the Goldstone fields associated to the symmetry breaking, not as coordinates. Chang and Mansouri[15] made use of the general nonlinear approach as we do, but they did not emphasize its relevance for the gauge teatment of the translations and thus for the link between tetrads and translational gauge fields. They also introduced an auxiliary coordinate manifold alien to the group. Lord[5] interpreted the gauge generalization of a spacetime group G in the language of fiber bundles as a gauge generalization of the stability subgroup, together with diffeomorphisms, following Hehl et al.[6]. The translations thus loose their Abelian character.

We will present a nonlinear gauge realization of the affine group paying a special attention to both, the rigourous treatment of the coordinates and the introduction of Lorentz–covariant fields, coupling to the general affine connections. The paper is organized as follows. In section 2 we shortly expose the basic general notions about nonlinear realizations. Section 3 is devoted to the introduction of the tetrads as the nonlinear connections of the translations. In section 4, the nonlinear realization of the affine group with the Lorentz group as the classification subgroup is presented, thus showing the compatibility of the affine theory with ordinary Dirac fields. In section 5, we relate the results of the latter section to the standard MAGT, which reveals itself as a degenerate case of ours, being unable to couple to fundamental particles. The gauge–theoretical origin of the degrees of freedom of the metric in a MAGT is clarified. There follow, in section 6, the conclusionsa and a discussion about some open questions. Our results are mainly contained in Refs.(16).

2. Nonlinear realization of spacetime groups and nonlinear connections

Here we will outline the basic nonlinear machinery briefly. Let $G = \{g\}$ be a Lie group including a subgroup $H = \{h\}$ whose linear representations $\rho(h)$ are known, acting on functions ψ belonging to a representation space of H. The elements of the quotient space G/H are equivalence classes of the form $gH = \{gh_1, gh_2 \ldots gh_n\}$, and they constitute a complete partition of the group space. We call the elements of the quotient space cosets to the left (right) of H with respect to g. Since we deal with Lie groups, the elements of G/H are labeled by continuous parameters, say ξ. We represent the elements of G/H by means of the coset indicators $c(\xi)$, parametrized by the coset parameters ξ, playing the role of a kind of coordinates. The nonlinear coset realizations[11] are based on the action of the group on G/H, i.e., on a partition of its own space. An arbitrary element $g \epsilon G$ acts on G/H transforming a coset into another, that is

$$g : G/H \rightarrow G/H$$
$$c(\xi) \rightarrow c(\xi'), \tag{2.1}$$

according to the general law

$$g\,c(\xi) = c(\xi')\,h(\xi,g)\ . \tag{2.2}$$

The elements $h(\xi,g)$ which appear in (2.2) belong to the subgroup H, that we will call in the following the *classification subgroup*, since the elements g of the whole group G considered in (2.2) act nonlinearly on the representation space of the classification subgroup H according to

$$\psi' = \rho(h(\xi,g))\psi\,, \tag{2.3}$$

where ρ, as mentioned above, is a linear representation of H in the space of the matter fields ψ. Therefore, the action of the total group G projects on the representations of the subgroup H through the dependence of $h(\xi,g)$ in (2.2) on the group element g, as given by eq.(2.3). The action of the group is realized on the couples (ξ,ψ). It reduces to the usual linear action of H when we take in particular for g in (2.2) an element of H.

Now we will construct the nonlinear connection of G suitable to define a covariant differential transforming like (2.3). Even in the global case, in which g does not depend on ξ, the appearence of ξ in the transformation $h(\xi,g)$, see (2.2), implies that h is not a constant, and a particular kind of covariant differentials is required, namely

$$\overset{\circ}{D}\psi := \left(d + \overset{\circ}{\Gamma}\right)\psi\,, \tag{2.4}$$

where $\overset{o}{\Gamma}$ is the Maurer–Cartan connection 1–form

$$\overset{o}{\Gamma} := c^{-1}dc, \tag{2.5}$$

with values on the group algebra, transforming as

$$\overset{o'}{\Gamma} = h\overset{o}{\Gamma}h^{-1} + hdh^{-1}. \tag{2.6}$$

The connections (2.5) do not involve dynamical degrees of freedom. The situation changes when local transformations are concerned. The previous scheme must then be extended to include a dependence of the parameters of $g\epsilon G$ on the *coset coordinates* ξ, and we generalize (2.5) to the dynamical connection corresponding to the nonlinear realization of the group, namely

$$\Gamma := c^{-1}\mathcal{D}c := c^{-1}(d + \Omega)c, \tag{2.7}$$

with the ordinary linear connection Ω of the whole group G transforming as

$$\Omega' = g\Omega g^{-1} + gdg^{-1}. \tag{2.8}$$

The nonlinear gauge field Γ defined in (2.7) transforms as

$$\Gamma' = h\Gamma h^{-1} + hdh^{-1} \tag{2.9}$$

under local transformations, thus allowing to define the local nonlinear covariant differential operator

$$\mathbf{D} := d + \Gamma. \tag{2.10}$$

The components of the connection Γ have very intersting transformation properties. In fact, it is easy to read out from (2.9) that only the components of Γ related to the generators of H behave as true connections, i.e. transform inhomogeneously, whereas the components of Γ over the generators associated with the cosets c transform as tensors with respect to the subgroup H, notwithstanding their nature of connections.

3. Gauge treatment of the tetrads

We are going to show that the coframes are to be interpreted as nonlinear connections of the translations, which transform as ordinary covectors. In this first approach, we will choose the general linear group as the classification subgroup of the affine group, and no metric will be taken into account, since it should be introduced *ad hoc*, without any dynamical reason. Let us consider the affine group $A(n, R) = GL(n, R) \rtimes R^n$ in n dimensions, defined as the semidirect product of the translations and the general linear transformations. The commutation relations read

$$
\begin{aligned}
[\Lambda^\alpha{}_\beta, \Lambda^\mu{}_\nu] &= i \left(\delta^\alpha_\nu \Lambda^\mu{}_\beta - \delta^\mu_\beta \Lambda^\alpha{}_\nu \right), \\
[\Lambda^\alpha{}_\beta, P_\mu] &= i \delta^\alpha_\mu P_\beta, \\
[P_\alpha, P_\beta] &= 0,
\end{aligned}
\tag{3.1}
$$

where $\Lambda^\alpha{}_\beta$ are the generators of the linear transformations, and P_α those of the translations. We will realize the group action on the coset space $A(n, R)/GL(n, R)$. We choose in particular for the cosets the following parametrization:

$$
c := e^{-i \xi^\alpha P_\alpha},
\tag{3.2}
$$

where ξ^α are the *coset coordinates*. As we will see below, they are equivalent to *Cartan's generalized radius vector* or the *Poincar coordinates* considered by other authors[2][3]. The group elements of the whole affine group $A(n, R)$ are parametrized as

$$
g = e^{i \epsilon^\alpha P_\alpha} e^{i \omega_\alpha{}^\beta \Lambda^\alpha{}_\beta},
\tag{3.3}
$$

and those of the classification subgroup $GL(n, R)$ are taken to be

$$
h := e^{i v_\alpha{}^\beta \Lambda^\alpha{}_\beta}.
\tag{3.4}
$$

Other parametrizations which lead to equivalent results are of course possible. The fundamental eq.(2.2) defining the nonlinear group action then reads

$$e^{i\,\epsilon^\alpha P_\alpha}\,e^{i\,\omega_\alpha{}^\beta \Lambda^\alpha{}_\beta}\,e^{-i\,\xi^\alpha P_\alpha} \;=\; e^{-i\,\xi'^\alpha P_\alpha}\,e^{i\,v_\alpha{}^\beta \Lambda^\alpha{}_\beta}\,. \tag{3.5}$$

Using the Campell–Hausdorff formula, the variation of the coset parameters ξ^α and the value of $v_\alpha{}^\beta$, in the r.h.s. of (3.5), are calculable. We get

$$\delta\xi^\alpha = -\omega_\beta{}^\alpha\,\xi^\beta - \epsilon^\alpha \quad, \qquad u_\alpha{}^\beta = \omega_\alpha{}^\beta\,. \tag{3.6}$$

Thus we see from (3.6) that the coset parameters ξ^α transform as affine covectors, as postulated by other authors[3] for *Cartan's generalized radius vector*. Observe that for the particular choice of the coset space we are dealing with, the parameters $v_\alpha{}^\beta$ of the r.h.s. of (3.5), i.e. of the parameters characterizing $h\epsilon H$, according to the general formulation (2.2), coincide with those $\omega_\alpha{}^\beta$ of the parametrization of $g\epsilon G$ in the l.h.s. of (3.5). This result is not valid for arbitrary choices of the coset space, see below, but it simplifies things in our case since the action (2.3) of the whole affine group on arbitrary fields of a representation space of $GL(n,R)$ reduces to $\psi' = \rho(h(g))\psi$. Actually, the infinitesimal variation of the fields reads

$$\delta\psi = i\,v_\alpha{}^\beta \rho(\Lambda^\alpha{}_\beta)\,\psi\,, \tag{3.7}$$

being ρ an arbitrary representation of $GL(n,R)$ transformations. Now we define the suitable connection for the nonlinear gauge realization in two steps, first introducing the ordinary linear affine connection Ω in (2.5) as

$$\Omega := -i\,\overset{(T)}{\Gamma}{}^\alpha P_\alpha - i\,\overset{(GL)}{\Gamma}{}_\alpha{}^\beta \Lambda^\alpha{}_\beta\,, \tag{3.8}$$

which includes the linear translational potential $\overset{(T)}{\Gamma}{}^\alpha$ and the $GL(n,R)$ connection $\overset{(GL)}{\Gamma}{}_\alpha{}^\beta$. The transformations (2.8) take the standard form

$$\delta\overset{(T)}{\Gamma}{}^\alpha = \overset{(GL)}{D}\epsilon^\alpha - \omega_\beta{}^\alpha\overset{(T)}{\Gamma}{}^\beta\,, \tag{3.9}$$

and

$$\overset{(GL)}{\delta \Gamma_\alpha{}^\beta} = \overset{(GL)}{D} \omega_\alpha{}^\beta ,\tag{3.10}$$

with $\overset{(GL)}{D}$ as the covariant differential constructed with the $GL(n,R)$ connection exclusively. Making then use of definition (2.7), we get

$$\tilde{\Gamma} := e^{i\xi^\alpha P_\alpha} (d + \Omega) e^{-i\xi^\alpha P_\alpha} = -i \left(\overset{(T)}{\Gamma^\alpha} + \overset{(GL)}{D} \xi^\alpha \right) P_\alpha - i \tilde{\Gamma}_\alpha{}^\beta \Lambda^\alpha{}_\beta .$$

$$\tag{3.11}$$

with

$$\tilde{\Gamma}_\alpha{}^\beta = \overset{(GL)}{\Gamma_\alpha{}^\beta} .\tag{3.12}$$

We denote the nonlinear objects with a tilde for later convenience. The components on P_α in the connection (3.11) play a crucial role in gravitational gauge theories. As we mentioned before, in spite of the fact that they arise as a constitutive part of the connection required in the nonlinear realization, they do not transform as a connection, but as a covector of the classification subgroup. Let us define them as the coframe

$$\tilde{\vartheta}^\alpha := \overset{(T)}{\Gamma^\alpha} + \overset{(GL)}{D} \xi^\alpha .\tag{3.13}$$

According to (2.9), it transforms as a covector under $GL(n,R)$, namely

$$\delta\tilde{\vartheta}^\alpha = -v_\beta{}^\alpha \tilde{\vartheta}^\beta .\tag{3.14}$$

In our scheme, the expression (3.13) reproduces the same results obtained in reference (3) without any *ad hoc* assumptions, since the variables ξ^α are constitutive elements of the gauge–theoretical approach.

4. Nonlinear gauge approach to the affine group with the Lorentz group as the classification subgroup

As we have discussed above, ordinary matter fields such as Dirac fields can only be included in an affine theory without breaking the symmetry if the affine group is realized nonlinearly, with the Lorentz group as the classification subgroup. Thus, let us consider the affine group $A(4, R) = GL(4, R) \rtimes R^4$ in 4 dimensions, with the generators $\Lambda^\alpha{}_\beta$ of the linear transformations splitted up into the Lorentz generators $L^\alpha{}_\beta$, plus the remaining generators $S^\alpha{}_\beta$ of the symmetric linear transformations, as $\Lambda^\alpha{}_\beta = L^\alpha{}_\beta + S^\alpha{}_\beta$. In addition, we have the generators P_α of the translations. The commutation relations (3.1) decompose into

$$
\begin{aligned}
[L_{\alpha\beta}, L_{\mu\nu}] &= -i \left(o_{\alpha[\mu}L_{\nu]\beta} - o_{\beta[\mu}L_{\nu]\alpha}\right), \\
[L_{\alpha\beta}, S_{\mu\nu}] &= i \left(o_{\alpha(\mu}S_{\nu)\beta} - o_{\beta(\mu}S_{\nu)\alpha}\right), \\
[S_{\alpha\beta}, S_{\mu\nu}] &= i \left(o_{\alpha(\mu}L_{\nu)\beta} + o_{\beta(\mu}L_{\nu)\alpha}\right), \\
[L_{\alpha\beta}, P_\mu] &= i\, o_{\mu[\alpha}P_{\beta]}, \\
[S_{\alpha\beta}, P_\mu] &= i\, o_{\mu(\alpha}P_{\beta)}, \\
[P_\alpha, P_\beta] &= 0.
\end{aligned}
\tag{4.1}
$$

In order to realize the group action on the coset space $A(4, R)/SO(1, 3)$, we make use of the general formula (2.2) which defines the nonlinear group action, choosing in particular for the cosets the parametrization

$$
c := e^{-i\xi^\alpha P_\alpha} e^{i h^{\mu\nu} S_{\mu\nu}}, \tag{4.2}
$$

where ξ^α and $h^{\mu\nu}$ are the coset parameters. The group elements of the whole affine group $A(4, R)$ are parametrized as

$$
g = e^{i\epsilon^\alpha P_\alpha} e^{i\alpha^{\mu\nu} S_{\mu\nu}} e^{i\beta^{\mu\nu} L_{\mu\nu}}, \tag{4.3}
$$

and those of the classification Lorentz subgroup are taken to be

$$
h := e^{i u^{\mu\nu} L_{\mu\nu}}. \tag{4.4}
$$

In the Appendix **A**, we show in some detail the calculations which lead to the explicit form of the infinitesimal transformations of the coset parameters. The variation of the translational ones reads

$$\delta\xi^\alpha = -(\alpha_\beta{}^\alpha + \beta_\beta{}^\alpha)\,\xi^\beta - \epsilon^\alpha\,, \qquad (4.5)$$

thus assigning these parameters the role of coordinates, transforming as usual under the affine group, compare with (3.6), with the obvious identification

$$\alpha_\beta{}^\alpha + \beta_\beta{}^\alpha = \omega_\beta{}^\alpha\,. \qquad (4.6)$$

On the other hand, we obtain the variation of the matrix

$$r^{\alpha\beta} := e^{h^{\alpha\beta}}\,, \qquad (4.7)$$

constructed from the coset parameters $h^{\alpha\beta}$ associated to the symmetric affine transformations. In the following, $r^{\alpha\beta}$ more than the coset parameters itself, will play the fundamental role. Their variation reads

$$\delta r^{\alpha\beta} = (\alpha^\alpha{}_\gamma + \beta^\alpha{}_\gamma)\,r^{\gamma\beta} + u^\beta{}_\gamma\,r^{\gamma\alpha}\,. \qquad (4.8)$$

Since $r^{\alpha\beta}$ is symmetric, the antisymmetric part of (4.8) must vanish. From this symmetry condition, as shown in Appendix **B**, follows for the nonlinear Lorentz parameter the expression

$$u^{\alpha\beta} = \beta^{\alpha\beta} - \alpha^{\mu\nu}\tanh\left\{\frac{1}{2}\log\left[r^\alpha{}_\mu\,(r^{-1})^\beta{}_\nu\right]\right\}\,, \qquad (4.9)$$

which shows how it consists of the linear Lorentz parameter $\beta^{\alpha\beta}$ plus a contribution depending on the symmetric affine parameter $\alpha^{\alpha\beta}$ *cum* $r^{\alpha\beta}$. The action (2.3) of the full affine group on arbitrary fields of a given representation space of the Lorentz group reads infinitesimally

$$\delta\psi = i\,u^{\alpha\beta}\rho(L_{\alpha\beta})\psi\,, \qquad (4.10)$$

being $u^{\alpha\beta}$ the nonlinear Lorentz parameter (4.9), and $\rho(L_{\alpha\beta})$ an arbitrary representation of the Lorentz group. This equation is the key which allows to include ordinary matter into an affine theory, since the action of the symmetric linear transformations on the fields occurs through the nonlinear Lorentz parameter, whereas the group generators are the ordinary generators of the Lorentz group. Thus, not only bosonic matter, but also Dirac fields, can be considered as the sources of the gravitational potentials.

Now we will define the suitable connection for the nonlinear gauge realization in two steps. We first introduce the ordinary linear affine connection Ω in (2.7) as

$$\Omega := -i \overset{(T)}{\Gamma^\alpha} P_\alpha - i \overset{(GL)}{\Gamma_\alpha}{}^\beta \left(S^\alpha{}_\beta + L^\alpha{}_\beta \right) . \tag{4.11}$$

Their transformations (2.8) of $\overset{(T)}{\Gamma^\alpha}$, and $\overset{(GL)}{\Gamma_\alpha}{}^\beta$ present the standard form

$$\delta \overset{(T)}{\Gamma^\alpha} = \overset{(GL)}{D} \epsilon^\alpha - (\alpha_\beta{}^\alpha + \beta_\beta{}^\alpha) \overset{(T)}{\Gamma^\gamma} , \tag{4.12}$$

and

$$\delta \overset{(GL)}{\Gamma_\alpha}{}^\beta = \overset{(GL)}{D} \left(\alpha_\alpha{}^\beta + \beta_\alpha{}^\beta \right) . \tag{4.13}$$

Compare (4.12,13) with (3.9,10). Eq.(4.13) shows that both, the symmetric and the antisymmetric parts of the linear connection $\overset{(GL)}{\Gamma_\alpha}{}^\beta$, transform as true connections, as expected. Making then use of definition (2.7), we get the nonlinear connection

$$\Gamma := c^{-1} (d + \Omega) c = -i \vartheta^\alpha P_\alpha - i \Gamma_\alpha{}^\beta \left(S^\alpha{}_\beta + L^\alpha{}_\beta \right) , \tag{4.14}$$

with the nonlinear translational connection ϑ^α and the nonlinear $GL(4, R)$ connection $\Gamma_\alpha{}^\beta$ respectively defined as

$$\vartheta^\alpha := r_\beta{}^\alpha \left(\overset{(T)}{\Gamma^\beta} + \overset{(GL)}{D} \xi^\beta \right) , \tag{4.15}$$

and

$$\Gamma_\alpha{}^\beta := \left(r^{-1}\right)_\alpha{}^\gamma \overset{(GL)}{\Gamma}_\gamma{}^\lambda r_\lambda{}^\beta - \left(r^{-1}\right)_\alpha{}^\gamma d\, r_\gamma{}^\beta \,. \tag{4.16}$$

In the following, we will interpret (4.15) and (4.16) geometrically, identifying ϑ^α with the coframe and $\Gamma_\alpha{}^\beta$ with a *geometrical* connection respectively. Eqs.(4.15,16) thus establish the correspondence between the *geometrical* objects in the l.h.s. and the original groupal objects in the r.h.s. According to (2.9), we find that the coframe and the connection transform respectively as

$$\delta\vartheta^\alpha = -u_\beta{}^\alpha \vartheta^\beta \,. \tag{4.17}$$

and

$$\delta\Gamma_\alpha{}^\beta = D\, u_\alpha{}^\beta \,, \tag{4.18}$$

with D constructed with the nonlinear connection (4.16) itself. Eqs.(4.17, 4.18) show that the coframe transforms as a Lorentz covector, with the nonlinear Lorentz parameter (4.9), and the connection behaves as a Lorentz connection. In view of (4.14), this connection is actually composed of two essentialy different parts, defined on different elements of the Lie algebra of the affine generators. Eq.(4.18) shows that only the antisymmetric part of (4.16), defined on the Lorentz generators, behaves as a true connection with respect to the Lorentz subgroup, whereas the symmetric part is tensorial, transforming without any inhomogeneous contribution, since $u^{\alpha\beta}$ is antisymmetric. The geometrical meaning of the nonlinear connection associated to the symmetric affine generators will become clearer in terms of the Minkowski metric, as we are going to show.

Since the nonlinear realization we are studying consists in a projection of the action of the whole affine group on its Lorentz subgroup, i.e. on the pseudoorthogonal group which, by definition, leaves invariant the symmetric tensor

$$o_{\alpha\beta} := diag(+ - - -), \tag{4.19}$$

this tensor appears automatically in the theory as a consequence of the nonlinear treatment, being a natural invariant of the Lorentz group. We interpret it geometrically in the common way as the Minkowskian metric tensor. No degrees of freedom are related to it. Its inverse reads

$$o^{\alpha\beta} := diag(+ - - -), \tag{4.20}$$

and, as mentioned above, both are Lorentz invariant:

$$\delta o_{\alpha\beta} = 0 \quad , \quad \delta o^{\alpha\beta} = 0. \tag{4.21}$$

Defining the nonmetricity $Q_{\alpha\beta}$ as usual[9], i.e. as minus the covariant differential of the metric tensor, we find that it is proportional to the symmetric part of the nonlinear $GL(4, R)$ connection, namely

$$Q_{\alpha\beta} := -Do_{\alpha\beta} = 2\Gamma_{(\alpha\beta)}. \tag{4.22}$$

Thus, the geometrical meaning of the nonlinear connection associated to the symmetric affine generators becomes apparent as the nonmetricity, which behaves as a Lorentz tensor. In order to show that, the transformation law (4.18) can be splitted up into two parts, corresponding to the Lorentz connection $\overset{(Lor)}{\Gamma}_{\alpha\beta} := \Gamma_{[\alpha\beta]}$, and to the nonmetricity respectively. We get

$$\delta \overset{(Lor)}{\Gamma}_{\alpha}{}^{\beta} = \overset{(Lor)}{D} u_{\alpha}{}^{\beta}, \tag{4.23}$$

and

$$\delta Q_{\alpha\beta} = 2 u_{(\alpha}{}^{\gamma} Q_{\beta)\gamma}. \tag{4.24}$$

The tensorial character of the symmetric part of the connection is a result of the nonlinear realization of the symmetric affine transformations, but it is also evident from the definition (4.22) of the nonmetricity, since $do_{\alpha\beta} = 0$.

Let us now find the natural field strengths of the theory from the commutation of two covariant differentials operators (2.10). This yields

$$\mathbf{D} \wedge \mathbf{D} = -i\, T^\alpha P_\alpha - i\, R_\alpha{}^\beta \left(S^\alpha{}_\beta + L^\alpha{}_\beta \right), \qquad (4.25)$$

with the torsion T^α and the curvature $R_\alpha{}^\beta$ respectively defined as

$$T^\alpha := D\vartheta^\alpha, \qquad (4.26)$$

and

$$R_\alpha{}^\beta := d\Gamma_\alpha{}^\beta + \Gamma_\gamma{}^\beta \wedge \Gamma_\alpha{}^\gamma. \qquad (4.27)$$

These are the field strengths of the translations and the general linear transformations respectively. The curvature has a symmetric and an antisymmetric part, corresponding to the symmetric and the antisymmetric (Lorentz) generators of the affine group respectively. Both, the torsion and the curvature, transform as Lorentz tensors, namely

$$\delta T^\alpha = -u_\beta{}^\alpha T^\beta, \qquad (4.28)$$

and

$$\delta R_\alpha{}^\beta = u_\alpha{}^\gamma R_\gamma{}^\beta - u_\gamma{}^\beta R_\alpha{}^\gamma. \qquad (4.29)$$

The geometrization of the gauge theory is completed by introducing vector bases which represent the reference frames. We interpreted the nonlinear translational connections (4.15) as the coframes, which play the role of the 1–forms bases. In terms of ϑ^α, we define their dual vector bases e_α by means of the interior product, as fulfiling the general relation

$$e_\alpha \rfloor \vartheta^\beta = \delta^\beta_\alpha. \qquad (4.30)$$

The vector bases thus transform as Lorentz vectors, namely

$$\delta e_\alpha = u_\alpha{}^\beta e_\beta. \qquad (4.31)$$

Our nonlinear approach contains all the elements which appear in the standard MAGT's, with the main difference of their transformation properties. In particular, the metric tensor is Lorentz invariant, i.e. it is fixed to be the Minkowskian metric, which does not posses any degrees of freedom. This seemengly makes a difference between the dynamical contents of both theories, since the metric tensor in the MAGT's involves in general ten degrees of freedom, but we will show below that these can be factorized into the coframes and the connections.

5. Correspondence to the standard metric–affine theory

We are interested in showing the correspondence between our theory and the standard MAGT. In section 3, we studied an affine gauge theory in which only the translations are realized nonlinearly, whereas the whole general linear group acts linearly. This purely affine theory is not equivalent to a MAGT, since it does not give account of the degrees of freedom of the metric, that are introduced by hand in the standard approaches[9]. Here we will show that the MAGT is in fact a degenerate case of the nonlinear theory with the Lorentz group as the classification subgroup. Such a theory depends on the variables ξ^α, $h^{\alpha\beta}$, $\overset{(T)}{\Gamma^\alpha}$, and $\overset{(GL)}{\Gamma_\alpha{}^\beta}$, i.e., on $4 + 10 + 16 + 64 = 94$ degrees of freedom. However, these variables occur factorized in such a manner that only the particular combinations ϑ^α and $\Gamma_\alpha{}^\beta$, see (4.15,16), i.e. $16 + 64 = 80$ degrees of freedom, are relevant. Neither ξ^α nor $h^{\alpha\beta}$ appear explicitly as independent degrees of freedom, since the symmetries to which they correspond are realized nonlinearly. But it is possible to rearrange the ten degrees of freedom of $h^{\alpha\beta}$ in such a way that they become manifest –through the metric tensor– whereas only ξ^α remain hidden. Formally, the transition from the nonlinear to the usual metric–affine objects resembles a finite gauge transformation, with $r^{\alpha\beta}$ as the matrix of the symmetric affine transformations. The resulting MAGT–metric tensor $\tilde{g}_{\alpha\beta} := r_\alpha{}^\mu r_\beta{}^\nu o_{\mu\nu}$, see (5.3) below, plays the role of a Goldstone–like field, that can be dropped out by means of the inverse

gauge transformation. We represent the standard metric–affine objects
signed by a tilde, since (up to the metric) they are identical to those studied in section 3. Thus, the corresponding coframes and connections are
those of a nonlinear realization of the affine group in which the role of the
classification group is played by the $GL(4, R)$ subgroup[11], namely

$$\tilde{\vartheta}^\alpha := \overset{(T)}{\Gamma^\alpha} + \overset{(GL)}{D} \xi^\alpha = \left(r^{-1}\right)_\beta{}^\alpha \vartheta^\beta , \tag{5.1}$$

and

$$\tilde{\Gamma}_\alpha{}^\beta := \overset{(GL)}{\Gamma_\alpha{}^\beta} = r_\alpha{}^\gamma \Gamma_\gamma{}^\lambda \left(r^{-1}\right)_\lambda{}^\beta - r_\alpha{}^\gamma d \left(r^{-1}\right)_\gamma{}^\beta . \tag{5.2}$$

In addition, the metric tensor, whose gauge–theoretical origin is not manifest if one simply includes it in the nonlinear realization with $GL(4, R)$
as the classification subgroup –in which the coset parameters $h^{\alpha\beta}$ are
absent–, reveals itself as a particular factorization of the degrees of freedom present in the nonlinear approach which takes the Lorentz group as
the classification subgroup. Actually, we have

$$\tilde{g}_{\alpha\beta} := r_\alpha{}^\mu r_\beta{}^\nu o_{\mu\nu} \quad , \quad \tilde{g}^{\alpha\beta} := \left(r^{-1}\right)_\mu{}^\alpha \left(r^{-1}\right)_\nu{}^\beta o^{\mu\nu} , \tag{5.3}$$

compare with Ref.(13). Thus, these objects are equivalent to those of
the framework of metric–affine theory. As a consequence, observe that
invariants like the line element may be alternatively expressed in terms of
the nonlinear or metric–affine objects respectively, namely

$$ds^2 = o_{\alpha\beta} \vartheta^\alpha \otimes \vartheta^\beta = \tilde{g}_{\alpha\beta} \tilde{\vartheta}^\alpha \otimes \tilde{\vartheta}^\beta , \tag{5.4}$$

where the transition from $o_{\alpha\beta}$ to $\tilde{g}_{\alpha\beta}$ or *vice versa* takes place by means of
the suitable factorization of the coset parameters associated to the sym-
metric affine transformations. The gauge–theoretical origin of the metric
tensor in the MAGT's is thus explained. Moreover, given a standard
MAGT, if one fixes the metric to be globally Minkowskian, the degrees of

freedom of the theory automatically rearrange themselves into the nonlinear theory developed in section 4. The possibility of factorizing the degrees of freedom of the metric into the coframes and the connections explains why the field equations found by varying with respect to the metric tensor in the framework of metric–affine theories are not essential. Hehl et al.[9] showed that they are redundant, when the field equations found from the coframes and the linear connections are taken into account.

Making use of the transformation properties of $r^{\alpha\beta}$, see (4.8), we find that the variations of (5.1–3) are the expected ones in a MAGT, namely

$$\delta\tilde{\vartheta}^\alpha = -\left(\alpha_\beta{}^\alpha + \beta_\beta{}^\alpha\right)\tilde{\vartheta}^\beta, \tag{5.5}$$

$$\delta\tilde{\Gamma}_\alpha{}^\beta = \tilde{D}\left(\alpha_\alpha{}^\beta + \beta_\alpha{}^\beta\right), \tag{5.6}$$

and

$$\delta\tilde{g}_{\alpha\beta} = 2\left(\alpha_{(\alpha}{}^\gamma + \beta_{(\alpha}{}^\gamma\right)\tilde{g}_{\beta)\gamma} \quad, \quad \delta\tilde{g}^{\alpha\beta} = -2\left(\alpha_\gamma{}^{(\alpha} + \beta_\gamma{}^{(\alpha}\right)\tilde{g}^{\beta)\gamma}. \tag{5.7}$$

The nonmetricity reads now

$$\tilde{Q}_{\alpha\beta} := -\overset{(GL)}{D}\tilde{g}_{\alpha\beta} = r_\alpha{}^\mu r_\beta{}^\nu Q_{\mu\nu}, \tag{5.8}$$

and still transforms as a tensor, namely

$$\delta\tilde{Q}_{\alpha\beta} = 2\left(\alpha_{(\alpha}{}^\gamma + \beta_{(\alpha}{}^\gamma\right)\tilde{Q}_{\beta)\gamma}, \tag{5.9}$$

but due to the fact that $d\,\tilde{g}_{\alpha\beta} \neq 0$, the symmetric part of the connection is no more a tensor, but a true connection. On the other hand, the metric–affine torsion and curvature relate to the nonlinear ones through

$$\tilde{T}^\alpha := \overset{(GL)}{D}\tilde{\vartheta}^\alpha = \left(r^{-1}\right)_\beta{}^\alpha T^\beta, \tag{5.10}$$

and

$$\tilde{R}_\alpha{}^\beta := d\tilde{\Gamma}_\alpha{}^\beta + \overset{(GL)}{\Gamma}_\gamma{}^\beta \wedge \overset{(GL)}{\Gamma}_\alpha{}^\gamma = r_\alpha{}^\mu \left(r^{-1}\right)_\nu{}^\beta R_\mu{}^\nu, \tag{5.11}$$

and their variations read

$$\delta \tilde{T}^{\alpha} = -\left(\alpha_{\beta}{}^{\alpha} + \beta_{\beta}{}^{\alpha}\right) \tilde{T}^{\beta},$$ (5.12)

and

$$\delta \tilde{R}_{\alpha}{}^{\beta} = \left(\alpha_{\alpha}{}^{\gamma} + \beta_{\alpha}{}^{\gamma}\right) \tilde{R}_{\gamma}{}^{\beta} - \left(\alpha_{\gamma}{}^{\beta} + \beta_{\gamma}{}^{\beta}\right) \tilde{R}_{\alpha}{}^{\gamma}.$$ (5.13)

This completes the MAGT scheme.

6. Conclusions and open questions

We claim that a certain gauge nonlinear realization of the affine group provides the natural framework for the gauge theories of gravitation. It allows to interpret the coframes as the nonlinear connections of the translations, and it makes it possible to include Dirac matter in an affine theory without breaking the symmetry. It can be noticed that the treatment of the translations in a coset formalism appears in our work as equivalent to the technique of induced representations when applied, as in (3.2), to the translational part of the states.

The choice of the Lorentz group as the classification subgroup leads to the metrization of the theory. The metric tensor is globally Minkowskian, and it does not play any dynamical role. The gravitational interaction is, strictly speaking, affine more than metric. The whole information about it is contained in the connections, as in the gauge theories of internal groups.

We have proven that the MAGT[9], metric tensor included, can be obtained from our fundamental approach as a degenerate case, in which ordinary fermionic matter is excluded. The essential difference between the nonlinear theory discussed in section 4 and the standard metric–affine theories consists in the transformation properties of the physical fields, which behave as representations of the Lorentz group, and in that the symmetric part of the connection is strictly proportional to the nonmetricity, transforming as a tensor. In practice, to deal with our approach, nothing has to be changed in the standard metric–affine formalism but the choice of the metric, and of course the interpretation. Since the Minkowskian metric is invariant under Lorentz transformations, it is globally fixed once and forever, so that space and time are everywhere well defined as distinguished quantities.

Let un mention a question which remains open to further developements. According to (4.10), the fields ψ of a representation space of H transform as

$$\delta\psi = i\, u^{\alpha\beta}\rho(L_{\alpha\beta})\,\psi\,. \tag{6.1}$$

In terms of ψ, we can formally define the fields

$$\varphi := e^{i\,h^{\mu\nu}S_{\mu\nu}}\psi\,, \tag{6.2}$$

which transform as

$$\delta\varphi = i\left(\alpha^{\alpha\beta}S_{\alpha\beta} + \beta^{\alpha\beta}L_{\alpha\beta}\right)\varphi\,. \tag{6.3}$$

Definition (6.2) does not present any problems as far as the regular representations are concerned. Eqs.(5.5,7,9,12,13) are particular examples of this case. However, the interpretation of (6.2) in general is dubitious, for instance as far as ψ is taken to be a spinor. Analogously, the following relation between the abstract differential operators holds

$$\mathbf{D}\psi = e^{-i\,h^{\mu\nu}S_{\mu\nu}}\,\tilde{\mathbf{D}}\varphi\,. \tag{6.4}$$

The problem pointed out by (6.2) is how to interpret the action of the generators $S_\alpha{}^\beta$ on arbitrary representation fields of the Lorentz group or, in general, the relationship between linear and nonlinear realizations, or between different nonlinear approaches. Indeed, in spite of the fact than one can construct a covariant differential of Dirac fields in terms of a connection restricted to the classification subgroup, the general relation (6.4) only mantains its validity if we include the whole connection, including the coupling of the matter fields to the nonmetricity. Thus, one has to give sense to the representation fields (6.2).

At this respect, we recall the presentation of nonlinear realizations as developped by Salam and Stradhee[4]. They considered the problem of constructing a nonlinear representation of G which becomes linear under H. This can be done by introducing a reduction matrix $L(\xi)$ depending on the coset parametres, transforming as

$$L(\xi') = gL(\xi)h^{-1}(\xi,g),\qquad(6.5)$$

where $g\in G$ and $h\in H$. The reduction matrix $L(\xi)$ is a selfrepresentation of G. Being ψ a nonlinear representation of H and φ a linear representation of G, the following relation, compare with (6.2), holds

$$\psi = \rho\left(L^{-1}(\xi)\right)\varphi.\qquad(6.6)$$

From (6.5) it is evident that $L(\xi)$ is to be identified with the cosets $c(\xi)$ of section 2. Thus, going back to our notation, we can obtain the relationship between two different nonlinear realizations

$$gc_1(\xi) = c_1(\xi')h_1\,,$$
$$gc_2(\xi) = c_2(\xi')h_2\,,\qquad(6.7)$$

where $h_1\in H_1$ and $h_2\in H_2$, being H_1 and H_2 two different subgroups of G. One verifies inmediately that

$$h_2 = \left[c_2^{-1}(\xi')c_1(\xi')\right]h_1\left[c_1^{-1}(\xi)c_2(\xi)\right],\qquad(6.8)$$

and

$$\psi_1 = c_1^{-1}(\xi)c_2(\xi)\psi_2\,,\qquad(6.9)$$

being ψ_1 and ψ_2 representations of H_1 and H_2 respectively. A particular case is given when one of the subgroups is a subgroup of the other one. In this case we can write

$$gc(\xi) = c(\xi')h(\xi,g),$$
$$hM(\chi) = M(\chi')e(\chi,h),\qquad(6.10)$$

with $h(g,c) \in H$ and $e(h,\chi) \in E \subset H$. One gets inmediately

$$\psi_e = M^{-1}\psi_h .$$ (6.11)

Relation (6.6) is a particular case of (6.11) when H becomes the group G itself. All these relations involving abstract elements of the group must be represented, and consequently their inverse version implies a further developement related with the concept of the infinitesimal operators when nonlinear realizations are concerned.

A further analysis of the geometrical implications of our approach requires to translate them to the language of fibre bundles.

Let us finally point out that, having the Lorentz group natural invariants, this is also the case for the affine group when realized nonlinearly with the Lorentz group as the classification subgroup. In the context of MAGT's of gravitation, McCrea[17] calculated the irreducible decomposition of the curvature, the torsion and the nonmetricity with respect to the Lorentz group. The utility of his work to construct all possible invariants becomes evident in view of the nonlinear realization presented here, since it enables us to work with an affine geometrical formalism whose objects are defined on representation spaces of the Lorentz group.

APPENDIX

A.– Let us show how the expressions (4.5) and (4.8) were deduced (cfr. Ref.(13)). We apply the general formula (2.2) defining the nonlinear action, namely

$$g\,c(\xi) = c(\xi')\,h(\xi,g) ,$$ (A.1)

with the particular choices

$$g = e^{i\,\epsilon^\alpha P_\alpha}\,e^{i\alpha^{\mu\nu}S_{\mu\nu}}\,e^{i\beta^{\mu\nu}L_{\mu\nu}} , \qquad c := e^{-i\xi^\alpha P_\alpha}\,e^{ih^{\mu\nu}S_{\mu\nu}} , \qquad h := e^{iu^{\mu\nu}L_{\mu\nu}} ,$$ (A.2)

as given in (4.2–4). The equation we have to solve then reads

$$e^{i\,\epsilon^\alpha P_\alpha}\,e^{i\,\alpha^{\mu\nu}S_{\mu\nu}}\,e^{i\,\beta^{\mu\nu}L_{\mu\nu}}\,e^{-i\,\xi^\alpha P_\alpha}\,e^{i\,h^{\mu\nu}S_{\mu\nu}} = e^{-i\,\xi'^\alpha P_\alpha}\,e^{i\,h'^{\mu\nu}S_{\mu\nu}}\,e^{i\,u^{\mu\nu}L_{\mu\nu}}\,.$$

$$(A.3)$$

We consider an affine transformation with infinitesimal group parameters ϵ^α, $\alpha^{\mu\nu}$ and $\beta^{\mu\nu}$. Thus, the transformed coset parameters in the r.h.s. of (A.3) reduce to $\xi'^\alpha = \xi^\alpha + \delta\xi^\alpha$ and $h'^{\mu\nu} = h^{\mu\nu} + \delta h^{\mu\nu}$, and $u^{\mu\nu}$ is also infinitesimal. Consequently, eq.(A.3) reduces to

$$e^{i\xi^\alpha P_\alpha}\left(1 + i\epsilon^\alpha P_\alpha + i\alpha^{\mu\nu}S_{\mu\nu} + i\beta^{\mu\nu}L_{\mu\nu}\right)e^{-i\xi^\alpha P_\alpha}$$
$$= \left(1 - i\delta\xi^\alpha P_\alpha\right)e^{i(h^{\mu\nu}+\delta h^{\mu\nu})S_{\mu\nu}}\left(1 + iu^{\mu\nu}L_{\mu\nu}\right)e^{-i h^{\mu\nu}S_{\mu\nu}}\,.$$

$$(A.4)$$

In order to simplify the calculations, we make use of the generators of the whole linear transformations $\Lambda^\alpha{}_\beta := L^\alpha{}_\beta + S^\alpha{}_\beta$, in terms of which, the commutation relations (4.1) reduce to (3.1). Making then use of the Campell–Hausdorff formula, we find the algebraic relations

$$e^{i\xi^\mu P_\mu}\,\lambda_\alpha{}^\beta\Lambda^\alpha{}_\beta\,e^{-i\xi^\mu P_\mu} = \lambda_\alpha{}^\beta\Lambda^\alpha{}_\beta + \lambda_\alpha{}^\beta\xi^\alpha P_\beta\,,\qquad(A.5)$$

and

$$e^{i\zeta_\mu{}^\nu\Lambda^\mu{}_\nu}\,\kappa_\alpha{}^\beta\Lambda^\alpha{}_\beta\,e^{-i\zeta_\mu{}^\nu\Lambda^\mu{}_\nu} = e^{\zeta_\alpha{}^\mu}\,\kappa_\mu{}^\nu\,e^{-\zeta_\nu{}^\beta}\,\Lambda^\alpha{}_\beta\,.\qquad(A.6)$$

Applying (A.5) to the l.h.s. of (A.4), it simplifies to

$$1 + i\left[\epsilon^\alpha + (\alpha_\beta{}^\alpha + \beta_\beta{}^\alpha)\xi^\beta\right]P_\alpha + i\alpha^{\mu\nu}S_{\mu\nu} + i\beta^{\mu\nu}L_{\mu\nu}\,,\qquad(A.7)$$

whereas in the r.h.s. we have to make use of the fact that

$$e^{i(h^{\mu\nu}+\delta h^{\mu\nu})S_{\mu\nu}} = e^{i h^{\mu\nu}S_{\mu\nu}}\left(1 + e^{-i h^{\mu\nu}S_{\mu\nu}}\,\delta e^{i h^{\mu\nu}S_{\mu\nu}}\right)$$
$$= e^{i h^{\mu\nu}S_{\mu\nu}}\left[1 + i e^{-h^\alpha{}_\gamma}\delta e^{h^{\gamma\beta}}\left(S_{\alpha\beta} + L_{\alpha\beta}\right)\right]\,,$$

$$(A.8)$$

in order to apply (A.6) particularized to the cases

$$e^{i h^{\mu\nu}S_{\mu\nu}}\,\sigma^{\alpha\beta}S_{\alpha\beta}\,e^{-i h^{\mu\nu}S_{\mu\nu}} = e^{h^\alpha{}_\mu}\,\sigma^{\mu\nu}e^{-h_\nu{}^\beta}\left(S_{\alpha\beta} + L_{\alpha\beta}\right)\,,\qquad(A.9)$$

and

$$e^{i\,h^{\mu\nu}\,S_{\mu\nu}}\,\tau^{\alpha\beta}\,L_{\alpha\beta}\,e^{-i\,h^{\mu\nu}\,S_{\mu\nu}} = e^{h^\alpha}{}_\mu\,\tau^{\mu\nu}\,e^{-h_\nu}{}^\beta\,(S_{\alpha\beta} + L_{\alpha\beta})\,. \tag{A.10}$$

Then, for ξ^α and $r^{\alpha\beta} := e^{h^{\alpha\beta}}$, it follows

$$\delta\xi^\alpha = -(\alpha_\beta{}^\alpha + \beta_\beta{}^\alpha)\,\xi^\beta - \epsilon^\alpha\,, \tag{A.11}$$

and

$$\delta r^{\alpha\beta} = (\alpha^\alpha{}_\gamma + \beta^\alpha{}_\gamma)\,r^{\gamma\beta} + u^\beta{}_\gamma\,r^{\gamma\alpha}\,. \tag{A.12}$$

Q.E.D.

B.–On the other hand, the nonlinear Lorentz parameter (4.8) is calculated as follows. First we rewrite the symmetry condition of (A.12), namely

$$u^{[\alpha}{}_\gamma\,r^{\beta]\gamma} = \left(\alpha^{[\alpha}{}_\gamma + \beta^{[\alpha}{}_\gamma\right)r^{\beta]\gamma}\,, \tag{B.1}$$

in the form

$$\left(u^{\alpha\beta} - \beta^{\alpha\beta}\right)\left[\delta_\alpha^\lambda\delta_\beta^\rho + (r^{-1})^{[\lambda}{}_\alpha\,r^{\rho]}{}_\beta\right] = \alpha^{\mu\nu}\,(r^{-1})^{[\lambda}{}_\mu\,r^{\rho]}{}_\nu\,, \tag{B.2}$$

and we resolve it formally as

$$u^{\alpha\beta} = \beta^{\alpha\beta} + \alpha^{\mu\nu}\,(r^{-1})^{[\lambda}{}_\mu\,r^{\rho]}{}_\nu\,\left[\delta_\alpha^\lambda\delta_\beta^\rho + (r^{-1})^{[\lambda}{}_\alpha\,r^{\rho]}{}_\beta\right]^{-1}\,. \tag{B.3}$$

Making then use of the fact that

$$(r^{-1})^{[\lambda}{}_\mu\,r^{\rho]}{}_\nu = \frac{1}{2}\left[e^{(h^\rho{}_\nu - h^\lambda{}_\mu)} - e^{-(h^\rho{}_\mu - h^\lambda{}_\nu)}\right]\,, \tag{B.4}$$

we recognize that

$$u^{\alpha\beta} = \beta^{\alpha\beta} - \alpha^{\mu\nu}\left\{\sinh\left(h^\lambda{}_\mu - h^\rho{}_\nu\right)\left[\delta_\alpha^\lambda\delta_\beta^\rho + \cosh\left(h^\lambda{}_\alpha - h^\rho{}_\beta\right)\right]^{-1}\right\}$$

$$= \beta^{\alpha\beta} - \alpha^{\mu\nu}\,\tanh\left(\frac{h^\alpha{}_\mu - h^\beta{}_\nu}{2}\right)$$

$$= \beta^{\alpha\beta} - \alpha^{\mu\nu}\,\tanh\left\{\frac{1}{2}\log\left[r^\alpha{}_\mu\,(r^{-1})^\beta{}_\nu\right]\right\}\,. \tag{B.5}$$

Q.E.D.

Acknowledgement

We are very grateful to Prof. F.W. Hehl for helpful comments.

REFERENCES

[1] R. Utiyama, *Phys. Rev.* **101** (1956) 1597

    T. W. B. Kibble, *J. Math. Phys.* **2** (1961) 212

    D. W. Sciama, *Rev. Mod. Phys.* **36** (1964) 463 and 1103

[2] K. Hayashi and T. Nakano, *Prog. Theor. Phys* **38** (1967) 491

    K. Hayashi and T. Shirafuji, *Prog. Theor. Phys* **64** (1980) 866 and **80** (1988) 711

    J. Hennig and J. Nitsch, *Gen. Rel. Grav.* **13** (1981) 947

    H.R. Pagels, *Phys. Rev.* **D 29** (1984) 1690

    T. Kawai, *Gen. Rel. Grav.* **18** (1986) 995

    G. Grignani and G. Nardelli, *Phys. Rev.* **D 45** (1992) 2719

[3] E. W. Mielke, J.D. McCrea, Y. Ne'eman and F.W. Hehl *Phys. Rev.* **D 48** (1993) 673, and references therein

[4] A. Salam and J. Strathdee, *Phys. Rev.* **184** (1969) 1750 and 1760

    C.J. Isham, A. Salam and J. Strathdee, *Ann. of Phys.* **62** (1971) 98

[5] E.A. Lord, *Gen. Rel. Grav.* **19** (1987) 983, and *J. Math. Phys.* **29** (1988) 258

[6] F. W. Hehl, P. von der Heyde, G. D. Kerlick and J. M. Nester, *Rev. Mod. Phys.* **48** (1976) 393

    P. von der Heyde, *Phys. Lett.* **58 A** (1976) 141

[7] E. Cartan, *Sur les varits connexion affine et la thorie de la relativit gnralise*, Ouvres completes, Editions du C.N.R.S. (1984), Partie III. 1, pgs. 659 and 921

[8] A. Trautman, in *Differential Geometry*, Symposia Mathematica Vol. 12 (Academic Press, London, 1973), p. 139

A. G. Agnese and P. Calvini, *Phys. Rev.* **D 12** (1975) 3800 and 3804

E.A. Ivanov and J. Niederle, *Phys. Rev.* **D25** (1982) 976 and 988

D. Ivanenko and G.A. Sardanashvily, *Phys. Rep.* **94** (1983) 1

E. A. Lord, *J. Math. Phys.* **27** (1986) 2415 and 3051

[9] F. W. Hehl, J. D. McCrea, E. W. Mielke, and Y. Ne'eman *Found. Phys.* **19** (1989) 1075

R. D. Hecht and F. W. Hehl, *Proc. 9th Italian Conf. G.R. and Grav. Phys.*, Capri (Napoli). R. Cianci et al.(eds.) (World Scientific, Singapore, 1991) p. 246

F.W. Hehl, J.D. McCrea, E.W. Mielke, and Y. Ne'eman, *Physics Reports*, to be published.

G.A. Sardanashvily, Preprint gr-qc/9405013

[10] Y. Ne'eman and Dj. Šijački, *Phys. Lett.* **B200** (1988) 489

Y. Ne'eman and Dj. Šijački, *Phys. Rev.* **D 37** (1988) 3267

[11] S. Coleman, J. Wess and B. Zumino, *Phys. Rev.* **117** (1969) 2239

C.G. Callan, S. Coleman, J. Wess and B. Zumino, *Phys. Rev.* **117** (1969) 2247

E. W. Mielke, *Fortschr. Phys.* **25** (1977) 401, and references therein

S. Coleman, *Aspects of Symmetry.* Cambridge University Press, Cambridge (1985)

[12] A.B. Borisov and I.V. Polubarinov, *Zh. ksp. Theor. Fiz.* **48** (1965) 1625, and V. Ogievetsky and I. Polubarinov, *Ann. Phys.* (NY) **35** (1965) 167

[13] A.B. Borisov and V.I. Ogievetskii, *Theor. Mat. Fiz.* **21** (1974) 329

[14] K.S. Stelle and P.C. West, *Phys. Rev.* **D 21** (1980) 1466

[15] L.N. Chang and F. Mansouri, *Phys. Lett.* **78 B** (1979) 274, and *Phys. Rev.* **D 17** (1978) 3168

[16] J. Julve, A. L?pez–Pinto, A. Tiemblo and R. Tresguerres, Preprint gr–qc/9412043, and A. L?pez–Pinto, A. Tiemblo and R. Tresguerres, Preprint gr–qc/9412045

[17] J. D. McCrea, *Class. Quantum Grav.* **9** (1992) 553

Gennadi A. Sardanashvily, Editor
New Frontiers in Gravitation
Hadronic Press, Palm Harbor, FL 34682-1577, U.S.A.
ISBN 0–911767–96–7, 1996, Pages 145–183

AFFINE-METRIC GRAVITY
WITH THE PROJECTIVE INVARIANCE

M. Yu. Kalmykov [1],

Bogoliubov Laboratory of Theoretical Physics, Joint Institute for Nuclear
Research, 141 980 Dubna (Moscow Region), Russian Federation

and

P. I. Pronin[2]

Department of Theoretical Physics, Physics Faculty
Moscow State University, 117234, Moscow, Russian Federation

Abstract

We consider the quantum affine-metric gravity with the projective
invariance at the one-loop level. In particular, we investigate the
influence of the projective invariance on renormalization properties
of theory. Also we research the role of the torsion field in the affine-
metric theory at the quantum level.

---

[1] E-mail: *kalmykov@thsun1.jinr.dubna.su*
Supported in part by RFFR grant # 94-02 03665-a
[2] E-mail: *pronin@theor.phys.msu.su*

This theory is renormalizable [21] and asymptotically free [22], [23] but it is not unitary because the ghosts and tachyons are present in the spectrum of the theory. It should be noted that it is impossible to restore the unitarity of the theory by means of loop corrections or adding an interaction with matter fields [24], [25]. Hence, one needs to use a new method in order to construct the theory of gravity.

The promosing way of the constructing the quantum theory of gravity is the increasing the number of symmetries of the initial Lagrangian. The presence of an additional symmetry in the theory may improve the renormalization properties of the theory. Such additional symmetry may be the Weyl symmetry. However at the quantum level the existing a lot of symmetry can give rise to anomaly violating the renormalization of the theory. The Weyl symmetry is this symmetry. All attempting to conserve the Weyl symmetry at the quantum level are unsuccesfully.

There is the most promising symmetry - the supersymmetry. The supersymmetry is the symmetry between the bosons and the fermions presenting in the theory. The local supersymmetry is supergravity. There are a lot of model of the supergravity. The simplest supergravity with ($N = 1$) [26], [27] is the first example of the gravity theory interacting with the matter field which has the finite elements of the S-matrix on mass-shell at one-loop level [28]. THe existing model of the supergravity ($N = 1$) are finite at two-loop level. But at three and higher loop level there are the non-vanishing counterterms violating the renormalizability of the theory. But supergravity with additional may be finite at higher loop level. For example this additional symmetry may be Weyl symmetry. It was shown [29] that the theories with the local conformal symmetry are non-renormalizable if there exist an ultraviolet divergences. But there are the finite model with the local conformal symmetry [30] - [32]. The other promising supergravity models are the extended with $N = 8$ [33]- [35] (consequence the model with $N < 8$ also was constructed). These models may be finite up to N loops [36]. But the interacting of the extended supergravity with matter

But the two-loop counterterms in the case of the pure gravitational theory is present [2], [3]. Moreover, the one-loop counterterms in the theory interacting with the matter fields are violated the renormalization of the theory at one-loop level [4] - [8].

Therefore, one needs to modify the theory or to show, that the difficulties presently encountered in the theory are only artifacts of perturbation theory. The non-perturbative treatment of the Einstein gravity are discussed in [9]. In general we may speak about the finite theory of gravity [10], [11]. In this theory the Green function are diverged but the elements of the S-matrix on mass-shell are finite. In the background field method the choice of the external lines on mass-shell correspond to use the classical equation for the background fields [12]- [16]. But in the last time the works was apeared stating that in non-renormalizable theory, such as Einstein gravity, there are problems connected with the gauge fixing term [17], [18]. In particular we can choose the gauge fixing term in such way that the two-loop counterterm will be absent. We think that this situation is the consequence of the perturbative non-renormalization theory. Therefore we will consider the perturbation renormalization of the theory as a main criterion of the true quantum gravity theory. We will assume that the perturbation expansion does exist, but the Einstein's theory of gravity is an incomplete theory. The simplest method of modifying the Einstein theory is to introduce terms quadratic in the curvature tensor in the action of the theory.

$$L_{gr} = \left(-\frac{1}{k^2} R + \alpha R_{\mu\nu}^2 + \beta R^2 \right) \sqrt{-g} \tag{1}$$

At th eclassical level this theory give rise to modifed Neuton potential [19], [20]

$$U(r) = -\frac{1}{r} + \frac{\alpha_1}{r} e^{-m_1 r} + \frac{\alpha_2}{r} e^{m_2 r} \tag{2}$$

where the constants $\alpha_1, \alpha_2, m_1, m_2$ are the linear combination of the coefficients α, β.

1 Introduction

The Einstein theory of gravity is incomplete theory already at the tree level. There are a lot of problems connected with the existence of the singularity, nonrenormalizability of the theory, the flatness problem and another. In this work we will attempt to consider a new class of gravity theory - so called affine-metric theory of gravity. The main aim of our work is to consider the quantum properties of the affine-metric theory with the projective invariance. The work is organized in the following way.

In section 1 we will consider the renormalization problems connected with the existing theory of gravity. In section 2 we will discuss the classical problems of the affine-metric theory of gravity. We will consider the metric-affine geometry of the space-time. Also we will consider the constructing the possible affine-metric Lagrangian, the role of the torsion fields in the affine-metric theory of gravity. In section 3 we will evaluate the one-loop counterterms in the different models of the affine-metric theory. In Conclusion we will summarize the obtained results.

We use the following notations:

$$c = \hbar = 1; \qquad \mu, \nu = 0, 1, 2, 3; \qquad k^2 = 16\pi G \qquad (g) = det(g_{\mu\nu})$$

The objects marked by the bar ¯ are constructed by means of the affine connection $\bar{\Gamma}^{\sigma}{}_{\mu\nu}$. The objects marked by the tilde ~ are constructed by means of the Riemannian-Kartan connection $\tilde{\Gamma}^{\sigma}{}_{\mu\nu}$ (see further). The others are the Riemannian objects. The needing notation will be given in the text.

2 The renormalization

The construction of quantum theory of gravity is an unresolved problem of modern theoretical physics. It is well know that the Einstein theory of gravity is not renormalizable in an ordinary sense. The one-loop counterterms are disappeared when gravity does not interacted witn the matter fields [1].

supersymmetry may give rise to appear of the non-vanishing counterterms violating renormalization of the theory. In our option it is imposibly to construct the supergravity model which is finite or renormalizable at all loop level [37].

In recent years hopes for renormalizable theory of quantum gravity have centered on the quantum superstrings [38], [39]. But the question about the existence of a perturbative renormalizable quantum gravity in the any string model is open [40].

The new type of the quantum gravity theory connect with the possibility that the quantum (and possible classical) treatment of space-time involve more than the Riemannian space-time [41] - [48].

The simplest non-Riemannian space-time is the space-time with the torsion (Riemann - Cartan space-time) . In this space-time there is a additional to metric tensor the torsion tensor defined as independent variable. The connection $\tilde{\Gamma}^\sigma_{\mu\nu}$ of the Riemann-Cartan space-time can be writen as

$$\tilde{\Gamma}^\sigma_{\mu\nu} = \Gamma^\sigma_{\mu\nu} + Q^\sigma_{\mu\nu} + Q_{\mu\nu}{}^\sigma + Q_{\nu\mu}{}^\sigma \qquad (3)$$

where $\Gamma^\sigma_{\mu\nu}$ is the Riemannian connection

$$\Gamma^\sigma_{\mu\nu} = \frac{1}{2} g^{\sigma\lambda} \left(-\partial_\lambda g_{\mu\nu} + \partial_\nu g_{\mu\lambda} + \partial_\mu g_{\lambda\nu} \right) \qquad (4)$$

We don't give the details of the Riemannian-Cartan geometry. THera are a lot of papers and books given the corresponding mathematical equipments [41] - [50]. It should be noted that the Riemann-Cartan are connected with the gauge aproach to the quantum gravity. The corresponding gauge gravity is called the Poincare gauge gravitational theory with the structure group P_{10}. In gauge treatment of gravity there are two dynamical variables, namely, the vierbein $h^a{}_\mu(x)$ and local Lorentz connection $\omega^a{}_{b\mu}(x)$. A curvature tensor $\tilde{R}^a{}_{b\mu\nu}(\tilde{\omega})$ and a torsion tensor $Q^a{}_{\mu\nu}(h, \tilde{\omega})$, which are the strength tensors of the Poincarè gauge gravitational theory, are defined by the following relations:

$$\tilde{R}^a{}_{b\mu\nu}(\tilde{\omega}) = \partial_\mu \tilde{\omega}^a{}_{b\nu} - \partial_\nu \tilde{\omega}^a{}_{b\mu} + \tilde{\omega}^a{}_{c\mu} \tilde{\omega}^c{}_{b\nu} - \tilde{\omega}^a{}_{c\nu} \tilde{\omega}^c{}_{b\mu} \tag{5}$$

$$Q^a{}_{\mu\nu}(h,\tilde{\omega}) = -\frac{1}{2} \left(\partial_\mu h^a{}_\nu - \partial_\nu h^a{}_\mu + \tilde{\omega}^a{}_{c\nu} h^c{}_\mu - \tilde{\omega}^a{}_{c\mu} h^c{}_\nu \right) \tag{6}$$

The Lagrangian of a gauge theory is built out of terms quadratic in the strength tensor of fields. In the Poincarè gauge theory the Lagrangian is defined as :

$$L_{P_{\Omega}} = \left(\frac{A_i}{k^2} Q^2(h,\tilde{\omega}) + B_j \tilde{R}^2(\omega) \right) h \tag{7}$$

where A_i, B_j are arbitrary constants and $\tilde{R}^2, Q^2$ are now a symbolic notation for the contractions of the curvature tensors or the torsion tensors respectively. For the classical limit, coinciding with the Einstein theory to exist one needs to add to the Lagrangian a term linear in the curvature tensor. The theory with the Lagrangian quadratic in the curvature tensor gives rise to a modification of the Newtonian potential. But in the Poincarè gauge gravitational theory there are models with the Lagrangian quadratic in the curvature and torsion tensors giving rise to the Newtonian potential [87] - [91]. In other words there are models satisfying the Birkhoff theorem.

The theory is invariant under the general coordinate transformations

$$x^\mu \rightarrow 'x^\mu = x^\mu + \xi^\mu(x)$$
$$h^a{}_\mu(x) \rightarrow 'h^a{}_\mu(x) = h^a{}_\mu(x) - \partial_\mu \xi^\alpha h^a{}_\alpha(x) - \xi^\alpha \partial_\alpha h^a{}_\mu(x)$$
$$\tilde{\omega}^a{}_{b\mu}(x) \rightarrow '\tilde{\omega}^a{}_{b\mu}(x) = \tilde{\omega}^a{}_{b\mu}(x) - \partial_\mu \xi^\alpha \tilde{\omega}^a{}_{b\alpha}(x) - \xi^\alpha \partial_\alpha \tilde{\omega}^a{}_{b\mu}(x) \tag{8}$$

and under the local Lorentz transformation

$$x^\mu \rightarrow 'x^\mu = x^\mu + \varepsilon^\mu{}_\nu \xi^\nu(x)$$
$$h^a{}_\mu(x) \rightarrow 'h^a{}_\mu(x) = h^a{}_\mu(x) + \varepsilon^a{}_b h^b{}_\mu(x)$$
$$\tilde{\omega}^a{}_{b\mu}(x) \rightarrow '\tilde{\omega}^a{}_{b\mu}(x) = \tilde{\omega}^a{}_{b\mu}(x) + \varepsilon^a{}_c \tilde{\omega}^c{}_{b\mu}(x) - \tilde{\omega}^a{}_{c\mu}(x) \varepsilon^c{}_b - \partial_\mu \varepsilon^a{}_b \tag{9}$$

where $\varepsilon^{ab}(x) = -\varepsilon^{ba}(x)$

At the present time there are a lot of papers concerning the classical problems of these theories. For example, it is possible to find some coefficients A_i and B_j in the Poincarè gauge gravitational theory in order to obtain a unitary model [51] - [57]. However, the renormalizability properties of the theories have been studied insufficiently. It was shown that the renormalizable Poincarè gauge gravitational theory must contain all possible invariant of the theory [59] with the mass dimension two or four constructed by means of the curvature and torsion tensors [58]. However the question about the unitary problems of this model have not been discussed.

In this way the Poincarè gauge gravitational theory have the following interesting properties:

1. There are the gauge treatment of the gravity.

2. There are unitary at the tree level model with propagating torsion and vierbein fields

3. There are the renormalizable model containing 194 terms.

4. There are the models satisfying the Birkhoff theorem.

However we can say nothing about the existing the renormalizable and unitary model. We think that in the Poincarè gauge gravitational theory we have the same problems as in Einstein gravity: there are the unitary but nonrenormalizable model or there are the renormalizable but non-unitary model. This problems can be solved in the supergravity treatment of the Poincarè gauge gravitational theory.

The further extendincy of the geometry of the space-time is the affine-metric geometry. In this treatmen exist a two dynamical variables: metric $g_{\mu\nu}(x)$ and affine connection $\bar{\Gamma}^{\sigma}{}_{\mu\nu}(x)$ independently defined an space-time manifold. The affine-metric geometry can be connected with the affine gauge group $GA(4, R)$. This theory is called the affine gauge gravitational

theory. The details description of the affine-metric geometry we will give
in the next section. Here we only note some feature of this theory. At the
present time there are a lot of papers concerning the classical problems of
this theory [60] - [73]. However, the renormalizability properties of the
theory have been studied insufficiently [74] - [99].

The strength tensor of the theory is the curvature tensor $\bar{R}^\sigma{}_{\lambda\mu\nu}(\bar{\Gamma})$ defined as:

$$\bar{R}^\sigma{}_{\lambda\mu\nu}(\bar{\Gamma}) = \partial_\mu \bar{\Gamma}^\sigma{}_{\lambda\nu} - \partial_\nu \bar{\Gamma}^\sigma{}_{\lambda\mu} + \bar{\Gamma}^\sigma{}_{\alpha\mu} \bar{\Gamma}^\alpha{}_{\lambda\nu} - \bar{\Gamma}^\sigma{}_{\alpha\nu} \bar{\Gamma}^\alpha{}_{\lambda\mu} \tag{10}$$

The Lagrangian of a gauge theory is built out of terms quadratic in
the strength tensor of fields. In the affine gauge theories the Lagrangian is
defined as :

$$L_{GA(4,R)} = C_j \bar{R}^2(\bar{\Gamma})\sqrt{-g} \tag{11}$$

where C_j are arbitrary constants and $\bar{R}^2$ is now a symbolic notation for the
contractions of the curvature tensors. In order to exisr the classical limit
coinsiding with the Einstein gravity one needs to add to the Lagrangian a
term linear in curvature tensor.

The torsion tensor $Q^\sigma{}_{\mu\nu}$ and nonmetricity tensor $W_{\sigma\mu\nu}$ defined as:

$$Q^\sigma{}_{\mu\nu} = \frac{1}{2}\left(\bar{\Gamma}^\sigma{}_{\mu\nu} - \bar{\Gamma}^\sigma{}_{\nu\mu}\right) \tag{12}$$

$$W_{\sigma\mu\nu} = \bar{\nabla}_\sigma g_{\mu\nu} \tag{13}$$

are only the auxiliary fields. They can not be present in the Lagrangian of
the affine gravity. The role of the these field in the affine-metric theory of
gravity are not understanding.

The affine-metric theory of gravity is invariant under general coordinate
transformation:

$$x^\mu \quad \rightarrow \quad 'x^\mu = x^\mu + \xi^\mu(x)$$
$$g_{\mu\nu}(x) \quad \rightarrow \quad 'g_{\mu\nu}(x) = g_{\mu\nu}(x) - \partial_\mu \xi^\alpha g_{\alpha\nu}(x) - \partial_\nu \xi^\alpha g_{\alpha\mu}(x) - \xi^\alpha \partial_\alpha g_{\mu\nu}(x)$$
$$\Gamma^\sigma_{\mu\nu}(x) \quad \rightarrow \quad '\Gamma^\sigma_{\mu\nu}(x) = \Gamma^\sigma_{\mu\nu}(x) - \partial_\mu \xi^\alpha \Gamma^\sigma_{\alpha\nu}(x) - \partial_\nu \xi^\alpha \Gamma^\sigma_{\mu\alpha}(x)$$
$$+ \partial_\alpha \xi^\sigma \Gamma^\alpha_{\mu\nu}(x) - \xi^\alpha \partial_\alpha \Gamma^\sigma_{\mu\nu}(x) - \partial_{\mu\nu} \xi^\sigma \tag{14}$$

In the affine-metric theory of gravity there are models possessing an extra projective symmetry. By the projective invariance we mean that the action is invariant under the following transformation of fields:

$$x^\mu \quad \rightarrow \quad 'x^\mu = x^\mu$$
$$g_{\mu\nu}(x) \quad \rightarrow \quad 'g_{\mu\nu}(x) = g_{\mu\nu}(x)$$
$$\Phi_{mat}(x) \quad \rightarrow \quad '\Phi_{mat}(x) = \Phi_{mat}(x)$$
$$\bar{\Gamma}^\sigma_{\mu\nu}(x) \quad \rightarrow \quad '\bar{\Gamma}^\sigma_{\mu\nu}(x) = \bar{\Gamma}^\sigma_{\mu\nu}(x) + \delta^\sigma_\mu C_\nu(x) \tag{15}$$

where $C_\nu(x)$ is an arbitrary vector.

The classical properties of models with the projective invariance have been discussed in papers [77] - [79]. However, the quantum properties of the projective invariance have not been investigated. As we mentioned the presence of an additional symmetry in the theory may improve the renormalization properties of the theory. So, the projective invariance may have the considerable role for the renormalizability of the theory.

The main aim of our work is to research the influence of the projective invariance on the renormalization properties of the theory and to understand the role of the torsion field in the affine-metric theory at the quantum level.

In order to investigate the influence of the projective invariance on renormalizability of the theory one needs to calculate the counterterms in some model possessing the projective invariance. The simplest model of this type is the model with the Lagrangian:

$$L_{gr} = -\frac{1}{k^2}\bar{R}(\bar{\Gamma})\sqrt{-g} \tag{16}$$

But because of the degeneracy of the four-dimensional space-time, the terms violating the renormalizability of the theory arise only at two-loop level [80]. The two-loop calculations are very cumbersome. Since we would like to restrict ourselves to the one-loop calculations and to investigate the influence of the projective invariance on the renormalizability of the models, we consider the interaction of the gravity with a matter field.

$$S_{gr} = \int d^4x\sqrt{-g}\left(\left(\xi\varphi^2 - \frac{1}{k^2}\right)\tilde{R}(\Gamma) + \frac{2}{k^2}\Lambda + \frac{1}{2}\partial_\mu\varphi\partial_\nu\varphi g^{\mu\nu}\right) \tag{17}$$

where Λ is a cosmological constant.

In particular, we consider the following problems connected with the projective invariance:

1. A necessity of introducing the term fixing the projective invariance at the quantum level.

2. The presence of the ghosts connected with the projective invariance.

3. The addition of the "projective" ghosts to the one-loop effective action

In order to investigate second problem we will calculate the one-loop counterterms in the model with the terms quadratic in the torsion fields. The Lagrangian of the model is following:

$$S_{gr} = -\frac{1}{k^2}\int d^4x\sqrt{-g}\left(\tilde{R}(\Gamma) - 2\Lambda - b_1 Q_{\sigma\mu\nu}Q^{\sigma\mu\nu} - b_2 Q_{\sigma\mu\nu}Q^{\nu\sigma\mu} - b_3 Q_\sigma Q^\sigma\right) \tag{18}$$

where Λ is a cosmological constant, $\{b_i\}$ are the arbitrary constants. We consider $\bar{\Gamma}^\sigma{}_{\mu\nu}(x), \varphi(x), g_{\mu\nu}(x)$ as independent dynamical fields.

3 The classical consideration

3.1 Geometry of the affine-metric space-time

Let us consider the four-dimensional affine-metric manifold M_4 without boundary. By the affine-metric manifold we mean the manifold with the metric structure $g_{\mu\nu}(x)$ and connection structure $\bar{\Gamma}^\sigma_{\mu\nu}$ defined independently in the arbitrary point of the manifold. The manifold M_4 is characterized by following geometrical objects:

1. the curvature tensor

$$\bar{R}^\alpha_{\beta\mu\nu} = \frac{\partial \bar{\Gamma}^\alpha_{\beta\nu}}{\partial x^\mu} - \frac{\partial \bar{\Gamma}^\alpha_{\beta\mu}}{\partial x^\nu} + \bar{\Gamma}^\alpha_{\sigma\mu}\bar{\Gamma}^\sigma_{\beta\nu} - \bar{\Gamma}^\alpha_{\sigma\nu}\bar{\Gamma}^\sigma_{\beta\mu} \tag{19}$$

2. the torsion tensor

$$Q^\alpha_{\mu\nu} = \frac{1}{2}\left(\bar{\Gamma}^\alpha_{\mu\nu} - \bar{\Gamma}^\alpha_{\nu\mu}\right) \tag{20}$$

The curvature and the torsion tensors satisfy the following identities:

$$\bar{R}^\sigma_{\lambda\mu\nu} + \bar{R}^\sigma_{\mu\nu\lambda} + \bar{R}^\sigma_{\nu\lambda\mu} + 2\,\bar{\nabla}_\lambda Q^\sigma_{\mu\nu} + 2\,\bar{\nabla}_\mu Q^\sigma_{\nu\lambda} + 2\,\bar{\nabla}_\nu Q^\sigma_{\lambda\mu} -$$
$$4\left(Q^\sigma_{\alpha\lambda}Q^\alpha_{\mu\nu} + Q^\sigma_{\alpha\mu}Q^\alpha_{\nu\lambda} + Q^\sigma_{\alpha\nu}Q^\alpha_{\lambda\mu}\right) = 0 \tag{21}$$

$$\bar{\nabla}_\lambda\bar{R}^\sigma_{\alpha\mu\nu} + \bar{\nabla}_\mu\bar{R}^\sigma_{\alpha\nu\lambda} + \bar{\nabla}_\nu\bar{R}^\sigma_{\alpha\lambda\mu} = 0 \tag{22}$$

where the covariant derivatives $\bar{\nabla}$ is defined in the following way:

$$\bar{\nabla}_\sigma T^{\alpha_1\cdots\alpha_q}_{\cdots\beta_1\cdots\beta_p} \equiv \frac{\partial T^{\alpha_1\cdots\alpha_q}_{\cdots\beta_1\cdots\beta_p}}{\partial x^\sigma} + \bar{\Gamma}^{\alpha_1}_{\lambda\sigma}T^{\lambda\alpha_2\cdots\alpha_q}_{\cdots\beta_1\cdots\beta_p} + \cdots + \bar{\Gamma}^{\alpha_q}_{\lambda\sigma}T^{\alpha_1\cdots\lambda}_{\cdots\beta_1\cdots\beta_p}$$
$$- \bar{\Gamma}^\lambda_{\beta_1\sigma}T^{\alpha_1\cdots\alpha_q}_{\cdots\lambda\beta_2\cdots\beta_p} - \cdots - \bar{\Gamma}^\lambda_{\beta_p\sigma}T^{\alpha_1\cdots\alpha_q}_{\cdots\beta_1\cdots\lambda}$$

where $T^{\alpha_1\cdots\alpha_q}_{\cdots\beta_1\cdots\beta_p}$ is an arbitrary tensor.

In general the affine connection $\bar{\Gamma}^\sigma{}_{\mu\nu}$ can be decompose into its irreducible parts:

$$\bar{\Gamma}^\sigma{}_{\mu\nu} = \Gamma^\sigma{}_{\mu\nu} + Q^\sigma{}_{\mu\nu} + Q_{\mu\nu}{}^\sigma + Q_{\nu\mu}{}^\sigma - \frac{1}{2}\left(-W^\sigma{}_{\mu\nu} + W_{\mu\nu}{}^\sigma + W_{\nu\mu}{}^\sigma\right)' \quad (23)$$

where $W_{\sigma\mu\nu}, \Gamma^\sigma{}_{\mu\nu}$ are defined in (13) and (4) respectively.

We don't give the details of mathematical equipment. The above mentioned definitions are sufficiently for our consideration.

3.2 Symmetries and Noether identities

The demanding the invariance action under the corresponding transformation give rise to the form of the action and type of interaction. We consider the affine-metric theory possessing two types of symmetries: the general coordinate (14) and projective (15) symmetries.

According to the second Noether theorem an invariance of the action functional $S = \int d^4 x L(u, \partial u)$ under the local transformation:

$$\delta x^\alpha = \mathbf{A}^\alpha{}_\mathbf{A} \epsilon^\mathbf{A} \tag{24}$$

$$\delta u = \epsilon^\mathbf{A} \mathbf{B}_\mathbf{A} u + \mathbf{C}^\mu{}_\mathbf{A} \partial_\mu \epsilon^\mathbf{A} \tag{25}$$

yields a set of identities:

$$\frac{\delta L}{\delta u}\left(\mathbf{B}_\mathbf{A} u - \mathbf{A}^\mu{}_\mathbf{A}\partial_\mu u\right) - \partial_\mu\left(\frac{\delta L}{\delta u}\mathbf{C}^\mu{}_\mathbf{A}\right) = 0 \tag{26}$$

$$\mathbf{A}^\mu{}_\mathbf{A} L + \frac{\partial L}{\partial(\partial_\mu u)}\left(\mathbf{B}_\mathbf{A} u - \mathbf{A}^\nu{}_\mathbf{A}\partial_\nu u\right) + \frac{\partial L}{\partial u}\mathbf{C}^\mu{}_\mathbf{A} + \frac{\partial L}{\partial(\partial_\nu u)}\partial_\nu \mathbf{C}^\mu{}_\mathbf{A} = 0 \tag{27}$$

$$\frac{\partial L}{\partial(\partial_\mu u)}\mathbf{C}^\nu{}_\mathbf{A} + \frac{\partial L}{\partial(\partial_\nu u)}\mathbf{C}^\mu{}_\mathbf{A} = 0 \tag{28}$$

Arranging $g_{\mu\nu}, \bar{\Gamma}^{\gamma}{}_{\mu\nu}$ into a generalised column one can easily find the matrices $\mathbf{A}^{\alpha}$, $\mathbf{B}_{\mathbf{A}}$ and $\mathbf{C}^{\mu}{}_{\mathbf{A}}$ from (14),(15). Then from (28) one sees that the Lagrangian can be expressed as an arbitrary function of the curvature, torsion and nonmetricity tensors. The equations (26),(27) connected with the projective invariance give the following relations:

$$\frac{\partial L}{\partial \bar{\Gamma}^{\sigma}{}_{\mu\nu}} \delta^{\sigma}_{\mu} = 0 \tag{29}$$

$$\frac{\partial L}{\partial \partial_{\lambda}\bar{\Gamma}^{\sigma}{}_{\mu\nu}} \delta^{\sigma}_{\mu} = 0 \tag{30}$$

We suggesste that the gravitational action is polynom of $\bar{R}^2, Q^2, W^2$, where $\bar{R}^2, Q^2, W^2$ are the symbolic notation for the constraction of the curvature tensors, the torsion tensors and nonmetricity tensors respectively. Then the equations (29), (30) we can rewrite as

$$
\begin{aligned}
\frac{\partial L}{\partial \bar{\Gamma}^{\sigma}{}_{\mu\nu}} \delta^{\sigma}_{\mu} &= \frac{\partial L}{\partial \bar{R}^{\rho}{}_{\omega\alpha\beta}} \frac{\partial \bar{R}^{\rho}{}_{\omega\alpha\beta}}{\partial \bar{\Gamma}^{\sigma}{}_{\mu\nu}} \delta^{\sigma}_{\mu} \\
&+ \frac{\partial L}{\partial Q^{\omega}{}_{\alpha\beta}} \frac{\partial Q^{\omega}{}_{\alpha\beta}}{\partial \bar{\Gamma}^{\sigma}{}_{\mu\nu}} \delta^{\sigma}_{\mu} + \frac{\partial L}{\partial W_{\omega\alpha\beta}} \frac{\partial W_{\omega\alpha\beta}}{\partial \bar{\Gamma}^{\sigma}{}_{\mu\nu}} \delta^{\sigma}_{\mu} \\
&= \frac{\partial L}{\partial Q^{\mu}{}_{\alpha\beta}} \delta^{\mu}_{[\alpha} \delta^{\nu}_{\beta]} - 2\frac{\partial L}{\partial W_{\nu\alpha\beta}} g^{\alpha\beta} = 0
\end{aligned} \tag{31}
$$

$$\frac{\partial L}{\partial \partial_{\lambda}\bar{\Gamma}^{\sigma}{}_{\mu\nu}} \delta^{\sigma}_{\mu} = \frac{\partial L}{\partial \bar{R}^{\rho}{}_{\omega\alpha\beta}} \frac{\partial \bar{R}^{\rho}{}_{\omega\alpha\beta}}{\partial \partial_{\lambda}\bar{\Gamma}^{\sigma}{}_{\mu\nu}} \delta^{\sigma}_{\mu} = \frac{\partial L}{\partial \bar{R}^{\rho}{}_{\rho\lambda\nu}} = 0 \tag{32}$$

The Noether theorem can be analogously applied to the matter field Lagrangian. We can verify the presence of the projective invariance in the models (17), (18). For example, the substituting the Lagrangian (18) into the equations (31),(32) give rise to the following condition of the projective invariance of the action (18):

$$2b_1 + 3b_3 - b_2 = 0 \tag{33}$$

This conditions it is easily obtain without the Noether identities. The torsion tensor $Q^\sigma_{\mu\nu}$ can be rewrite as the sum of its irreducible parts:

$$Q^\sigma_{\mu\nu} = \bar{Q}^\sigma_{\mu\nu} + \frac{1}{3}\left(Q_\mu \delta^\sigma_\nu - Q_\nu \delta^\sigma_\mu\right) + \frac{1}{6}\varepsilon^\sigma_{\ \mu\nu\lambda}\check{Q}^\lambda \tag{34}$$

where $\bar{Q}^\sigma_{\mu\nu}$ is traceless part satisfying the following conditions

$$\bar{Q}_{\sigma\mu\nu} + \bar{Q}_{\nu\sigma\mu} + \bar{Q}_{\mu\nu\sigma} = 0 \tag{35}$$

$$\bar{Q}^\sigma_{\ \mu\sigma} = 0 \tag{36}$$

and Q_λ and $\check{Q}_\lambda$ are the trace and axial parts of torsion respectively:

$$Q_\nu = Q^\mu_{\ \nu\mu} \tag{37}$$

$$\check{Q}_\mu = \varepsilon_{\mu\alpha\beta\nu}Q^{\alpha\beta\nu} \tag{38}$$

It is easy to show that under the projective transformations (15) the curvature and the torsion tensors transform in the following way:

$$Q^\sigma_{\ \mu\nu} \rightarrow' Q^\sigma_{\ \mu\nu} = Q^\sigma_{\ \mu\nu} + \frac{1}{2}\left(\delta^\sigma_\mu C_\nu - \delta^\sigma_\nu C_\mu\right) \tag{39}$$

$$Q_\sigma \rightarrow' Q_\sigma = Q_\sigma - \frac{3}{2}C_\sigma \tag{40}$$

$$\check{Q}_\sigma \rightarrow' \check{Q}_\sigma = \check{Q}_\sigma \tag{41}$$

$$\bar{Q}_{\sigma\mu\nu} \rightarrow' \bar{Q}_{\sigma\mu\nu} = \bar{Q}_{\sigma\mu\nu} \tag{42}$$

$$\bar{R}^\sigma_{\ \lambda\mu\nu}(\bar{\Gamma}) \rightarrow' \bar{R}^\sigma_{\ \lambda\mu\nu}('\bar{\Gamma}) = \bar{R}^\sigma_{\ \lambda\mu\nu}(\bar{\Gamma}) + \delta^\sigma_\lambda\left(\partial_\mu C_\nu - \partial_\nu C_\mu\right) \tag{43}$$

$$\bar{R}_{\mu\nu}(\bar{\Gamma}) \rightarrow' \bar{R}_{\mu\nu}('\bar{\Gamma}) = \bar{R}_{\mu\nu}(\bar{\Gamma}) + \partial_\mu C_\nu - \partial_\nu C_\mu \tag{44}$$

$$\bar{R}(\bar{\Gamma}) \rightarrow' \bar{R}('\bar{\Gamma}) = \bar{R}(\bar{\Gamma}) \tag{45}$$

$$W_{\sigma\mu\nu} \rightarrow' W_{\sigma\mu\nu} = W_{\sigma\mu\nu} - 2\, g_{\mu\nu}C_{\sigma} \tag{46}$$

Taking into account the expansion (34) we can rewrite the action (18) in the following form:

$$
\begin{aligned}
S_{gr} \;=\; & -\frac{1}{k^2} \int d^4x \sqrt{-g}\left(\tilde{R}(\Gamma) - 2\Lambda - \left(\frac{b_1 + b_2}{6}\right) \check{Q}_{\sigma}\check{Q}^{\sigma} \right. \\
& \left. - \left(b_1 - \frac{1}{2}b_2 \right) \bar{Q}_{\sigma\mu\nu}\bar{Q}^{\sigma\mu\nu} - \left(\frac{2}{3}b_1 + b_3 - \frac{1}{3}b_2 \right) Q_{\sigma}Q^{\sigma} \right)
\end{aligned} \tag{47}
$$

Hence, the action (18) is invariant under the projective transformation (15) at the tree level only under the condition

$$2b_1 + 3b_3 - b_2 = 0 \tag{48}$$

The considerating the model (17) is more easy. In summerrazing, the model (17) is projective invariance, but the existence of the projective invariance in the model (18) depend on the chooice of the coefficients. We will consider two case:

- the theory without the projective invariance (the condition (33) is not satisfied)

- the theory with the projective invariance (the condition (33) is fulfilled).

4   One-loop counterterms

4.1   Background field method

When treating theories with nonlinear realization of a symmetry like σ model or quantum gravity, one faces extraordinary complexity of perturbative calculations. To simplify them, one usually applied the so called background field method which allow one to handle all calculations in a strictly covariant way. This method was successfully applied to multiloop calculations in various gauge and scalar models, being combined with the minimal subtraction scheme based on some invariant regularization.

We repeat only the same aspect and formulate the algotithm for the computation of the one-loop counterterms. We use the supercondence De-Witt notations.

Let $S(\varphi)$ be the action for gauge fields. The gauge theory is invariant under the following gauge transformations:

$$\delta\varphi^k = \mathbf{R}^k{}_A(\varphi)\xi^A(x) \tag{49}$$

where $\xi^A(x)$ is gauge transformation parameters and the generators $\mathbf{R}^k{}_A(\phi)$ form the close algebra:

$$\mathbf{R}^k{}_{A,j}\mathbf{R}^j{}_B(\varphi) - \mathbf{R}^k{}_{B,j}\mathbf{R}^j{}_A(\varphi) = c^M{}_{AB}\mathbf{R}^k{}_M(\varphi) \tag{50}$$

where $c^M{}_{AB}$—the structure group constant and

$$\mathbf{R}^k{}_{B,j} \equiv \frac{\delta\mathbf{R}^k{}_B(\varphi)}{\delta\phi^j} \tag{51}$$

In accordance with the background field method all dynamical variables are rewritten as the sum of the classical and quantum parts:

$$\varphi^k = \phi^k + q^k \tag{52}$$

The partition function of the connected Green functions is:

$$exp\{i\Omega(\phi, J)\} \equiv N' \int dq^k \ det\left\{\frac{\delta P^A(\phi, q)}{\delta q^k} \mathbf{R}^k{}_B(\phi + q)\right\} \times$$

$$exp\left(i\{S(\phi + q) + J_k q^k + \frac{1}{2} P^A(\phi, q) P_A(\phi, q)\}\right) (53)$$

where

$$P^A(\phi, q) = P^A_k(\phi) q^k \qquad (54)$$

is the linear gauge fixing term and P^A_k– is the arbitrary differential operator containing no more than one derivatives,

N—is the constant,

J is the source of the quantum field

$\chi_{AB}(\varphi)$—is the arbitrary nondegenerate matrix

The action $S(\phi + q)$ is expanded in power of $\phi^k(x)$

$$S(\phi + q) = S(\phi) + q^k \frac{\delta S(\phi)}{\delta \phi^k} + \frac{1}{2} q^i \frac{\delta^2 S(\phi)}{\delta \phi^i \delta \phi^j} q^j + \dots \qquad (55)$$

Then the one-loop effective action has the following form:

$$\Gamma^{(1)} = -i \ln\left(\{det D_{kj}\}^{-\frac{1}{2}}\{det V^A_B\}\right) = \frac{i}{2}\left(\ln det D_{kj} - 2 \ln det V^A_B\right) \quad (56)$$

where $D_{ij} = \frac{\delta^2 S(\phi)}{\delta \phi^i \delta \phi^j} + P^A_i(\phi) P_{Aj}(\phi)$

$V^A_B = P^A_k(\phi) \mathbf{R}^k{}_B(\phi)$

Using the dimensional regularization one can show that the divergences of this expression is equal to

$$\Gamma^{(1)}{}_\infty = \frac{-1}{\varepsilon}\left(B_4(D) - 2\ B_4(V)\right) \qquad (57)$$

where the coefficient B_4 is the coefficient of the spectral expansion of second order elliptic operators. For the following operator

$$D_{kj} = - (\nabla_\mu \nabla_\mu g^{\mu\nu} \mathbf{1}_{kj} + 2S_{\mu kj}(\phi) \nabla_\nu g^{\mu\nu} + X_{kj}(\phi)) \tag{58}$$

the coefficients of the spectral expansion are defined as

$$B_0 = \frac{1}{32\pi^2} Sp\ \mathbf{1} \tag{59}$$

$$B_2 = \frac{1}{32\pi^2} Sp\left(Z + \frac{1}{6}R\right) \tag{60}$$

$$B_4 = \frac{1}{32\pi^2} Sp(\frac{1}{180}R_{\mu\nu\alpha\beta}R^{\mu\nu\alpha\beta} - \frac{1}{180}R_{\mu\nu}R^{\mu\nu} +$$
$$\frac{1}{72}R^2 + \frac{1}{2}Z^2 + \frac{1}{6}RZ + \frac{1}{12}Y_{\mu\nu}Y^{\mu\nu}) \tag{61}$$

where $\mathbf{1}$ is unit $N \times N$ matrix,

$$Z = X - \nabla_\mu S^\mu - S_\mu S^\mu \tag{62}$$

$$Y_{\mu\nu} = \nabla_\mu S_\nu - \nabla_\nu S_\mu + S_\mu S_\nu - S_\mu S_\nu + [\nabla_\mu, \nabla_\nu]\mathbf{1} \tag{63}$$

Coefficient B_6 was defined in paper [80]

4.2 The affine-metric gravity interacting with the matter field

For calculating the one-loop effective action we will use the background field method [100], [101] and the Schwinger-DeWitt technique ([82] - [84]). In gauge theories, the renormalization procedure may violate the gauge invariance at the quantum level, thus destroying the renormalizability of the theory. Therefore, one is bound to apply an invariant renormalization. This can be achieved by applying an invariant regularization and using the minimal subtraction scheme [102], [103]. It has been proved that the dimensional regularization ([104] - [107]) is an invariant regularization preserving all the symmetries of the classical action that do not depend explicitly on the space-time dimension [103], [108]. To sum up, we will use the dimensional regularization and minimal subtraction scheme in our loop calculation. This is the invariant renormalization.

In accordance with the background field method, all dynamical variables are rewritten as a sum of classical and quantum parts. In general case, the dynamical variables in the affine-metric theory are $\Gamma^\sigma_{\mu\nu}, \bar{g}_{\mu\nu} = g_{\mu\nu}(-g)^r$ or $\bar{g}^{\mu\nu} = g^{\mu\nu}(-g)^s$, where r, s are the numbers satisfying the only condition: $r \neq -\frac{1}{4}, s \neq \frac{1}{4}$. The one-loop counterterms on the mass-shell do not depend on the value of r and s. To simplify our calculation, we use the following numbers $r = s = 0$.

The fields $\bar{\Gamma}^\sigma_{\mu\nu}, g_{\mu\nu}, \varphi$ are now rewritten according to

$$
\begin{aligned}
\bar{\Gamma}^\sigma_{\mu\nu} &= \bar{\Gamma}^\sigma_{\mu\nu} + k\gamma^\sigma_{\mu\nu} \\
g_{\mu\nu} &= g_{\mu\nu} + kh_{\mu\nu} \\
\varphi &= \frac{1}{k}\varphi + \phi
\end{aligned}
\tag{64}
$$

where $\bar{\Gamma}^\sigma_{\mu\nu}, g_{\mu\nu}, \varphi$ are the classical parts satisfying the following equations

$$
\frac{\delta S}{\delta \bar{\Gamma}^\sigma_{\mu\nu}} = 0 \Rightarrow D^\sigma_{\mu\nu} = -\frac{1}{2}\frac{1}{\alpha(\varphi)}\partial_\lambda\alpha(\varphi)(g^{\lambda\sigma}g_{\mu\nu} - \delta^\lambda_\mu\delta^\sigma_\nu) + \delta^\sigma_\mu C_\nu
$$

$$
\frac{\delta S}{\delta g_{\mu\nu}} = 0 \Rightarrow -\alpha(\varphi)\bar{R}_{(\mu\nu)}(\Gamma) = \frac{1}{2}\partial_\mu\varphi\partial_\nu\varphi + \Lambda g_{\mu\nu}
$$

$$
\frac{\delta S}{\delta \varphi} = 0 \Rightarrow 2\xi\varphi\bar{R}(\Gamma) - g^{\mu\nu}\nabla_\mu\nabla_\nu\varphi = 0
\tag{65}
$$

where

$$
D^\sigma_{\mu\nu} = \bar{\Gamma}^\sigma_{\mu\nu} - g^{\sigma\lambda}\frac{1}{2}(-\partial_\lambda g_{\mu\nu} + \partial_\mu g_{\nu\lambda} + \partial_\nu g_{\mu\lambda})
\tag{66}
$$

$$
\alpha(\varphi) = \xi\varphi^2 - 1
\tag{67}
$$

C_ν is an arbitrary vector.

Using the expansion (64) we have:

$$g^{\mu\nu}\sqrt{-g} = \sqrt{-g}\left(g^{\mu\nu} + k\left(\frac{1}{2}hg^{\mu\nu} - h^{\mu\nu}\right)\right)$$
$$+\sqrt{-g}k^2\left(h^{\mu\alpha}h^\nu{}_\alpha - \frac{1}{2}h^{\mu\nu}h + \frac{1}{2}g^{\mu\nu}\left(\frac{1}{4}h^2 - \frac{1}{2}h_{\alpha\beta}h^{\alpha\beta}\right)\right) + O(k^3) \qquad (68)$$

$$\sqrt{-g} = \sqrt{-g}\left(1 + \frac{k}{2}h + \frac{k^2}{8}h^2 - \frac{k^2}{4}h_{\alpha\beta}h^{\alpha\beta} + O(k^3)\right) \qquad (69)$$

where

$$h \equiv h^\alpha{}_\alpha \qquad (70)$$

The action (17) expanded as a power series in the quantum fields (64) defines the effective action for calculating the loop counterterms. The one-loop effective Lagrangian quadratic in the quantum fields is:

$$L_{eff} = \Bigg(\alpha(\varphi)\frac{1}{2}\gamma^\sigma{}_{\mu\nu}F_\sigma{}^{\mu\nu}{}_\lambda{}^{\alpha\beta}\gamma^\lambda{}_{\alpha\beta}$$
$$+\alpha(\varphi)\frac{1}{2}h_{\mu\nu}h_{\sigma\lambda}D^{\mu\nu\sigma\lambda} - \frac{1}{4}h_{\alpha\beta}h_{\mu\nu}\Lambda P^{-1\alpha\beta\mu\nu} + \xi\phi^2 R$$
$$+\frac{1}{2}g^{\mu\nu}\nabla_\mu\phi\nabla_\nu\phi - \frac{1}{2}\alpha(\varphi)h_{\alpha\beta}P^{-1\alpha\beta\mu\nu}\left(B_\lambda{}^{\epsilon\tau\sigma}{}_{\mu\nu}\nabla_\sigma + \Delta_\lambda{}^{\epsilon\tau}{}_{\mu\nu}\right)\gamma^\lambda{}_{\epsilon\tau}$$
$$+2\xi\varphi\phi\left(\left(B_\lambda{}^{\epsilon\tau\sigma}\nabla_\sigma + \Delta_\lambda{}^{\epsilon\tau}\right)\gamma^\lambda{}_{\epsilon\tau} - \frac{1}{2}h_{\alpha\beta}P^{-1\alpha\beta\mu\nu}R_{\mu\nu}\right)$$
$$+\frac{1}{2}\nabla_\mu\varphi\nabla_\nu\varphi\left(h^{\mu\lambda}h^\nu{}_\lambda - \frac{1}{2}hh^{\mu\nu} - \frac{1}{8}h_{\alpha\beta}h_{\sigma\lambda}g^{\mu\nu}P^{-1\alpha\beta\sigma\lambda}\right)$$
$$-\frac{1}{2}\nabla_\mu\varphi\nabla_\nu\phi h_{\alpha\beta}P^{-1\alpha\beta\mu\nu}\Bigg)\sqrt{-g} \qquad (71)$$

where

$$
\begin{aligned}
P^{-1\alpha\beta\mu\nu} &= g^{\alpha\mu}g^{\beta\nu} + g^{\alpha\nu}g^{\beta\mu} - g^{\alpha\beta}g^{\mu\nu} \\
\Delta_\lambda{}^{\alpha\beta}{}_{\mu\nu} &\equiv D^\alpha{}_{\mu\nu}\delta^\beta_\lambda + D_\lambda\delta^\alpha_\mu\delta^\beta_\nu - D^\alpha{}_{\mu\lambda}\sigma^\beta_\nu - D^\beta{}_{\lambda\nu}\delta^\alpha_\mu \\
B_\lambda{}^{\alpha\beta\sigma}{}_{\mu\nu} &= \delta^\sigma_\lambda\delta^\alpha_\mu\delta^\beta_\nu - \delta^\beta_\lambda\delta^\alpha_\mu\delta^\sigma_\nu \\
F_\alpha{}^{\beta\lambda}{}_\mu{}^{\nu\sigma} &= g^{\beta\lambda}\delta^\nu_\mu\delta^\sigma_\alpha - g^{\beta\sigma}\delta^\nu_\alpha\delta^\lambda_\mu + g^{\nu\sigma}\delta^\lambda_\alpha\delta^\beta_\mu - g^{\lambda\nu}\delta^\sigma_\alpha\delta^\beta_\mu \\
\Delta_\lambda{}^{\epsilon\tau} &= \Delta_\lambda{}^{\epsilon\tau}{}_{\mu\nu}g^{\mu\nu} \\
B_\lambda{}^{\epsilon\tau\sigma} &= B_\lambda{}^{\alpha\beta\sigma}{}_{\mu\nu}g^{\mu\nu} \\
D^{\alpha\beta\mu\nu} &= 2R^{\alpha\mu}g^{\beta\nu} - RP^{\alpha\beta\mu\nu} - R^{\alpha\beta}g^{\mu\nu}
\end{aligned}
\tag{72}
$$

Now we may define the propagators of the quantum fields $\gamma^\sigma{}_{\mu\nu}, h_{\mu\nu}, \phi$. The propagator of the quantum field $\gamma^\sigma{}_{\mu\nu}$ satisfies two conditions:

$$
F^{-1\sigma}{}_{\mu\nu}{}^\lambda{}_{\alpha\beta} = F^{-1\lambda}{}_{\alpha\beta}{}^\sigma{}_{\mu\nu}
\tag{73}
$$

$$
F^{-1\sigma}{}_{\mu\nu}{}^\lambda{}_{\alpha\beta}F_\lambda{}^{\alpha\beta}{}_\rho{}^{\tau\epsilon} = \delta^\sigma_\rho\delta^\tau_\mu\delta^\epsilon_\nu
\tag{74}
$$

However, because of the projective invariance of the effective Lagrangian (71) the propagator does not exist. Under transformation (15) the quantum part of the connection transforms as

$$
\gamma^\sigma{}_{\mu\nu}(x) \to' \gamma^\sigma{}_{\mu\nu}(x) = \gamma^\sigma{}_{\mu\nu}(x) + \delta^\sigma_\mu C_\nu(x)
\tag{75}
$$

In order to fix the projective invariance we use the following condition:

$$
f_\lambda = \left(B_1 g_{\lambda\sigma}g^{\alpha\beta} + B_2\delta^\alpha_\sigma\delta^\beta_\lambda + B_3\delta^\beta_\sigma\delta^\alpha_\lambda\right)\gamma^\sigma{}_{\alpha\beta} \equiv f_{\lambda\sigma}{}^{\alpha\beta}\gamma^\sigma{}_{\alpha\beta}
\tag{76}
$$

$$
L_{gf} = \frac{1}{2}f_\mu f^\mu
\tag{77}
$$

where B_j are the constants satisfying the only condition:

$$
B_1 + B_3 + 4B_2 \neq 0
\tag{78}
$$

The action of the projective ghosts defined by the standard way has the following structure:

$$L_{gh} = \overline{\chi}^{\mu} g_{\mu\nu}(-g)^{\alpha} \chi^{\nu} \tag{79}$$

where

$\overline{\chi}^{\mu}, \chi^{\nu}$ are the grassmann variables; α is a constant.

The one-loop contribution of the projective ghosts to the effective action is proportional to the $\delta^4(0)$. In the dimensional regularization $[\delta^4(0)]_R = 0$ and the contribution of the projective ghosts to the one-loop counterterms is equal to zero.

Now, we must change the equation (74). The propagator of the quantum field $\gamma^{\sigma}_{\mu\nu}$ satisfies equation (73) and new condition:

$$F^{-1\sigma}_{\mu\nu}{}^{\lambda}_{\alpha\beta} F_{\lambda}{}^{\alpha\beta}{}^{\tau\epsilon}_{\rho} = \delta^{\sigma}_{\rho}\delta^{\tau}_{\mu}\delta^{\epsilon}_{\nu} \tag{80}$$

where

$$
\begin{aligned}
F_{\sigma}{}^{\alpha\beta\,\mu\nu}_{\lambda} &= F_{\sigma}{}^{\alpha\beta\,\mu\nu}_{\lambda} + f_{\tau\sigma}{}^{\alpha\beta} f^{\tau}_{\lambda}{}^{\mu\nu} \\
&= g^{\mu\nu}\delta^{\alpha}_{\lambda}\delta^{\beta}_{\sigma}(1 + B_1 B_3) + g^{\alpha\beta}\delta^{\mu}_{\sigma}\delta^{\nu}_{\lambda}(1 + B_1 B_3) - g^{\nu\alpha}\delta^{\mu}_{\sigma}\delta^{\beta}_{\lambda} - g^{\mu\beta}\delta^{\nu}_{\sigma}\delta^{\alpha}_{\lambda} \\
&\quad + B_1 B_2 g^{\alpha\beta}\delta^{\nu}_{\sigma}\delta^{\mu}_{\lambda} + B_1 B_2 g^{\mu\nu}\delta^{\alpha}_{\sigma}\delta^{\beta}_{\lambda} + B_1^2 \, g_{\sigma\lambda}g_{\mu\nu}g_{\alpha\beta} + B_3^2 \, g^{\alpha\mu}\delta^{\nu}_{\lambda}\delta^{\beta}_{\sigma} + \\
&\quad + B_2 B_3 g^{\mu\beta}\delta^{\alpha}_{\sigma}\delta^{\nu}_{\lambda} + B_2 B_3 g^{\alpha\nu}\delta^{\beta}_{\sigma}\delta^{\mu}_{\lambda} + B_2^2 \, g^{\nu\beta}\delta^{\alpha}_{\sigma}\delta^{\mu}_{\lambda} \tag{81}
\end{aligned}
$$

Having solved equations (73),(80) we obtain the following result:

$$
\begin{aligned}
F^{-1\alpha}_{\beta\sigma}{}^{\mu}_{\nu\lambda} &= -\frac{1}{4}g^{\alpha\mu}g_{\beta\sigma}g_{\nu\lambda} + \frac{1}{2}g^{\alpha\mu}g_{\beta\nu}g_{\sigma\lambda} - \frac{1}{4}g_{\nu\beta}\delta^{\mu}_{\lambda}\delta^{\alpha}_{\sigma} \\
&\quad + \frac{1}{4}\left(g_{\nu\lambda}\delta^{\mu}_{\beta}\delta^{\alpha}_{\sigma} + g_{\beta\sigma}\delta^{\alpha}_{\nu}\delta^{\mu}_{\lambda}\right) - \frac{1}{2}\left(g_{\nu\sigma}\delta^{\alpha}_{\lambda}\delta^{\mu}_{\beta} + g_{\beta\lambda}\delta^{\mu}_{\sigma}\delta^{\alpha}_{\nu}\right) \\
&\quad + \frac{1}{4}\left(\frac{B_1 - B_3 + 2B_2}{B_1 + B_3 + 4B_2}\right)\left(g_{\nu\lambda}\delta^{\mu}_{\sigma}\delta^{\alpha}_{\beta} + g_{\beta\sigma}\delta^{\alpha}_{\lambda}\delta^{\mu}_{\nu}\right)
\end{aligned}
$$

$$+ \frac{1}{4}\left(\frac{B_3 - B_1 + 2B_2}{B_1 + B_3 + 4B_2}\right)\left(g_{\beta\lambda}\delta^\mu_\nu\delta^\alpha_\sigma + g_{\beta\nu}\delta^\alpha_\beta\delta^\mu_\lambda\right)$$

$$+ \frac{1}{4}\frac{1}{(B_1 + B_3 + 4B_2)^2}(4 - B_1^2 - B_3^2 - 12B_2^2 +$$
$$+ 10B_1B_3 - 4B_1B_2 - 4B_2B_3)g_{\sigma\lambda}\delta^\mu_\nu\delta^\alpha_\beta \qquad (82)$$

To get the diagonal form of the effective Lagrangian we are to replace the dynamical variables in the following way:

$$\gamma^\sigma_{\mu\nu} \to \tilde{\gamma}^\sigma_{\mu\nu} = \gamma^\sigma_{\mu\nu} + \frac{1}{2}F^{-1\sigma}{}_{\mu\nu}{}^\lambda{}_{\alpha\beta}\left(B_\lambda{}^{\alpha\beta\tau}{}_{\rho\epsilon}\nabla_\tau - \Delta_\lambda{}^{\alpha\beta}{}_{\rho\epsilon}\right)P^{-1\rho\epsilon\kappa\nu}h_{\kappa\nu}$$
$$+ \frac{1}{2}F^{-1\sigma}{}_{\mu\nu}{}^\lambda{}_{\alpha\beta}P^{-1\rho\epsilon\kappa\nu}h_{\kappa\nu}B_\lambda{}^{\alpha\beta\eta}{}_{\rho\epsilon}\frac{1}{\alpha(\varphi)}\nabla_\eta\alpha(\varphi)$$
$$+ 2\xi\phi\varphi\frac{1}{\alpha(\varphi)}F^{-1\sigma}{}_{\mu\nu}{}^\lambda{}_{\alpha\beta}\Delta_\lambda{}^{\alpha\beta} - \frac{2\xi}{\alpha(\varphi)}F^{-1\sigma}{}_{\mu\nu}{}^\lambda{}_{\alpha\beta}B_\lambda{}^{\alpha\beta\tau}\nabla_\tau(\phi\varphi) \qquad (83)$$

This replacement does not change the functional measure:

$$det\frac{\partial\tilde{\gamma}}{\partial\gamma} = 1 \qquad (84)$$

We don't give the details of the cumbersome one-loop calculations that have been performed by means of the special REDUCE package program. One should note, that we violate the invariance of the action (71) under the general coordinate transformation by means of the following gauge:

$$F_\mu = \nabla_\nu h_\mu^\nu - \frac{1}{2}\nabla_\mu h - \frac{2\xi\varphi}{\alpha(\varphi)}\nabla_\mu\phi \qquad (85)$$

$$L_{gf} = \frac{1}{2}F_\mu F^\mu \qquad (86)$$

The action of the coordinate ghost is

$$L_{gh} = \bar{c}^\mu\left(g_{\mu\nu}\nabla^2 + R_{\mu\nu} - \frac{2\xi\varphi}{\alpha(\varphi)}(\nabla_\nu\varphi)\nabla_\mu - \frac{2\xi\varphi}{\alpha(\varphi)}(\nabla_\mu\nabla_\nu\varphi)\right)c^\nu \qquad (87)$$

The one-loop counterterms on the mass-shell including the contributions of the quantum and ghost fields are

$$\Delta\Gamma^1_\infty = -\frac{1}{32\pi^2\varepsilon}\int d^4x\sqrt{-g}\left(\frac{71}{60}\left(R_{\alpha\beta\mu\nu}R^{\alpha\beta\mu\nu} - 4R_{\mu\nu}R^{\mu\nu} + R^2\right)\right.$$

$$+\frac{203}{40}R^2 + \frac{\Lambda^2}{\alpha^2(\varphi)}\left(\frac{463}{5} + 52\xi^2\right)$$

$$+\Lambda R\left(\frac{1}{\alpha(\varphi)}\left(5\xi^2 - \frac{4}{3}\xi + \frac{463}{10}\right) + \frac{\xi^2\varphi^2}{\alpha^2(\varphi)}\left(75\xi + \frac{20}{3}\right) - \frac{700}{3}\frac{\xi^4\varphi^4}{\alpha^3(\varphi)}\right)\right) \quad (88)$$

4.3   The minimal gauge theory of gravity

Now let us consider the one-loop effective action in the minimal gauge theory of gravity with the action (18). One rewrite the fields $\bar{\Gamma}^\sigma{}_{\mu\nu}, g_{\mu\nu}$ in accordance with (64) where $\bar{\Gamma}^\sigma{}_{\mu\nu}, g_{\mu\nu}$ are now the classical parts satisfying the following equations

$$\begin{aligned}\frac{\delta S_{gr}}{\delta g^{\mu\nu}} &= \tilde{R}_{(\mu\nu)} - \frac{1}{2}\tilde{R}g_{\mu\nu} + \Lambda g_{\mu\nu}\\ &+ b_1 Q_{\mu\alpha\beta}Q_\nu{}^{\alpha\beta} - 2b_1 Q_{\alpha\beta\mu}Q^{\alpha\beta}{}_\nu + b_2 Q^{\alpha b}{}_\mu Q_{\beta\alpha\nu} - b_3 Q_\mu Q_\nu\\ &- \frac{1}{2}g_{\mu\nu}\left(b_1 Q_{\sigma\alpha\beta}Q^{\sigma\alpha\beta} + b_2 Q_{\sigma\alpha\beta}Q^{\beta\sigma\alpha} + b_3 Q_\sigma Q^\sigma\right) = 0 \quad (89)\end{aligned}$$

and

$$\begin{aligned}\frac{\delta S_{gr}}{\delta\Gamma^\sigma_{\alpha\beta}} &= D^{\alpha\lambda}_\lambda\delta^\beta_\sigma + D_\sigma g^{\alpha\beta} - \left(1 + \frac{1}{2}b_2\right)D^{\alpha\beta}_\sigma - \left(1 + \frac{1}{2}b_2\right)D^\beta_\sigma{}^\alpha\\ &- b_1 D_\sigma{}^{\alpha\beta} + b_1 D_\sigma{}^{\beta\alpha} + \frac{1}{2}D^\alpha{}_\sigma{}^\beta + \frac{1}{2}D^{\beta\alpha}_\sigma\\ &- \frac{1}{2}b_3 D^\alpha\delta^\beta_\sigma + \frac{1}{2}b_3 D^\beta\delta^\alpha_\sigma + \frac{1}{2}b_3 D_\lambda{}^{\lambda\alpha}\delta^\beta_\sigma - \frac{1}{2}b_3 D_\lambda{}^{\lambda\beta}\delta^\alpha_\sigma = 0 \quad (90)\end{aligned}$$

where $D^\sigma{}_{\mu\nu}$ is defined in (66)

The equation (89) has two solutions:

1. if $2b_1 + 3b_3 - b_2 = 0$,

$$D^{\sigma}{}_{\mu\nu} = \delta^{\sigma}_{\mu} C_{\nu}(x) \tag{91}$$

where C_{ν} is an arbitrary vector.

2. if $2b_1 + 3b_3 - b_2 \neq 0$

$$D^{\sigma}{}_{\mu\nu} = 0 \tag{92}$$

Taking into account (91) or (92) we obtain from (65)

$$R_{\mu\nu} = \Lambda g_{\mu\nu} \tag{93}$$

The one-loop effective Lagrangian quadratic in the quantum fields is:

$$L_{eff} = -\frac{1}{2} \gamma^{\sigma}{}_{\mu\nu} \tilde{F}_{\sigma}^{\ \mu\nu}{}_{\lambda}^{\alpha\beta} \gamma^{\lambda}_{\alpha\beta} -$$

$$\frac{1}{2} h^{\alpha\beta} h^{\mu\nu} \left(X_{\alpha\beta\mu\nu} - 2 H_{\alpha\beta\mu\nu\sigma}^{\ \ \ \ \ \rho\tau}{}_{\lambda}^{\kappa\epsilon} Q^{\sigma}{}_{\rho\tau} Q^{\lambda}{}_{\kappa\epsilon} \right) +$$

$$\gamma^{\lambda}_{\alpha\beta} \left(B_{\lambda}^{\alpha\beta\sigma}{}_{\mu\nu} \nabla_{\sigma} - \Delta_{\lambda}^{\alpha\beta}{}_{\mu\nu} \right) \left(\frac{1}{2} h g^{\mu\nu} - h^{\mu\nu} \right) -$$

$$h_{\mu\nu} V_{\lambda}^{\ \alpha\beta\rho}{}_{\nu\epsilon\kappa\tau}^{\ \ \ \sigma} E^{\mu\nu}{}_{\rho}{}^{\nu\epsilon}{}_{\sigma}{}^{\kappa\tau} \gamma^{\lambda}_{\alpha\beta} \tag{94}$$

where

$$
\begin{aligned}
\tilde{F}_{\alpha}^{\ \beta\lambda}{}_{\mu}^{\ \nu\sigma} &= g^{\beta\lambda}\delta^{\nu}_{\alpha}\delta^{\sigma}_{\mu} + g^{\nu\sigma}\delta^{\lambda}_{\alpha}\delta^{\beta}_{\mu} - \left(1 - \frac{b_2}{2}\right) g^{\beta\sigma}\delta^{\nu}_{\alpha}\delta^{\lambda}_{\mu} - \left(1 - \frac{b_2}{2}\right) g^{\lambda\nu}\delta^{\sigma}_{\alpha}\delta^{\beta}_{\mu} \\
&+ b_1\, g_{\alpha\mu}g^{\beta\nu}g^{\sigma\lambda} - b_1\, g_{\alpha\mu}g^{\lambda\nu}g^{\beta\sigma} - \frac{b_2}{2} g^{\lambda\sigma}\delta^{\beta}_{\mu}\delta^{\nu}_{\alpha} - \frac{b_2}{2} g^{\beta\nu}\delta^{\lambda}_{\mu}\delta^{\sigma}_{\alpha} \\
&+ \frac{b_3}{2} g^{\beta\nu}\delta^{\lambda}_{\alpha}\delta^{\sigma}_{\mu} - \frac{b_3}{2} g^{\beta\sigma}\delta^{\nu}_{\mu}\delta^{\lambda}_{\alpha} - \frac{b_3}{2} g^{\lambda\nu}\delta^{\beta}_{\alpha}\delta^{\sigma}_{\mu} + \frac{b_3}{2} g^{\sigma\lambda}\delta^{\beta}_{\alpha}\delta^{\nu}_{\mu} \tag{95}
\end{aligned}
$$

$$E^{\alpha\beta}{}_{\sigma}{}^{\mu\nu}{}_{\lambda}{}^{\rho\tau} = \frac{1}{2} G_{\sigma}{}^{\mu\nu}{}_{\lambda}{}^{\rho\tau} g^{\alpha\beta} - b_3 \delta^{\tau}_{\lambda}\delta^{\nu}_{\sigma}g^{\alpha\mu}g^{\beta\rho} - b_3 \delta^{\rho}_{\sigma}\delta^{\nu}_{\lambda}g^{\alpha\mu}g^{\beta\tau}$$

$$+ b_1 \left(g^{\mu\rho}g^{\nu\tau}\delta^{\alpha}_{\sigma}\delta^{\beta}_{\lambda} - 2g_{\sigma\lambda}g^{\nu\tau}g^{\alpha\mu}g^{\beta\rho} \right) \tag{96}$$

$$G_\sigma^{\mu\nu}{}_\alpha^{\beta\lambda} = b_1 g_{\sigma\alpha} g^{\mu\beta} g^{\nu\lambda} + b_2 g^{\mu\lambda} \delta_\alpha^\nu \delta_\sigma^\beta + b_3 g^{\mu\beta} \delta_\sigma^\nu \delta_\alpha^\lambda \tag{97}$$

$$V_\epsilon^{\rho\tau\sigma}{}_{\mu\nu}{}^\lambda_{\alpha\beta} = 2 Q^\lambda_{\alpha\beta} \delta_\epsilon^\sigma \delta_\mu^\rho \delta_\nu^\tau \tag{98}$$

$$
\begin{aligned}
H^{\gamma\rho\epsilon\tau}{}_\sigma{}^{\mu\nu}{}_\lambda{}^{\alpha\beta} &= -\frac{1}{2} P^{\gamma\rho\epsilon\tau} G_\sigma^{\mu\nu}{}_\lambda^{\alpha\beta} - b_1\, g^{\nu\beta} g^{\mu\epsilon} g^{\tau\alpha} \delta_\sigma^\gamma \delta_\lambda^\rho + b_1\, g_{\sigma\lambda} g^{\mu\gamma} g^{\rho\alpha} \delta_\sigma^\gamma \delta_\lambda^\rho \\
&\quad - b_1 g_{\mu\alpha} g_{\beta\tau} g_{\nu\epsilon} \delta_\sigma^\gamma \delta_\lambda^\rho + \frac{1}{2} b_1 g^{\gamma\rho} \left(g^{\mu\alpha} g^{\nu\beta} \delta_\sigma^\epsilon \delta_\lambda^\tau - 2 g_{\sigma\lambda} g^{\mu\gamma} g^{\rho\alpha} g^{\nu\epsilon} \right) \\
&\quad + b_1 g_{\sigma\lambda} g^{\alpha\mu} g^{\nu\gamma} g^{\rho\tau} g^{\epsilon\beta} - \frac{b_2}{2} g^{\gamma\rho} g^{\mu\epsilon} g^{\beta\tau} \delta_\lambda^\nu \delta_\sigma^\alpha - \frac{b_3}{2} g^{\mu\epsilon} g^{\alpha\tau} g^{\gamma\rho} \delta_\sigma^\nu \delta_\lambda^\beta \\
&\quad + b_2 g^{\mu\gamma} g^{\rho\tau} g^{\beta\epsilon} \delta_\lambda^\nu \delta_\sigma^\alpha + \left(b_1 g_{\sigma\lambda} g^{\nu\beta} + b_3 \delta_\lambda^\beta \delta_\sigma^\nu \right) g^{\mu\gamma} g^{\rho\tau} g^{\alpha\epsilon} \tag{99}
\end{aligned}
$$

$$X_{\alpha\beta\mu\nu} = 2 R_{\alpha\mu} g_{\beta\nu} - R_{\mu\nu} g_{\alpha\beta} + \Lambda g_{\alpha\mu} g_{\beta\nu} - \frac{1}{2} \Lambda g_{\alpha\beta} g_{\mu\nu} + \frac{1}{4} R g_{\mu\nu} g_{A B} - \frac{1}{2} R g_{\alpha\mu} g_{\beta\nu} \tag{100}$$

and $P^{-1\alpha\beta\mu\nu}, \Delta_\lambda{}^{\alpha\beta}{}_{\mu\nu}, B_\lambda{}^{\alpha\beta\sigma}{}_{\mu\nu}, \Delta_\lambda{}^{\epsilon\tau}, B_\lambda{}^{\epsilon\tau\sigma}$, are defined in (72)

Let us consider the first case: the theory without the projective invariance (the condition (33) is not satisfied). To get the diagonal form of the effective Lagrangian we are to replace the dynamical variables in the following way:

$$
\begin{aligned}
\tilde{\gamma}^\sigma_{\mu\nu} &= \gamma^\sigma_{\mu\nu} + F^{-1\sigma}{}_{\mu\nu}{}^\lambda_{\alpha\beta} (B_\lambda{}^{\alpha\beta\tau}{}_{\rho\epsilon} \nabla_\tau \varphi^{\rho\epsilon} - \Delta_\lambda{}^{\alpha\beta}{}_{\rho\epsilon} \\
&\quad - 2 V_\lambda{}^{\alpha\beta\gamma}{}_{\chi\eta}{}^\kappa_{\tau\omega} E^{\delta\zeta}{}_\gamma{}^{\chi\eta}{}_\kappa{}^{\tau\omega} P_{\rho\epsilon\delta\zeta}) \varphi^{\rho\epsilon} \\
\varphi^{\mu\nu} &= \frac{1}{2} P^{-1\mu\nu\alpha\beta} h_{\alpha\beta} \tag{101}
\end{aligned}
$$

where $F^{-1\sigma}{}_{\mu\nu}{}^\lambda_{\alpha\beta}$ is the propagator of the quantum field $\gamma^\sigma_{\mu\nu}$ satisfying two conditions (73) and (74).

Having solved equations (73) and (74) we obtain the following result:

$$F^{-1\alpha}{}_{\beta\sigma}{}^{\mu}{}_{\nu\lambda} = \quad - \frac{1}{4}g^{\alpha\mu}g_{\beta\sigma}g_{\nu\lambda} + A_2 g^{\alpha\mu}g_{\beta\nu}g_{\sigma\lambda} + \left(\frac{1}{12} - \frac{1}{3}(A_2 - A_1)\right)g_{\nu\beta}\delta^{\mu}_{\lambda}\delta^{\alpha}_{\sigma}$$

$$+ \frac{1}{4}\left(g_{\nu\lambda}\delta^{\mu}_{\beta}\delta^{\alpha}_{\sigma} + g_{\beta\sigma}\delta^{\alpha}_{\nu}\delta^{\mu}_{\lambda}\right) + A_1\left(g_{\nu\sigma}\delta^{\alpha}_{\lambda}\delta^{\mu}_{\beta} + g_{\beta\lambda}\delta^{\mu}_{\sigma}\delta^{\alpha}_{\nu}\right)$$

$$+ \frac{1}{4}\left(g_{\nu\lambda}\delta^{\mu}_{\sigma}\delta^{\alpha}_{\beta} + g_{\beta\sigma}\delta^{\alpha}_{\lambda}\delta^{\mu}_{\nu}\right) - \left(A_2 - \frac{1}{2}\right)g^{\alpha\mu}g_{\sigma\nu}g_{\beta\lambda}$$

$$+ \left(\frac{1}{3}(A_2 - A_1) - \frac{1}{4}\right)\left(g_{\beta\lambda}\delta^{\mu}_{\nu}\delta^{\alpha}_{\sigma} + g_{\beta\nu}\delta^{\alpha}_{\beta}\delta^{\mu}_{\lambda}\right)$$

$$+ \left(\frac{1}{12} - \frac{1}{3}(A_2 - A_1) + \frac{2}{3(2b_1 + 3b_3 - b_2)}\right)g_{\sigma\lambda}\delta^{\mu}_{\nu}\delta^{\alpha}_{\beta}$$

$$- \left(\frac{1}{2} + A_1\right)g_{\nu\beta}\delta^{\mu}_{\sigma}\delta^{\alpha}_{\lambda} - \left(\frac{1}{2} + A_1\right)g_{\sigma\lambda}\delta^{\mu}_{\beta}\delta^{\alpha}_{\nu} \tag{102}$$

where the constants A_2, A_1 are defined by the following expressions :

$$A_2 = \frac{2b_2^2 - 4b_1^2 - 2b_1 b_2 - 6b_2 - 2b_1 + 4}{d}$$

$$A_1 = -A_2 - \frac{4b_1}{d} + \frac{8}{d} \tag{103}$$

where

$$d \equiv 8(b_2^2 - 2b_2 + 1 + b_1 - b_1 b_2 - 2b_1^2) \neq 0 \tag{104}$$

The replacement (101) does not change the functional measure:

$$det \left|\frac{\partial(\varphi, \tilde{\gamma})}{\partial(h, \gamma)}\right| = 1 \tag{105}$$

We violate the coordinate invariance of the action (94) by means of the following gauge:

$$F_\mu = \nabla_\nu \varphi^\nu{}_\mu \tag{106}$$

$$L_{gh} = \frac{1}{2} F_\mu F^\mu \tag{107}$$

The action of the coordinate ghost is

$$L_{gh} = \bar{c}^\mu \left(g_{\mu\nu} \nabla^2 + R_{\mu\nu} \right) c^\nu \tag{108}$$

We don't give the details of the cumbersome calculations. The one-loop counterterms on the mass-shell including the contributions of the quantum and ghost fields are

$$\Delta\Gamma^1_\infty = -\frac{1}{32\pi^2\varepsilon} \int d^4x \sqrt{-g} \left(\frac{53}{45} R_{\alpha\beta\mu\nu} R^{\alpha\beta\mu\nu} - \frac{58}{5} \Lambda^2 \right) \tag{109}$$

Let us consider second case: the theory possessing the projective invariance (the condition (33) is fulfilled). In this case the propagator $F^{-1\alpha}{}_{\beta\sigma}{}^\mu{}_{\nu\lambda}$ of the quantum field $\gamma^\sigma_{\mu\nu}$ does not exist because of the projective invariance of the effective Lagrangian (94).

In order to fix the projective invariance we use the following condition:

$$f_\lambda = A \delta^\beta_\sigma \delta^\alpha_\lambda \gamma^\sigma_{\alpha\beta} \equiv f_{\lambda\sigma}{}^{\alpha\beta} \gamma^\sigma_{\alpha\beta} \tag{110}$$

$$L_{gf} = \frac{1}{2} f_\mu f^\mu \tag{111}$$

where the constant A does not equal to zero. The action of the projective ghost coincide with (79). We as in th epreviously case can discard the contribution of the projective ghost to the one-loop counterterms. We also change the equation (74). The new conditions coinside with (80), where

$$F_\sigma{}^{\alpha\beta}{}_\lambda{}^{\mu\nu} = \tilde{F}_\sigma{}^{\alpha\beta}{}_\lambda{}^{\mu\nu} + f_{\tau\sigma}{}^{\alpha\beta} f^\tau_\lambda{}^{\mu\nu} = b_1 g_{\sigma\lambda} g^{\beta\nu} g^{\alpha\mu}$$
$$- b_1 g_{\sigma\lambda} g^{\beta\mu} g^{\alpha\nu} - \left(1 - \frac{b_2}{2}\right) g^{\nu\alpha} \delta^\mu_\sigma \delta^\beta_\lambda - \left(1 - \frac{b_2}{2}\right) g^{\mu\beta} \delta^\nu_\sigma \delta^\alpha_\lambda$$

$$+ \left(A^2 + \frac{b_3}{2}\right) g^{\alpha\mu} \delta^\nu_\lambda \delta^\beta_\sigma - \frac{b_3}{2} g^{\mu\beta} \delta^\alpha_\sigma \delta^\nu_\lambda - \frac{b_3}{2} g^{\alpha\nu} \delta^\beta_\sigma \delta^\mu_\lambda + \frac{b_3}{2} g^{\nu\beta} \delta^\alpha_\sigma \delta^\mu_\lambda$$

$$+ g^{\mu\nu} \delta^\alpha_\lambda \delta^\beta_\sigma + g^{\alpha\beta} \delta^\mu_\sigma \delta^\nu_\lambda - \frac{b_2}{2} g^{\alpha\mu} \delta^\beta_\lambda \delta^\nu_\sigma - \frac{b_2}{2} g^{\beta\nu} \delta^\alpha_\lambda \delta^\mu_\sigma \tag{112}$$

Having solved equations (73) and (80) we obtain the following result:

$$F^{-1\alpha}{}_{\beta\sigma}{}^\mu{}_{\nu\lambda} =$$

$$-\frac{1}{4} g^{\alpha\mu} g_{\beta\sigma} g_{\nu\lambda} + A_2 g^{\alpha\mu} g_{\beta\nu} g_{\sigma\lambda} + \left(\frac{1}{12} - \frac{1}{3}(A_2 - A_1)\right) g_{\nu\beta} \delta^\mu_\lambda \delta^\alpha_\sigma$$

$$+\frac{1}{4}\left(g_{\nu\lambda}\delta^\mu_\beta\delta^\alpha_\sigma + g_{\beta\sigma}\delta^\mu_\nu\delta^\alpha_\lambda\right) + A_1\left(g_{\nu\sigma}\delta^\alpha_\lambda\delta^\mu_\beta + g_{\beta\lambda}\delta^\mu_\sigma\delta^\alpha_\nu\right)$$

$$-\frac{1}{4}\left(g_{\nu\lambda}\delta^\mu_\sigma\delta^\alpha_\beta + g_{\beta\sigma}\delta^\alpha_\lambda\delta^\mu_\nu\right) - \left(A_2 - \frac{1}{2}\right) g^{\alpha\mu} g_{\sigma\nu} g_{\beta\lambda}$$

$$+\left(\frac{1}{3}(A_2 - A_1) - \frac{1}{12}\right)\left(g_{\beta\lambda}\delta^\mu_\nu\delta^\alpha_\sigma + g_{\beta\nu}\delta^\alpha_\sigma\delta^\mu_\lambda\right)$$

$$+\left(\frac{1}{12} - \frac{1}{3}(A_2 - A_1) + A^2\right) g_{\sigma\lambda}\delta^\mu_\nu\delta^\alpha_\beta$$

$$-\left(\frac{1}{2} + A_1\right) g_{\nu\beta}\delta^\mu_\sigma\delta^\alpha_\lambda - \left(\frac{1}{2} + A_1\right) g_{\sigma\lambda}\delta^\mu_\beta\delta^\alpha_\nu \tag{113}$$

where the constants A_2, A_1 are defined from the expressions (103).

The abandonment calculations are coincide with the previously case. Having made the replacement of the variables (101) one needs to change $F^{-1\alpha}{}_{\beta\sigma}{}^\mu{}_{\nu\lambda} \rightarrow F^{-1\alpha}{}_{\beta\sigma}{}^\mu{}_{\nu\lambda}$. The coordinate invariance we fix by means of conditions (106), (107) and action of the coordinate ghosts is defined by (108). The one-loop counterterms on mass-shell coincide with expression (109).

5   Conclusion

In our work we have investigated the following problems:

1. the influence of the projective invariance on the renormalizability of the theory

2. the role of the torsion field at the quantum level in the affine-metric theory of gravity.

It turns out that:

1. In order to define the propagator of the quantum fields $\gamma^\sigma_{\mu\nu}$, one needs to fix the projective invariance.

2. The gauge fixing term (76) has the algebraic structure, that is it does not contain derivatives of the fields.

3. The action of the projective ghosts (79) has also the algebraic structure. The one-loop contribution of the projective ghosts is proportional to the $\delta^4(0)$ Hence its contribution is equal to zero in the dimensional regularization.

4. The theory (17) is not renormalizable. The term violating the renormalizability of the theory is equal to the R^2.

5. The renormalizability of the theory is not affected by the presence of the projective invariance.

About the role of torsion field at the quantum level in the affine-metric theory of gravity we established the following results. It turn out that the terms quadratic in the torsion tensor play the auxiliary role. They are serve for violating the projective invariance of the action and are not contribute to the one-loop counterterms.

It is very interesting the additional conditions (104)) arising in the definition of the quantum field propagator. It is easy to show that

$$d = 8(1 - b_1 - b_2)(1 + 2b_1 - b_2) \tag{114}$$

Let us consider the action (17). In accordance with (23) we can rewrite the connection $\bar{\Gamma}^{\sigma}{}_{\mu\nu}$ as the following sum:

$$\bar{\Gamma}^{\sigma}{}_{\mu\nu} = \Gamma^{\sigma}{}_{\mu\nu} + D^{\sigma}{}_{\mu\nu} \tag{115}$$

where $D^{\sigma}{}_{\mu\nu}$ are defined in (66) and $\Gamma^{\sigma}{}_{\mu\nu}$ is the Riemannian connection. $D^{\sigma}{}_{\mu\nu}$ can be decomposed into its irreducible parts:

$$D^{\sigma}{}_{\mu\nu} = A^{\sigma}g_{\mu\nu} + B_{\mu}\delta^{\sigma}_{\nu} + C_{\nu}\delta^{\sigma}_{\mu} + \frac{1}{6}\varepsilon^{\sigma}{}_{\mu\nu\lambda}\check{D}^{\lambda} + \bar{D}^{\sigma}{}_{\mu\nu} \tag{116}$$

where $\check{D}^{\lambda}$ is axial part, $A^{\sigma}, B_{\mu}, C_{\nu}$ are the vector fields defined as :

$$
\begin{aligned}
A^{\sigma} &\equiv \frac{1}{18}\left(5D^{\sigma\lambda}{}_{\lambda} - D^{\lambda\sigma}{}_{\lambda} - D_{\lambda}{}^{\lambda\sigma}\right) \\
B^{\sigma} &\equiv \frac{1}{18}\left(-D^{\sigma\lambda}{}_{\lambda} + 5D^{\lambda\sigma}{}_{\lambda} - D_{\lambda}{}^{\lambda\sigma}\right) \\
C^{\sigma} &\equiv \frac{1}{18}\left(-D^{\sigma\lambda}{}_{\lambda} - D^{\lambda\sigma}{}_{\lambda} + D_{\lambda}{}^{\lambda\sigma}\right)
\end{aligned} \tag{117}
$$

and $\bar{D}^{\sigma}{}_{\mu\nu}$ is traceless part satisfying the following conditons:

$$\bar{D}^{\nu}{}_{\mu\nu} \equiv \bar{D}^{\mu}{}_{\mu\nu} \equiv \bar{D}^{\sigma}{}_{\mu\nu}g^{\mu\nu} \equiv 0 \tag{118}$$

$$\bar{D}_{\sigma\mu\nu} + \bar{D}_{\nu\sigma\mu} + \bar{D}_{\mu\nu\sigma} = 0 \tag{119}$$

Let us remain that

$$Q^{\sigma}{}_{\mu\nu} = \frac{1}{2}\left(D^{\sigma}{}_{\mu\nu} - D^{\sigma}{}_{\nu\mu}\right) \tag{120}$$

Then it is easily to find the following relations between the irreducible decompositions of the torsion and connection defect tensors:

$$\check{Q}^{\lambda} = \check{D}^{\lambda}$$

$$\bar{Q}_{\sigma\mu\nu} = \bar{D}_{\sigma\mu\nu}$$
$$Q_\mu = \frac{3}{2}\left(B_\mu - C_\mu\right) \tag{121}$$

The coefficients $(1 - b_1 - b_2)$ and $(1 + 2b_1 - b_2)$ are proportional to the quadratic irreducible term. In the linear field approximation the quadratic term is proportional to mass term. Hence the coefficients $(1 - b_1 - b_2)$ and $(1 + 2b_1 - b_2)$ are proportional to the particles masses arising in the linear field approximation [49], [85], [86]. The condition $d = 0$ correspond to the presence of the massless particles in the theory. In this case the propagator of the quantum field $\gamma^\sigma_{\mu\nu}$ does not defined. Hence, the appearance of the new massless particles is connected with the presence of the new type symmetry in the theory. We do not known the transformation rule of the fields under these new symmetries [86], [109], [110]. It is easy to show that the only the connection field is transformed under these symmetries. The metric field is not change.

The theory with the action (18) is renormalizable at one-loop level. The expression $\int d^4 x \sqrt{-g}\left(R_{\alpha\beta\mu\nu}R^{\alpha\beta\mu\nu} - 4R_{\mu\nu}R^{\mu\nu} + R^2\right)$ is proportional to topological number - so called the Euler number χ of space-time:

$$\chi = \frac{1}{32\pi^2}\int d^4 x \sqrt{-g}\left(R_{\alpha\beta\mu\nu}R^{\alpha\beta\mu\nu} - 4R_{\mu\nu}R^{\mu\nu} + R^2\right) \tag{122}$$

Hence, this expression is some number. In the topologically trivial space-time this number is equal to zero. At one-loop level on mass-shell one needs to renormalize only the cosmological constant. Let us represent the cosmological constant in the following form:

$$\Lambda = \frac{\lambda}{k^2} \tag{123}$$

where λ is the dimensionless constant. Then from the explicit calculations in the previous section we get the renormalization group equation:

$$\beta(\lambda) = \mu^2 \frac{\partial \bar{\lambda}}{\partial \mu^2} = -\frac{29}{160\pi^2}\lambda^2 \tag{124}$$

where μ^2 is the subtraction point. Hence, we have the asymptotic freedom for λ.

The result of the one-loop calculations on mass-shell are coincide with one-loop counterterms of the Einstein gravity with the cosmological constant [81]. This coincidence is accidental one. The considered theory coincide with Einstein gravity on tree level. But because the Einstein gravity and theory under consideration are not renormalizable at two-loop level, the equivalence of the above mentioned theories can be violate at the quantum level. Therefore one cannot to predict the result of the one-loop calculations (109) without the corresponding calculations.

References

[1] G. t'Hooft and M.Veltman Ann. Inst. Henri Poincare **20** (1974) 69

[2] M.H.Goroff and A Sagnotti Nucl. Phys. **B266** (1986) 709

[3] A.E.M. van de Ven Nucl. Phys. **B378** (1992) 309

[4] S.Deser and P.van Nieuwenhuizen Phys. Rev. **D10** (1974) 401

[5] S.Deser and P.van Nieuwenhuizen Phys. Rev. **D10** (1974) 411

[6] S.Deser, P.van Nieuwenhuizen and H.S.Tsao Phys. Rev. **D10** (1974) 3337

[7] D.M.Capper and M.J.Duff Nucl. Phys. **B82** (1974) 147

[8] D.M.Capper, M.J.Duff and L.Halpern Phys. Rev. **D10** (1974) 461

[9] A.Ashtekar, New Perspective in Canonical Gravity (Bibliopolis, Napoli 1988)

[10] R.E.Kallosh, O.V.Tarasov and I.V.Tutin Nucl. Phys. **B137** (1978) 145

[11] D.M.Capper and J.J.Dulwich Nucl. Phys. B**221** (1983) 349

[12] G. t'Hooft Nucl. Phys. B**62** (1973) 444

[13] R.Kallosh Nucl. Phys. B**78** (1974) 293

[14] M.T.Grisaru, P.van Nieuwenhuisen and C.C.Wu Phys. Rev. D**12** (1975) 3203

[15] L.F.Abbott, M.T.Grisaru and R.K.Schaefere Nucl. Phys. B**229** (1983) 372

[16] A.Rebhan and G.Wirthumer Z.Phys.C - Particle and Fields **28** (1985) 269

[17] S.Ichinose Phys. Lett. B**284** (1992) 234

[18] S.Ichinose Nucl. Phys. B**395** (1993) 433

[19] K.S.Stelle Gen. Rel. Grav.**9** (1978) 353

[20] V.De Sabbata, V.N.Melnikov and P.I.Pronin Prog. Theor. Phys.**88** (1992) 623

[21] K.S.Stelle Phys. Rev. D**16** (1977) 953

[22] J.Julve and M.Tonin Nuovo Cim. B **46** (1978) 137

[23] E.S.Fradkin and A.A.Tseytlin Nucl. Phys. B**201** (1982) 469

[24] I.Antoniadis and E.T.Tomboulis Phys. Rev. D**33** (1986) 2756

[25] D.A.Johnston Nucl. Phys. B**297** (1988) 721

[26] D.Z.Freedman, P. van Nieuwenhuizen and S.Ferrara Phys. Rev. D **13** (1976) 3214

[27] S. Deser and B.Zumino Phys. Lett. B **62** (1976)335

[28] M.T.Grisaru, P. van Nieuwenhuizen and J.A.M.Vermaseren Phys. Rev. Lett 37 (1976) 1662

[29] E.S.Fradkin and A.A.Tseytlin Phys. Lett. B **134** (1984) 187

[30] E.S.Fradkin and A.A.Tseytlin Phys. Lett. B **104** (1981) 377

[31] E.S.Fradkin and A.A.Tseytlin Nucl. Phys. B **203** (1982) 157

[32] E.S.Fradkin and A.A.Tseytlin Phys. Rep. **119** (1985) 233

[33] B.De Wit and M.Nicolai Nucl. Phys. B **128** (1981) 98

[34] B.De Wit and M.Nicolai Nucl. Phys. B **208** (1982) 323

[35] P.Howe and H.Nicolai Phys. Lett. B **109** (1982) 209

[36] R.Kallosh Phys. Lett. B **99** (1981) 122

[37] SUPERGRAVITY' 81 ed.by S.Ferrara and J.G.Taylor (Cambridge University Press 1982)

[38] M.B.Green, J.H.Schwarz and E.Witten Superstring Theory, 2 volumes (Cambridge University Press, 1987)

[39] J.H.Schwarz Superstring, the First 15 Years of Superstrings Theory, volumes 1 and 2 (World Scientific, Singapore, 1985)

[40] D.J.Gross and V.Periwal Phys. Rev. Lett.**60** (1988) 2105

[41] L.P.Eisenhart Non-Riemannian Geometry (Americ. Math. Soc. Coll. Publication, New York, 1927)

[42] J.A.Schouten Ricci-Calculus, 2nd ed (Springer, Berlin, 1954)

[43] E.Cartan Om Manifolds with an Affine Connection and the Theory of General Relativity, English translational of the French original (Bibliopolis, Napoli, 1986)

[44] F.W.Hehl, P.van der Heyde, G.D.Kerlick and I.M.Nester Rev. Mod. Phys. **48** (1976) 393

[45] D.D.Ivanenko, P.I.Pronin and G.A.Sardanashvily Gauge theory of Gravity (University Publ.House, Moscow, 1985)

[46] V.N. Ponomarev, A.O.Barvinsky and Yu.N.Obukhov, Geometrodynamical Methods and Gauge Approach to the Theory of Gravitational Interaction, in Russian (Energoatomisdat, Moscow, 1985)

[47] E.W.Mielke Geometrodynamics of Gauge Fields (Akademie-Verlag, Berlin, 1987)

[48] F.W.Hehl (1985) Found. Phys. **15**, 451

[49] K.Hayashi and T.Shirafyji Prog. Theor. Phys.**64** (1980) 866, 883, 1435, 2222; ibid **65** (1981) 525

[50] A.A.Tsesytlin Phys. Rev. D**26** (1982) 3327

[51] D.Neville Phys. Rev. D**18** (1978) 3535

[52] D.Neville Phys. Rev. D**21** (1980) 867

[53] E.Sezgin and P. van Nieuwenhuizen Phys. Rev. D**21** (1980) 3269

[54] D.Neville Phys. Rev. D**23** (1981) 1244

[55] E.Sezgin Phys. Rev. D**24** (1981) 1677

[56] C.Rovelli Nuv. Cim. B **78** (1983) 167

[57] R.Kuhfuss and J.Nitsh Gen. Rel. Grav.**18** (1986) 1207

[58] S.M.Christensen J. Phys. A: Math. Gen., **13** (1980) 3001

[59] M.L.Yan Commun. Theor. Phys. (China) **2** (1983) 1281

[60] F.W.Hehl, E.A.Lord and Y.Ne'emann Phys. Lett. **B71** (1977) 432

[61] F.W.Hehl, E.A.Lord and Y.Ne'emann Phys. Lett. **B71** (1977) 432

[62] W.R.Davis Letter Nuovo Cimento **18** (1977) 319

[63] F.W.Hehl, E.A.Lord and Y.Ne'emann Phys. Rev. **D17** (1978) 428

[64] E.A.Lord Phys. Lett. **A65** (1978) 1

[65] J.Kijowski Gen. Rel. Grav.**9** (1978) 857

[66] F.W.Hehl and G.David Kerlic Gen. Rel. Grav.**9** (1978) 691

[67] Y.Ne'eman and Dj.Silacki Ann. of Phys. **120** (1979) 292

[68] E.W.Mielke, J.D.McCrea, Y.Ne'eman and F.W.Hehl Phys. Rev. **D48** (1993) 673

[69] L.Smolin Nucl. Phys. **B160** (1979) 253

[70] V.N.Ponomarev and A.A.Tseytlin Phys. Lett. **A70** (1979) 164

[71] M.Martellini Phys. Rev. Lett.**51** (1983) 152

[72] L.Smolin Nucl. Phys. **B247** (1984) 511

[73] J.Dell, J.L.deLyra and L.Smolin Phys. Rev. **D34** (1986) 3012

[74] C.Y.Lee and Y.Ne'eman Phys. Lett. **B233** (1989) 286

[75] C.Y.Lee and Y.Ne'eman Phys. Lett. **B242** (1990) 59

[76] C.Y.Lee Class. Quant. Grav**9** (1982) 2001

[77] V.D.Sandberg Phys. Rev. **D12** (1975) 3013

[78] W.R.Davis Letter Nuovo Cimento, **22** (1978) 101

[79] L.L.Smalley Lett. Nuovo Cim. **24** (1979) 406

[80] P.van Nieuwenhuizen Ann. of Phys. **104** (1977) 197

[81] S.M.Christensen and M.J.Duff Nucl. Phys. **B170** [FS1] (1980) 480

[82] P.B.Gilkey J. Differ. Geomet. **10** (1975) 601

[83] S.M.Christensen and M.J.Duff Nucl. Phys. **B154** (1979) 301

[84] A.O.Barvinsky and G.A.Vilkovisky Phys. Rep. **119** (1985) 1

[85] M.Blagoevic and J.A.Nikolic Nuovo Cim. B **73** (1983) 258

[86] M.Blagoevic and M.Vasilic Phys. Rev. **D34** (1986) 357

[87] D.Neville Phys. Rev. **D21** (1980) 2770

[88] H.T.Nieh and R.Rauch Phys. Lett. **A81** (1981) 113

[89] R.Rauch and H.T.Nieh Phys. Rev. **D24** (1981) 2029

[90] R.Rauch, J.C Shaw and H.T.Nieh Gen. Rel. Grav.**14** (1982) 331

[91] R.Rauch Phys. Rev. **D25** (1982) 577

[92] F.Mansouri and L.N.Chang Phys. Rev. D **13** (1976) 3192

[93] Y.Ne'emann and D.Šijački Phys. Lett. B **200** (1988) 489

[94] F.W.Hehl, G.D.Kerlic and P.von der Heyde Phys. Lett. B **63** (1976) 446

[95] F.W.Hehl, E.A.Lord and Y.Ne'emann Phys. Lett. B **71** (1977) 432; Phys. Rev. D **17** (1978) 428

[96] F.W.Hehl, J.D.McCrea, E.W.Mielke and Y.Ne'emann Found. Phys. **19** (1989) 1075

[97] M.Yu.Kalmykov and P.I.Pronin Nuovo Cimento B **106** (1991) 1401

[98] F.W.Hehl, W.Kopchynski, I.D.McCrea and E.W.Mielke J. Math. Phys. **32** (1991) 2169

[99] M.Yu.Kalmykov, P.I.Pronin and K.V.Stepanyantz Class. Quantum Grav. **11** (1994) 2645

[100] B.S.DeWitt (1967) Phys. Rev. **162**, 1195, 1239

[101] B.S.DeWitt (1965) Dynamical Theory Groups and Fields (Gordon and Breach, New York)

[102] G. 't Hooft Nucl. Phys. B **61** (1973) 455

[103] E. R. Speer J. Math. Phys. **15** (1974) 1

[104] G. 't Hooft and M. Veltman (1972) Nucl. Phys. B **44**, 189

[105] C. G. Bollini and J. J. Giambiagi (1972) Nuovo Cim. B **12**, 20; (1972) Phys. Lett. B **40**, 566

[106] J. Ashmore (1972) Lett. Nuovo Cim. **4**, 289

[107] G. M. Cicuta and E. Montaldi (1972) Lett. Nuovo Cim. **4**, 329

[108] P. Breitenlohner and D. Maison (1977) Commun. Math. Phys. **52**, 11

[109] I.Bars and S.W.MacDowell (1977) Phys. Lett. B **129**, 182

[110] K.Sundermeyer (1984) Phys. Lett. B **134**, 415

Gennadi A. Sardanashvily, Editor
New Frontiers in Gravitation
Hadronic Press, Palm Harbor, FL 34682-1577, U.S.A.
ISBN 0–911767–96–7, 1996, Pages 185–202

FROM THE POINCARÉ–CARTAN FORM TO A GERSTENHABER ALGEBRA OF THE POISSON BRACKETS IN FIELD THEORY

Igor V. Kanatchikov

Institut für Theoretische Physik
RWTH Aachen, D-52056 Aachen, Germany

Abstract

We consider the generalization of the basic structures of classical analytical mechanics to field theory within the framework of the De Donder-Weyl (DW) covariant canonical theory. We start from the Poincaré-Cartan form and construct the analogue of the symplectic form – the polysymplectic form of degree $(n + 1)$, n is the dimension of the space-time. The dynamical variables are represented by differential forms and the polysymplectic form leads to a natural definition of the Poisson brackets on forms. The Poisson brackets equip the exterior algebra of dynamical variables with the structure of a Gerstenhaber algebra. We also briefly discuss a possible approach to field quantization which proceeds from the DW Hamiltonian formalism and the Poisson brackets of forms.

1. INTRODUCTION

In this communication I discuss the canonical structure underlying the so-called De Donder–Weyl (DW) Hamiltonian formulation in field theory and its possible application to a quantization of fields. The abovementioned structure was found recently in my paper[1] to which I refer both for further references and for additional details. In particular, I am going to show that the relationships between the Poincaré-Cartan form, symplectic structure and the Poisson structure, which are well known in the mathematical formalism of classical mechanics, have their natural counterparts also in field theory within the framework of the DW canonical theory. This leads to the analogue of the symplectic structure, which I call polysymplectic, and to the analogue of the Poisson brackets which are defined on differential forms.

Recall that the Euler-Lagrange field equations may be written in the following form (see e.g.[2, 3, 4])

$$\frac{\partial p_a^i}{\partial x^i} = -\frac{\partial H}{\partial y^a}, \qquad \frac{\partial y^a}{\partial x^i} = \frac{\partial H}{\partial p_a^i} \qquad (1.1)$$

in terms of the variables

$$p_a^i := \frac{\partial L}{\partial(\partial_i y^a)}, \qquad (1.2)$$

$$H := p_a^i \partial_i y^a - L \qquad (1.3)$$

which are to be refered to as the DW momenta and the DW Hamiltonian function respectively. Here $L = L(y^a, \partial_i y^a, x^i)$ is the Lagrangian density, $x^i, i = 1, ..., n$ are space-time coordinates and $y^a, a = 1, ..., m$ are field variables. Eqs. (1) are reminiscent of Hamilton's canonical equations in mechanics and, therefore, may be thought of as a specific covariant Hamiltonian formulation of field equations. We call eqs. (1) the DW Hamiltonian field equations and the formulation of field theory in terms of the variables p_a^i and H above the DW Hamiltonian formulation. The formulation above originates from the work of De Donder and Weyl (1935) on the variational calculus of multiple integrals.

The mathematical structures underlying this formulation of field theory were considered earlier by several authors in the context of the so-called multisymplectic formalism[5] which was recently studied in detail in[6, 7, 8]. However, the possible analogues of the symplectic structure and the Poisson brackets, which are known to be so fruitful in the canonical formulation of classical mechanics, still are not properly understood within the DW canonical theory.

Our interest to this subject is motivated by the explicit covariance of the formulation above, in the sense that the space and time variables are not discriminated as usual, and its finite dimensionality, in the sense that the formulation refers to the finite dimensional analogue of the phase space namely, the space of variables (y^a, p^i_a), as well as by the attempts to understand if or how it is possible to construct a formulation of quantum field theory which would be based on the DW Hamiltonian formulation. Clearly, the answer to the latter question requires the analogue of the Poisson brackets and the bracket representation of the equations of motion corresponding to the DW formulation.

The canonical formalism in classical mechanics is related to the variational principle of least action and it may be derived from the fundamental object of the calculus of variations – the Poincaré-Cartan (P-C) form (see e.g.[9]). The corresponding construction leads to the structures which are known to be important for quantization. Conventional generalization to field theory implies setting off the time dimension from other space-time dimensions and leads to the infinite dimensional functional version of the abovementioned construction. Here we are interested in the field theoretical generalization of these structures within the space-time symmetric DW formulation.

2. POINCARÉ–CARTAN FORM, CLASSICAL EXTREMALS AND THE POLYSYMPLECTIC FORM

In field theory, which is related to the variational problems with several independent variables, the analogue of the P-C form written in terms of the DW Hamiltonian variables (1.2), (1.3) reads[6, 7, 8]

$$\Theta = p_a^i dy^a \wedge \omega_i - H\omega, \tag{2.1}$$

where $\omega := dx^1 \wedge ... \wedge dx^n$ and $\omega_i := \partial_i \lrcorner \omega$. The equations of motion in the DW Hamiltonian form, eqs. (1.1), may be shown to follow from the statement that the classical extremals are the integral hypersurfaces of the multivector field of degree n, $\overset{n}{X}$,

$$\overset{n}{X} := \tfrac{1}{n!} X^{M_1...M_n}(z) \partial_{M_1 ... M_n}, \tag{2.2}$$

where $\partial_{M_1 ... M_n} := \partial_{M_1} \wedge ... \wedge \partial_{M_n}$, which annihilates the canonical $(n+1)$-form

$$\Omega_{DW} := d\Theta, \tag{2.3}$$

that is

$$\overset{n}{X} \lrcorner \, \Omega_{DW} = 0. \tag{2.4}$$

The integral hypersurfaces of $\overset{n}{X}$ are defined as the solutions of the equations

$$\overset{n}{X}{}^{M_1...M_n}(z) = \mathcal{N} \frac{\partial(z^{M_1}, ..., z^{M_n})}{\partial(x^1, ..., x^n)} \tag{2.5}$$

where a multiplier $\mathcal{N}$ depends on the choosen parametrization of a hypersurface and $z^M := (x^i, y^a, p_a^i)$. The component calculations show that eq. (2.4) specifies only a part of the components of $\overset{n}{X}$ and that the DW canonical equations (1.1) actually follow from the "vertical" components $X^{vi_1 ... i_{n-1}}$. We call vertical the field and the DW momenta variables $z^v := (y^a, p_a^i)$ and horizontal the space-time (independent) variables x^i.

Introducing the notions of the vertical multivector field of degree p:

$$\overset{p}{X}{}^V := \frac{1}{(p-1)!} X^{v i_1 \dots i_{p-1}} \partial_{v i_1 \dots i_{p-1}}, \tag{2.6}$$

the vertical exterior differential, d^V, $d^V \dots := dz^v \wedge \partial_v \dots$, and the form

$$\Omega := -dy^a \wedge dp_a^i \wedge \omega_i, \tag{2.7}$$

one may check that (2.4) is equivalent to

$$\overset{n}{X}{}^V \lrcorner \, \Omega = (-)^n d^V H, \tag{2.8}$$

if the parametrization in (2.5) is choosen such that

$$\frac{1}{n!} \overset{n}{X}{}^{i_1 \dots i_n} \partial_{i_1 \dots i_n} \lrcorner \, \omega = 1.$$

The form Ω in (2.7) is to be refered to as *polysymplectic*.

The appearance of the DW field equations in the form of (2.8) suggests (cf. mechanics!) that the polysymplectic form is a field theoretical analogue of the symplectic form, so that its properties should be taken seriously as a starting point for the canonical formalism.

As a generalization of (2.8) it is easy to see that the polysymplectic form maps in general the horizontal q-forms, $\overset{q}{F}$,

$$\overset{q}{F} := \frac{1}{q!} F_{i_1 \dots i_q}(z) dx^{i_1 \dots i_q}, \tag{2.9}$$

where

$$dx^{i_1 \dots i_q} := dx^{i_1} \wedge \dots \wedge dx^{i_q},$$

to the vertical multivectors of degree $(n-q)$:

$$\overset{n-q}{X} \lrcorner \, \Omega = d^V \overset{q}{F}. \tag{2.10}$$

for all $q = 0, ..., n - 1$. Evidently, the horizontal forms play a role of dynamical variables within the present formalism. Henceforth we omit the superscripts ^{V} labelling the vertical multivectors.

The hierarchy of maps (2.10) may be viewed as a local consequence of the hierarchy of "graded canonical symmetries"

$$\pounds_{\overset{p}{X}} \Omega = 0, \tag{2.11}$$

$p = 1, ..., n$, which are formulated in terms of the generalized Lie derivatives with respect to the vertical multivector fields. By definition (cf.[10]), for any form μ

$$\pounds_{\overset{p}{X}} \mu := \overset{p}{X} \lrcorner \, d^V \mu - (-1)^p \, d^V (\overset{p}{X} \lrcorner \, \mu). \tag{2.12}$$

Now, by analogy with the terminology known from mechanics, I call the vertical multivector fields fulfilling (2.11) *locally Hamiltonian* and those fulfilling (2.10) (globally) *Hamiltonian*. Correspondingly, the forms to which the Hamiltonian multivector fields can be associated through the map (2.10) are refered to as the *Hamiltonian forms*.

The notion of a Hamiltonian form implies certain restriction on the dependence of its components on the DW momenta. For example, the components of the vector field $X_F := X^a \partial_a + X_a^i \partial_i^a$ associated through the map $X_F \lrcorner \Omega = d^V F$ with the $(n - 1)$–form $F := F^i \omega_i$ are given by

$$X_a^i = \partial_a F^i, \quad -X^a \delta_j^i = \partial_j^a F^i. \tag{2.13}$$

The latter relation restricts the admissible $(n-1)$–forms to those which have a simple dependence on the DW momenta namely, $F^i(y, p, x) = f^a(y, x) \, p_a^i + g^i(y, x)$.

Note also that the Hamiltonian multivector field associated with a form through the map (2.10) is actually defined up to an addition of *primitive* fields which annihilate the polysymplectic form

$$\overset{p}{X}_0 \lrcorner \Omega = 0. \tag{2.14}$$

Therefore, the image of a Hamiltonian form under the map (2.10) given by the polysymplectic form is rather the equivalence class of Hamiltonian multivector fields of corresponding degree modulo an addition of primitive fields.

3.   THE POISSON BRACKETS ON FORMS AND A GERSTENHABER ALGEBRA

It is natural to define the bracket of two locally Hamiltonian multivector fields as follows:

$$[\overset{p}{X}_1 , \overset{q}{X}_2] \lrcorner \; \Omega := \pounds_{\overset{p}{X}_1}(\overset{q}{X}_2 \lrcorner \; \Omega). \tag{3.1}$$

From the definition it follows

$$deg([\overset{p}{X}_1 , \overset{q}{X}_2]) \;=\; p+q-1, \tag{3.2}$$

$$[\overset{p}{X}_1 , \overset{q}{X}_2] \;=\; -(-1)^{(p-1)(q-1)}[\overset{q}{X}_2, \overset{p}{X}_1], \tag{3.3}$$

$$(-1)^{g_1 g_3}[\overset{p}{X} , [\overset{q}{X} , \overset{r}{X}]] \;+\; (-1)^{g_1 g_2}[\overset{q}{X} , [\overset{r}{X} , \overset{p}{X}]]$$
$$+\; (-1)^{g_2 g_3} \, [\overset{r}{X} , [\overset{p}{X} , \overset{q}{X}]] = 0, \tag{3.4}$$

where $g_1 = p-1$, $g_2 = q-1$ and $g_3 = r-1$.

These properties allow us to identify the bracket in (3.1) with the vertical (i.e. taken w.r.t. the vertical variables) of Schouten–Nijenhuis (SN) bracket multivector fields and to conclude that the space of LH fields is a graded Lie algebra with respect to the (vertical) SN bracket.

For two Hamiltonian multivector fields one obtains

$$[\overset{p}{X}_1 , \overset{q}{X}_2] \lrcorner \; \Omega \;=\; \pounds_{\overset{p}{X}_1} d^V \overset{s}{F}_2$$

$$=\; (-1)^{p+1} d^V(\overset{p}{X}_1 \lrcorner \; d^V \overset{s}{F}_2) \tag{3.5}$$

$$=:\; -d^V \{\overset{r}{F}_1, \overset{s}{F}_2\}, \tag{3.6}$$

where $r = n - p$ and $s = n - q$. From (3.5) it follows that the SN bracket of two Hamiltonian fields is a Hamiltonian field (as in mechanics). In (3.6) one defines the bracket operation on Hamiltonian forms which is induced by the vertical SN bracket of multivector fields associated with them.

From the definition in (3.6) it follows

$$\{\overset{r}{F_1}, \overset{s}{F_2}\} = (-1)^{(n-r)} X_1 \lrcorner \, d^V \overset{s}{F_2} = (-1)^{(n-r)} X_1 \lrcorner \, X_2 \lrcorner \, \Omega \qquad (3.7)$$

and

$$deg\{\overset{r}{F_1}, \overset{s}{F_2}\} = r + s - n + 1, \qquad (3.8)$$

$$\{\overset{p}{F_1}, \overset{q}{F_2}\} = -(-1)^{g_1 g_2} \{\overset{q}{F_2}, \overset{p}{F_1}\}, \qquad (3.9)$$

$$\{\overset{p}{F}, \overset{q}{F} \wedge \overset{r}{F}\} = \{\overset{p}{F}, \overset{q}{F}\} \wedge \overset{r}{F} + (-1)^{q(n-p-1)} \overset{q}{F} \wedge \{\overset{p}{F}, \overset{r}{F}\}, \qquad (3.10)$$

$$(-1)^{g_1 g_3} \{\overset{p}{F}, \{\overset{q}{F}, \overset{r}{F}\}\} +$$

$$(-1)^{g_1 g_2} \{\overset{q}{F}, \{\overset{r}{F}, \overset{p}{F}\}\} + (-1)^{g_2 g_3} \{\overset{r}{F}, \{\overset{p}{F}, \overset{q}{F}\}\} = 0, \qquad (3.11)$$

where $g_1 = n - p - 1$, $g_2 = n - q - 1$ and $g_3 = n - r - 1$.

The algebraic construction which satisfies the axioms (3.9)–(3.11) together with the familiar properties of the exterior product is known as the Gerstenhaber algebra[11].

Remark: Strictly speaking, the space of Hamiltonian forms is not closed with respect to the exterior product, so that the full justification of the Leibniz rule (3.10) requires a generalization of the above construction which admits arbitrary horizontal forms as the dynamical variables. Such a generalization is discussed in[12].

4. EQUATIONS OF MOTION IN THE BRACKET FORM

By analogy with mechanics one can expect that the equations of motion are given by the bracket with the DW Hamiltonian function. Indeed, for the bracket of H with the $(n-1)$–form $F := F^i \omega_i$ one obtains

$$
\begin{aligned}
\{\!\!\{H, F\}\!\!\} &= X_F \lrcorner\, d^V H = X_F{}^a \partial_a H + X_{F_a}^i \partial_i^a H \\
&= \partial_i p_a^j \partial_j^a F^i + \partial_i y^a \partial_a F^i
\end{aligned}
$$

where we have used (2.3) and (1.1). Introducing the *total* (i.e. evaluated on extremals) exterior differential $\boldsymbol{d}$ of a horizontal form of degree p, $\overset{p}{F}$:

$$
\boldsymbol{d}\overset{p}{F} := \partial_i z^M dx^i \wedge \partial_M \overset{p}{F} = \partial_i z^v dx^i \wedge \partial_v \overset{p}{F} + dx^i \wedge \partial_i \overset{p}{F} = \boldsymbol{d}^V F + d^{hor} F
$$

one can write the equation of motion of Hamiltonian $(n-1)$–form F as (by definition, $*^{-1}\omega := 1$)

$$
*^{-1} \boldsymbol{d}F = \{\!\!\{H, F\}\!\!\} + \partial_i F^i. \tag{4.1}
$$

The bracket of a p–form with H vanishes for $p < n-1$. The equations of motion of arbitrary forms may be written in terms of the bracket with the n–form $H\omega$. This implies certain extension of the construction in Sect. 2. Namely, we map $H\omega$ to a vector-valued form $\tilde{X} := \tilde{X}_i^v dx^i \otimes \partial_v$ by

$$
\tilde{X} \lrcorner\, \Omega = d^V H\omega \tag{4.2}
$$

where $\tilde{X} \lrcorner\, \Omega := X^v_{\cdot k} dx^k \wedge (\partial_v \lrcorner\, \Omega)$ is the Frölicher-Nijenhuis inner product. From (4.2) it follows

$$
\tilde{X}^a_{\cdot k} = \partial_k^a H, \qquad \tilde{X}^i_{ak} \delta_i^k = -\partial_a H. \tag{4.3}
$$

Substitution of the natural parametrization of $\tilde{X}$:

$$
\tilde{X}^v_{\cdot k} = \frac{\partial z^v}{\partial x^k},
$$

into (4.3) leads to the DW Hamiltonian equations (1.1).

Now, we define the bracket with $H\omega$ (cf. (3.7))

$$
\{\!\!\{H\omega, \overset{p}{F}\}\!\!\} := \tilde{X}_{H\omega} \lrcorner\, d^V \overset{p}{F} \tag{4.4}
$$

and reveal that

$$d\overset{p}{F} = \{\!\!\{H\omega, \overset{p}{F}\}\!\!\} + d^{hor}\overset{p}{F}. \tag{4.5}$$

Thus, we have shown that the bracket with the DW Hamiltonian n–form $H\omega$ is related to the exterior differential of a form.

Remark: The bracket which is naively defined in (4.4) does not satisfy in general the axioms of a Gerstenhaber algebra. Appropriate extension of a Gerstenhaber algebra structure to n–forms is a part of the generalization of the present construction to the forms which are not Hamiltonian according to the definition in Sect. 2 (see[12]).

5. TOWARDS A QUANTIZATION

Appropriate quantization of a Gerstenhaber algebra of exterior forms, which generalizes to field theory the Poisson algebra of dynamical variables, may in principle lead to certain quantization procedure in field theory. The purpose of this section is to discuss briefly a possible heuristic approach to such a quantization.

We start from the observation that

$$\{\!\!\{p_a, y^b\}\!\!\} = \delta_a^b, \tag{5.1}$$

where $p_a := p_a^i \omega_i$ is the $(n-1)$–form which may be considered as the momentum variable canonically conjugate to fields y^a. Applying Dirac's quantization prescription $[\ ,\ ]_\pm = i\hbar\{\!\!\{\ ,\ \}\!\!\}_\pm$ one obtains the canonical commutation relation for the operators corresponding to fields and the $(n-1)$–form momenta

$$[\hat{p}_a, \hat{y}^b] = i\hbar\delta_a^b. \tag{5.2}$$

In "y–representation" one finds the differential operator realization of $\hat{p}_a$

$$\hat{p}_a = i\hbar\frac{\partial}{\partial y^a}. \tag{5.3}$$

Based on the analogy with the quantization of classical mechanics in Schrödinger's representation and the observation in Sect. (4) that the exterior differential is related to the DW Hamiltonian n-form, one can conjecture the following form of the covariant "Schrödinger equation"

$$i\hbar \, d\Psi = (H\omega)^{op}\Psi \tag{5.4}$$

for the "wave function" $\Psi = \Psi(x^i, y^a)$ which depends on the space-time and field variables which form the analogue of a configuration space within the present formulation.

In the particular example of a system of scalar fields y^a interacting through the potential $V(y)$, which is given by the Lagrangian

$$L = -\frac{1}{2}\partial_i y^a \partial^i y_a - V(y),$$

the DW Hamiltonian function takes the form

$$H = -\frac{1}{2}p_a^i p_i^a + V(y). \tag{5.5}$$

In terms of the $(n-1)$-form momenta variables p_a the n-form $H\omega$ may be written as

$$H\omega = \frac{1}{2} * p_a \wedge p^a + V(y)\omega \tag{5.6}$$

where $*p_a = -p_a^i dx_i$ (the Minkowski metric in the x-space is assumed). The realization of the operator corresponding to the non-Hamiltonian one-form $*p_a$

$$\widehat{*p_a} = * \hat{p}_a \tag{5.7}$$

is suggested by the quantization of the bracket

$$\{ *p_a, y^b \omega_i \} = -\delta_a^b dx_i = *\{ p_a, y^b \omega_i \} \tag{5.8}$$

which may be calculated either with the help of the Leibniz rule (3.10) or within a more general scheme (see[12]) where one associates arbitrary horizontal forms with the differential operators on exterior algebra which are represented by the multivector-valued forms instead of the multivectors as in the case of Hamiltonian forms.

Further, the classical identity $\omega = *1$ suggests that $\hat{\omega} = *$ and, therefore, one can write

$$(H\omega)^{op} = *(-\frac{\hbar^2}{2}\Delta + V(y)) =: *H^{op}, \tag{5.9}$$

where $\Delta := \partial^a\partial_a$ is the Laplace operator in a field space. Thus, the Schrödinger equation (5.4) may also be written as

$$i\hbar *^{-1} d\Psi = H^{op}\Psi. \tag{5.10}$$

Evidently, this equation makes sense only if the wave function Ψ is a non-homogeneous horizontal form. In the simple case of the DW Hamiltonian operator (5.9) which does not depend explicitly on the space-time coordinates one can take into account only the zero- and $(n-1)$-form contributions, so that

$$\Psi = \psi_0(x,y) + \psi^i(x,y)\,\omega_i. \tag{5.11}$$

Substituting (5.11) into (5.10) one obtains the component form of the Schrödinger equation:

$$i\hbar\partial_i\psi^i = H^{op}\psi_0, \tag{5.12}$$
$$-i\hbar\partial_i\psi_0 = H^{op}\psi_i. \tag{5.13}$$

Integrability condition of this set of equations is

$$\delta\Psi = 0. \tag{5.14}$$

By a straightforward calculation one can derive from (5.12) and (5.13) the following conservation law

$$\partial_i[\bar{\psi}_0\psi^i + \psi_0\bar{\psi}^i] = -\frac{i\hbar}{2}\partial_a[\bar{\psi}_0\overleftrightarrow{\partial_a}\psi_0 - \bar{\psi}^i\overleftrightarrow{\partial_a}\psi_i]. \tag{5.15}$$

If one assumes the sufficiently rapid decay of the wave function $\Psi(x,y)$ for large values of fields $|y| \to \infty$, by Gauss' theorem one obtains

$$\partial_i \int dy\,[\bar{\psi}_0\psi^i + \psi_0\bar{\psi}^i] = 0. \tag{5.16}$$

Thus, the current

$$j^i := \int dy\, [\bar{\psi}_0 \psi^i + \psi_0 \bar{\psi}^i]$$

is the conserved space-time current of the theory. It suggests the inner product of nonhomogeneous forms Ψ which one needs for the calculation of quantum theoretical expectation values.

The covariant Schrödinger equation may be solved by means of the separation of field and space-time variables. Namely, let us write

$$\Psi(x,y) = \Phi(x)f(y), \tag{5.17}$$

where $\Phi(x)$ is a nonhomogeneous form with the components depending on x:

$$\Phi(x) := \phi_0(x) + \phi^i(x)\omega_i \tag{5.18}$$

and $f(y)$ is a function of field variables. Substituting this ansatz into the Schrödinger equation (5.10) we arrive at the eigenvalue problem for the DW Hamiltonian operator

$$H^{op} f = \kappa f, \tag{5.19}$$

and the equation on $\Phi(x)$:

$$i\hbar *^{-1} d\Phi(x) = \kappa \Phi(x). \tag{5.20}$$

From the latter equation it follows

$$\Box \phi_0 = \frac{\kappa^2}{\hbar^2}\phi_0, \quad \phi_i = -\frac{i\hbar}{\kappa}\partial_i \phi_0. \tag{5.21}$$

The solutions of (5.19) and (5.21) provide us with a basis for decomposition of an arbitrary solution of the covariant Schrödinger equation.

Remarks:

1. The canonical bracket (5.1) belongs to the subalgebra of zero- and $(n-1)$-forms of a Gerstenhaber algebra of dynamical variables. Other canonical brackets from this subalgebra are

$$\{\!\{p^i_a, y^b\omega_j\}\!\} = \delta^b_a \delta^i_j, \tag{5.22}$$

$$\{\!\{p_a, y^b\omega_i\}\!\} = \delta^b_a \omega_i. \tag{5.23}$$

Quantization of these three brackets is a part of the problem of quantization of the center of a Gerstenhaber algebra which is formed by the forms of the kind $p_a^i dx^{\cdots}$ and $y^a dx^{\cdots}$, where $dx^{\cdots}$ denotes the basis elements of Grassmann algebra of horizontal forms. The question as to which subalgebra of a Gerstenhaber algebra of dynamical variables should or can be quantized remains open and deserves the same careful study as the similar question concerning the quantizable subalgebra of the Poisson algebra of observables in mechanics. The minimal subalgebra is that of $(n-1)$-forms and the canonical bracket from this subalgebra is given by (5.23). Its quantization rather than a quantization of (5.1) gives rise to the operator realization of p_a in (5.3). The quantization of the subalgebra of zero- and $(n-1)$-forms with the canonical brackets (5.1), (5.22) and (5.23) leads to the problem of realization of the operator $\hat{p}_a^i$ which would be consistent with the realization of $\hat{p}_a$ and the requirement $\hat{p}_a = \hat{p}_a^i \circ \hat{\omega}_i$, as well as to the problem of the proper realization of the operation $\circ$ of the multiplication of quantum operators. When quantizing the (centre of the) Gerstenhaber algebra the latter problem is that of the proper realization of the quantized wedge product which is in this case a generalization of the Jordan symmetric product of operators in quantum mechanics.

2. The quantization of the bracket (5.1) leads to the operator realization of the $(n-1)$–form p_a which is the 0-form. In general, the form degree of the operator corresponding to a dynamical variable is different from the classical form degree of the latter. This gives rise to an additional problem of which degree should define the graded products of operators which correspond to the exterior product and the quantized Poisson bracket respectively.

3. It is interesting to note that the realization (5.3) is not consistent with the classical property $dx^i \wedge p_a = (-)^{n-1} p_a \wedge dx^i$ which one may require to be also fulfilled on the quantum level. This may be achieved if the quantization prescription is modified in such a way that

$$[\, , \,]_\pm = \gamma \hbar \{ \, , \, \}_\pm \tag{5.24}$$

where γ denotes the imaginary unit corresponding to the Clifford algebra of the n-dimensional space-time over which a field theory under quantization is formulated. In Minkowski space-time $\gamma := \gamma_0\gamma_1\gamma_2\gamma_3$. In the case of mechanics $(n = 1)$ $\gamma = i$ and the above quantization prescription reduces to that of Dirac. The quantization according to (5.24) leads to the realization

$$\hat{p}_a = \gamma\hbar\partial_a \quad \text{and} \quad \widehat{dx^i}\wedge = \gamma^i\wedge, \tag{5.25}$$

where $\wedge$ at the right denotes the graded symmetrized Clifford product. Correspondingly, the wave function may be considered as taking values in the Clifford–Kähler algebra of nonhomogeneous forms which corresponds to the n-dimensional space-time (see e.g.[13] and the references quoted there). The latter reduces to complex numbers in the case of mechanics. This quantization prescription leads to the same realization of the DW Hamiltonian operator as in (5.9). However, in general, it is not clear which quantization prescription is more appropriate both physically and mathematically for the quantization of the suitable "quantizable" subalgebra of a Gerstenhaber algebra of forms–dynamical variables in field theory.

4. The elements of quantum theory presented above possess the basic features of a quantum description of dynamics and its connections with the structures of classical mechanics. These elements are easily seen to reduce to the corresponding elements of quantum mechanics at $n = 1$. In this sense at least our formulation may be viewed as an approach to the quantum description of fields. Establishing the possible links with the known approaches and results in quantum field theory and a physical interpretation of the present formulation poses many conceptual questions and needs a further study which we hope to communicate elsewhere. In particular, it would be interesting to understand a possible relation of our nonhomogeneous form-valued wave function $\Psi(x,y)$ to the Schrödinger wave functional $\Psi(t, [y(\mathbf{x})])$ and of our covariant Schrödinger equation to the functional Schrödinger equation.

Acknowledgements. I thank Prof. A. Odzijewicz and the organizers for inviting me to present this talk. I acknowledge useful discussions with F. Cantrijn, M. Gotay, M. Modugno and J. Śniatycki during the time of the workshop. Thanks to Z. Oziewicz for several inspirating discussions on the subject of this paper and encouragement.

References

1. I.V. Kanatchikov, On the canonical structure of the De Donder-Weyl covariant Hamiltonian formulation of field theory I. Graded Poisson brackets and equations of motion, PITHA 93/41 (November 1993) and hep-th/9312162.

2. H. Rund, "The Hamilton-Jacobi Theory in the Calculus of Variations", D. van Nostrand Co. Ltd., Toronto etc. (1966)

3. H. Kastrup, Canonical theories of Lagrangian dynamical systems in physics, *Phys. Rep.* 101:1 (1983)

4. E. Binz, J. Śniatycki, H. Fisher, "Geometry of Classical Fields", North-Holland, Amsterdam (1989)

5. J. Kijowski, A finite dimensional canonical formalism in the classical field theory, *Comm. Math. Phys.* 30:99 (1973);
   J. Kijowski, Multiphase Spaces and Gauge in the Calculus of Variations, *Bull. de l'Acad. Polon. des Sci., Sér sci. math., astr. et Phys.* XXII:1219 (1974);
   J. Kijowski and W. Szczyrba, A Canonical Structure for Classical Field Theories, *Comm. Math. Phys.* 46:183 (1976)

6. M.J. Gotay, An Exterior Differential Systems Approach to the Cartan Form, *in:* " Géométrie Symplectique & Physique Mathématique", P. Donato, C. Duval e.a. eds., Birkhäuser, Boston (1991)
   M.J. Gotay, A multisymplectic framework for classical field theory and the calculus of variations I. Covariant Hamiltonain formalism, *in:* "Mechanics, Analysis and Geometry: 200 Years after Lagrange", M. Francaviglia ed., North Holland, Amsterdam (1991)

M.J. Gotay, A multisymplectic framework for classical field theory and the calculus of variations II. Space + time decomposition, *Diff. Geom. and its Appl.* 1:375 (1991)

7. M. J. Gotay, J. Isenberg, J. E. Marsden, R. Montgomery, J. Śniatycki and Ph. B. Yasskin: "Momentum maps and classical relativistic fields: The Lagrangian and Hamiltonian structure of classical field theories with constraints", Preprint, Berkeley (1992)

8. J.F. Cariñena, M. Crampin, L.A. Ibort, On the multisymplectic formalism for first order field theories, *Diff. Geom. and its Appl.* 1:345 (1991)

9. R. Abraham and J.E. Marsden, "Foundations of Mechanics", 2nd ed., Benjamin and Cummings, N.Y. (1978)

10. W.M. Tulczyjew, The graded Lie algebra of multivector fields and the generalized Lie derivative of forms, *Bull. de l'Acad. Polon. sci., Sér sci. math., astr. et phys.* XXII:937 (1974)

11. M. Gerstenhaber, The cohomology structure of an associative ring, Ann. Math. 78:267 (1963);
M. Gerstenhaber and S.D. Schack, Algebraic cohomology and deformation theory, *in*: "Deformation Theory of Algebras and Structures and Applications", M. Hazewinkel and M. Gerstenhaber eds., Kluwer Academic Publ., Dordrecht (1988);
B.H. Lian and G.J. Zuckerman, New perspectives of the BRST-algebraic structure of string theory, *Commun. Math. Phys.* 154:613 (1993)

12. I.V. Kanatchikov, Basic structures of the covariant canonical formalism for fields based on the De Donder–Weyl theory, preprint PITHA 94/17 and hep-th/9410238;

I.V. Kanatchikov, On the finite dimensional covariant Hamiltonian formalism in field theory, to be published *in*: New Frontiers in Gravitation, R. Santilli and G. Sardanashvily eds., Hadronic Press, Palm Harbor (1995)

13. P. Becher and H. Joos, The Dirac-Kähler equation and fermions on the lattice, *Z. Phys. C* 15:343 (1982),
    I.M. Benn and R.W. Tucker, Fermions without spinors, *Comm. Math. Phys.* 89:341 (1983),
    N.A. Salingaros, G.P. Wene, The Clifford algebra of differential forms, *Acta Appl. Math.* 4:271 (1985)

Gennadi A. Sardanashvily, Editor
New Frontiers in Gravitation
Hadronic Press, Palm Harbor, FL 34682-1577, U.S.A.
ISBN 0–911767–96–7, 1996, Pages 203–214

QUANTUM GRAVITATIONAL EFFECTS IN DE SITTER SPACE

Claus Kiefer

Fakultät für Physik, Universität Freiburg
Hermann-Herder-Str. 3, D-79104 Freiburg, Germany

Abstract

We calculate the first quantum gravitational correction term to the trace anomaly in De Sitter space from the Wheeler-DeWitt equation. This is obtained through an expansion of the full wave functional for gravity and a conformally coupled scalar field in powers of the Planck mass. We also discuss a quantum gravity induced violation of unitarity and comment on its possible relevance for inflation.

A central role in the study of quantum field theory on a given classical background spacetime is played by the semiclassical Einstein equations

$$R_{\mu\nu} - \frac{1}{2}g_{\mu\nu}R = -8\pi G\langle T_{\mu\nu}\rangle, \tag{1}$$

in which the renormalised expectation value of the energy-momentum tensor acts as a "back reaction" on the metric of some classical spacetime. The quantum matter state with respect to which this expectation value is taken is assumed to obey, in the Schrödinger picture, a functional Schrödinger equation, where the time evolution is generated by the matter Hamiltonian. A prominent example is the case of a conformally coupled scalar field in De Sitter spacetime. If one assumes this field to be in the Bunch-Davies vacuum state (which is the unique De Sitter invariant vacuum state [1]), one finds for the expectation value of the energy-momentum tensor the result (see e.g. [2])

$$\langle T_{\mu\nu} \rangle = \frac{H_0^4 \hbar}{960\pi^2} g_{\mu\nu},$$ (2)

where H_0 is the (constant) Hubble parameter of De Sitter space. Since the trace of this expression is non-vanishing, it leads to the so-called *trace anomaly* because conformal invariance would lead to a vanishing trace at the classical level.

Since one expects that the gravitational field is fundamentally described by quantum theory, (1) can at best hold approximately. There have been many discussions in the literature which have investigated the range of validity of the semiclassical Einstein equations. Ford [3], e.g., has compared the emission of classical gravitational waves in the semiclassical theory with graviton emission in linear quantum gravity and found that this can be drastically different except if the mean deviation of $T_{\mu\nu}$ is small. This is fulfilled, for example, if the quantum state approximately evolves adiabatically. A number of papers have strengthened this result by the attempt to derive (1) from the Wheeler-DeWitt equation, the central equation of canonical quantum gravity, in a semiclassical approximation and to study the emergence of the back reaction term with the help of Wigner's function (see, e.g., [4]). A similar discussion was made for quantum electrodynamics [5].

If it is possible to derive the limit of quantum field theory in a classical background from the Wheeler-DeWitt equation [6], one should also be able to go beyond this limit and study quantum gravitational corrections. This has been achieved through an expansion with respect to the gravitational constant [6, 7], although in a formal sense only, since regularisation issues have not been adressed. More precisely, one obtains correction terms to the functional Schrödinger equation for matter fields on a given spacetime – the first quantum gravity - induced "post-Schrödinger approximation".

In the present paper these correction terms are explicitly calculated for a conformally coupled scalar field in De Sitter space. Since the general discussion in [7] only dealt with minimally coupled fields, it is necessary to extend the approximation scheme to the case of conformally coupled fields. This is nontrivial since the canonical formalism is very different for non-minimally coupled fields [8].

The action for a massless scalar field ϕ which is conformally coupled to gravity reads

$$S = \int d^4x \sqrt{-g} \left(\frac{{}^{(4)}R - 2\Lambda}{16\pi G} - \frac{1}{2} g^{\mu\nu} \partial_\mu \phi \partial_\nu \phi - \frac{1}{12} {}^{(4)}R\phi^2 \right). \qquad (3)$$

Canonical quantisation proceeds by first casting the theory into Hamiltonian form. This is achieved by the usual 3+1 splitting of spacetime into a foliation of spacelike hypersurfaces. The Hamiltonian constraint found by this procedure is then implemented in the usual way by applying its (naive) operator version on physically allowed wave functionals, i.e., through the Wheeler-DeWitt equation. It reads explicitly [8]

$$\mathcal{H}\Psi \equiv \left(\frac{3\sqrt{h}}{16M} \frac{\delta^2}{\delta(\sqrt{h})^2} - \frac{1}{2M\sqrt{h}} \frac{1}{1 - \frac{\phi^2}{24M}} \tilde{h}_{ac}\tilde{h}_{bd} \frac{\delta^2}{\delta\tilde{h}_{ab}\delta\tilde{h}_{cd}} \right.$$
$$- \frac{\phi}{8M} \frac{\delta^2}{\delta\sqrt{h}\delta\phi} - \frac{1}{2\sqrt{h}} \left(1 - \frac{\phi^2}{24M} \right) \frac{\delta^2}{\delta\phi^2} - 2\sqrt{h}MR + \frac{\sqrt{h}\phi^2}{12} R$$
$$\left. + 4\sqrt{h}M\Lambda + \frac{\sqrt{h}}{2} h^{ab} \phi_{,a}\phi_{,b} \right) \Psi \left[\sqrt{h}(\mathbf{x}), \tilde{h}_{ab}(\mathbf{x}), \phi(\mathbf{x}) \right] = 0, \qquad (4)$$

where $M = (32\pi G)^{-1}$, $h_{ab} = h^{1/3}\tilde{h}_{ab}$, $h = \det(h_{ab})$, and R is the three-dimensional Ricci scalar.

We note that there exists a critical field value $\phi_c^2 = 3/4\pi G$ for which the second term in (4) diverges and the signature of the kinetic term changes its sign. While this is a crucial feature in full quantum gravity [8], it does not affect the semiclassical expansion, as will be shown below.

The semiclassical expansion proceeds by writing

$$\Psi \equiv \exp(iS) \tag{5}$$

and expanding S in powers of M:

$$S = MS_0 + S_1 + M^{-1}S_2 + \dots. \tag{6}$$

This ansatz is inserted into (4), and equal powers of M are compared. The denominator in the second term is handled by expanding

$$\left(1 - \frac{\phi^2}{24M}\right)^{-1} = 1 + \frac{\phi^2}{24M} + \left(\frac{\phi^2}{24M}\right)^2 + \dots, \tag{7}$$

and one recognises explicitly that the pole does not present any problem in the semiclassical expansion.

The highest order in the semiclassical expansion is M^2, and it leads to the condition that S_0 depend on the three-metric only. The next order (M) yields the Hamilton-Jacobi equation for gravity *alone*,

$$-\frac{3\sqrt{h}}{16}\left(\frac{\delta S_0}{\delta\sqrt{h}}\right)^2 + \frac{1}{2\sqrt{h}}\tilde{h}_{ac}\tilde{h}_{bd}\frac{\delta S_0}{\delta h_{ab}}\frac{\delta S_0}{\delta h_{cd}} - 2\sqrt{h}(R - 2\Lambda) = 0. \tag{8}$$

Each solution of this equation describes a family of solutions to the classical equations of motion (the vacuum Einstein equations), i.e., a family of classical spacetimes. We shall choose a special solution which corresponds to De Sitter spacetime being foliated into flat spatial slices, i.e., we consider regions of configuration space where $R = 0$. Looking thus for a solution of (8) which depends only on the three-dimensional volume, one finds

$$S_0 = \pm 8\sqrt{\frac{\Lambda}{3}}\int\sqrt{h}d^3x. \tag{9}$$

In the following we shall choose the solution with the minus sign. It can be easily seen that (9) leads to an exponential expansion for the scale factor a

$(\sqrt{h} \equiv a^3)$, since

$$\frac{\partial}{\partial t}\sqrt{h} \equiv \int d^3y \frac{\delta\sqrt{h}(\mathbf{x})}{\delta\tau(\mathbf{y})} = \sqrt{3\Lambda h} \Rightarrow a(t) = e^{\sqrt{\frac{\Lambda}{3}}t} \equiv e^{H_0 t}. \qquad (10)$$

Note that the local "WKB time" $\tau(\mathbf{x})$ follows from S_0 according to

$$\frac{\delta}{\delta\tau(\mathbf{x})} \equiv -\frac{3\sqrt{h}}{8}\frac{\delta S_0}{\delta\sqrt{h}}\frac{\delta}{\delta\sqrt{h}} \equiv \sqrt{3h\Lambda}\frac{\delta}{\delta\sqrt{h}}. \qquad (11)$$

Note also that a is chosen here to be dimensionless.

The next order (M^0) of our approximation scheme leads to an equation involving S_1. Using the fact that S_0 does not depend on $\tilde{h}_{ab}$, one obtains

$$\frac{3i\sqrt{h}}{16}\frac{\delta^2 S_0}{\delta(\sqrt{h})^2} - \frac{3\sqrt{h}}{8}\frac{\delta S_0}{\delta\sqrt{h}}\frac{\delta S_1}{\delta\sqrt{h}} + \frac{\phi}{8}\frac{\delta S_0}{\delta\sqrt{h}}\frac{\delta S_1}{\delta\phi} - \frac{i}{2\sqrt{h}}\frac{\delta^2 S_1}{\delta\phi^2}$$
$$+\frac{1}{2\sqrt{h}}\left(\frac{\delta S_1}{\delta\phi}\right)^2 + \frac{\sqrt{h}\phi^2}{12}R + \frac{\sqrt{h}}{2}h^{ab}\phi_{,a}\phi_{,b} = 0. \qquad (12)$$

We note that terms involving $\tilde{h}_{ab}$ begin to show up only at order M^{-2}, which is one order beyond the orders discussed in this paper. This demonstrates that the influence of three-geometries which are not "tangential" to curves in configuration space is not seen in the present orders of approximation. The expansion scheme thus proceeds as in the minimally coupled case [6, 7].

Writing $\psi \equiv D[\sqrt{h}]\exp(iS_1)$ and choosing the usual prefactor equation for D [6, 7], (12) leads to

$$-i\frac{3\sqrt{h}}{8}\frac{\delta S_0}{\delta\sqrt{h}}\frac{\delta\psi}{\delta\sqrt{h}} = \mathcal{H}_m\psi, \qquad (13)$$

where $\mathcal{H}_m$ is the matter Hamiltonian density which reads explicitly

$$\mathcal{H}_m = -\frac{1}{2\sqrt{h}}\frac{\delta^2}{\delta\phi^2} - \frac{i\phi}{8}\frac{\delta S_0}{\delta\sqrt{h}}\frac{\delta}{\delta\phi} + \frac{\sqrt{h}}{2}\left(\frac{\phi^2}{6}R + h^{ab}\phi_{,a}\phi_{,b}\right). \qquad (14)$$

The left-hand side of Eq. (13) is often written as $i\delta\psi/\delta\tau$, see (11), but one must keep in mind that this notion is misleading, since the presence of such a time function would contradict the commutation relations between the Hamiltonian densities at different space points [9]. Anyway, the important equation for the following discussion is the *integrated* version of (13) along a particular choice of the slicing. This functional Schrödinger equation reads

$$i\frac{\partial\psi}{\partial t} = \int d^3x \left(-\frac{1}{2a^3}\frac{\delta^2}{\delta\phi^2} + i\phi H_0\frac{\delta}{\delta\phi} + \frac{a}{2}(\nabla\phi)^2\right)\psi \equiv H_m\psi. \qquad (15)$$

Since De Sitter space is homogeneous, it is convenient to introduce the Fourier transform of $\phi(x)$,

$$\phi(\mathbf{x}) = \int \frac{d^3k}{(2\pi)^3}\chi(\mathbf{k})e^{i\mathbf{k}\mathbf{x}} \equiv \int d^3\tilde{k}\chi_k e^{i\mathbf{k}\mathbf{x}}. \qquad (16)$$

Note that

$$\frac{\delta}{\delta\phi(\mathbf{x})} = \int d^3\tilde{k}e^{i\mathbf{k}\mathbf{x}}\frac{\delta}{\delta\chi_k} \Rightarrow \frac{\delta\chi_k}{\delta\chi_{k'}} = (2\pi)^3\delta(\mathbf{k}+\mathbf{k}'). \qquad (17)$$

Since ϕ occurs only quadratically in (15), it is suggesting to make a Gaussian ansatz for the wave functional ψ,

$$\psi[\chi_k,t] = N(t)\exp\left(-\frac{1}{2}\int d^3\tilde{k}\Omega(\mathbf{k},t)\chi_k\chi_{-k}\right). \qquad (18)$$

Such a state describes a general vacuum state (independent of any Fock space) for the scalar field in the gravitational background. Inserting (18) into (15), one immediately obtains two equations for N and Ω,

$$i\frac{\dot{N}}{N} = \frac{V}{2a^3}\int d^3\tilde{k}\Omega \equiv \frac{1}{2a^3}\mathrm{Tr}\Omega, \qquad (19)$$

$$i\dot{\Omega} = \frac{\Omega^2}{a^3} - ak^2 + 2iH_0\Omega, \qquad (20)$$

where $k \equiv |\mathbf{k}|$, and V is the space volume which is introduced for regularisation. Given an initial state ψ_0, these equations uniquely determine the state ψ for all times (we assume the normalisation $\langle\psi|\psi\rangle = 1$). Eq. (20) can easily be solved by introducing a quantity y according to

$$\Omega = -ia^3\frac{\dot{y}}{y} \tag{21}$$

which then leads to a linear equation for y,

$$\ddot{y} + H_0\dot{y} + \frac{k^2}{a^2}y = 0. \tag{22}$$

Introducing the conformal time coordinate η according to

$$dt = a(\eta)d\eta \Rightarrow a(\eta) = -\frac{1}{H_0\eta}, \quad \eta \in (0, -\infty), \tag{23}$$

and denoting derivatives with respect to η by primes, this reduces to the simple form

$$y'' + k^2y = 0. \tag{24}$$

We choose the solution

$$y(\eta) = \frac{1}{\sqrt{2k}}e^{ik\eta} \tag{25}$$

which selects the positive frequency solution $\Omega = \text{Re}\,\Omega = a^2k$. Eq. (25) corresponds to the conformal vacuum state which is known to agree with the adiabatic vacuum state in the massless limit [2].

One important point has to be emphasised. Our matter Hamiltonian (14) differs from the corresponding Hamiltonian density which is obtained by directly inserting a solution of the classical Einstein equations into (3) [10]. The reason for this discrepancy is the non-minimal coupling of ϕ to R, which couples kinetic gravitational terms to the matter field. It thus makes a difference whether gravity is described by quantum theory at a fundamental level and a semiclassical approximation is performed, or whether gravity is treated classically ab initio.

Proceeding with the expansion scheme to the next order (M^{-1}), one finds the same correction terms to the Schrödinger equation than in the minimally coupled case [6, 7]. The "corrected Schrödinger equation" thus reads (re-inserting $\hbar$)

$$i\hbar\frac{\partial\psi}{\partial t} = H_m\psi - \frac{2\pi G}{\Lambda a^3}\int d^3x\, \mathcal{H}_m^2\psi - i\hbar\frac{2\pi G}{V\Lambda a^3}\left(\frac{\partial}{\partial t}H_m\right)\psi. \qquad (26)$$

In the following we shall use these correction terms to evaluate the quantum gravity-induced correction to the expectation value (2). To this purpose we need the expectation value of the Hamiltonian density $\mathcal{H}_m$ with respect to the Gaussian state (18). With the explicit form given in (14), one finds[1]

$$\langle\mathcal{H}_m\rangle = \frac{1}{4a^3}\int d\tilde{k}\frac{|\Omega|^2}{\Omega_R} + \frac{H_0}{2}\int d\tilde{k}\frac{\Omega_I}{\Omega_R} + \frac{a}{4}\int d\tilde{k}\frac{k^2}{\Omega_R}, \qquad (27)$$

where $d\tilde{k} \equiv dk/(2\pi)^3$. Note that

$$\langle\phi^2\rangle = \int\frac{d\tilde{k}}{2\Omega_R} = 2\pi H_0^2\eta^2\int_0^\infty d\tilde{k}k = \frac{H_0^2}{4\pi^2}\int_0^\infty u\,du, \qquad (28)$$

which is formally independent of conformal time η (this is a property of the special Gaussian state chosen). This, as well as

$$\langle\mathcal{H}_m\rangle = \frac{H_0^4}{4\pi^4}\int_0^\infty u^3\,du,$$

is of course ultraviolet divergent. One thus needs a regularisation prescription to arrive at a physically sensible, finite, result. For ultraviolet regularisation the high frequency modes in (18) are important. For such modes the Hamiltonian density in [10] coincides with our Hamiltonian density. One can thus use the result for $\langle T_{\mu\nu}\rangle$ already found in [10]. However, one must keep in mind that for non-minimally coupled fields T_{00} does *not* coincide with the Hamiltonian density. In fact, one finds that

$$a^2\langle T_{00}\rangle - \langle\mathcal{H}_m\rangle = \frac{a^3 H_0^2}{4}\int\frac{d\tilde{k}}{\Omega_R} - H_0\int d\tilde{k}\frac{\Omega_I}{\Omega_R}. \qquad (29)$$

---

[1]We also take into account an imaginary part for Ω, Ω_I, since this is necessary for the dimensional regularisation of the expectation values (in dimensions away from 3 space dimensions, Ω is *complex*)

Using (20) as well as the results of [10], one has

$$\langle \phi^2 \rangle = -\frac{1}{a^3} \frac{\langle \mathcal{H}_m \rangle}{H_0^2}$$

and

$$\langle \mathcal{H}_m \rangle = -\frac{2}{3} a^3 \langle T_{00} \rangle.$$

Using (2), one eventually finds

$$\langle \mathcal{H}_m \rangle = \frac{a^3 \hbar H_0^4}{1440 \pi^2}. \tag{30}$$

Considering now the quantum-gravity induced correction terms to the functional Schrödinger equation, given in (26), one obtains from the first term a shift $\delta \epsilon$ to the expectation value (30). The second term describes a quantum gravity induced unitarity violation and will be discussed below. The shift $\delta \epsilon$ is then given by

$$\delta \epsilon = -\frac{2\pi G}{3a^3 H_0^2} \langle \mathcal{H}_m^2 \rangle. \tag{31}$$

This expression is in general utterly divergent and has to be regularised. In the present case, however, the state evolves adiabatically, i.e., the mean deviation of $\mathcal{H}_m$ can be assumed to be small: $\langle \mathcal{H}_m^2 \rangle \approx \langle \mathcal{H}_m \rangle^2$. As was mentioned above, this is the condition under which the semiclassical Einstein equations (1) are valid. This fact, together with (30), immediately leads to the result

$$\delta \epsilon \approx -\frac{2\pi G}{3a^3 H_0^2} \langle \mathcal{H}_m \rangle^2 = -\frac{2G\hbar^2 H_0^6 a^3}{3(1440)^2 \pi^3}. \tag{32}$$

It is clear that, due to the presence of $G\hbar^2$, this shift is in general very small. We emphasise that (32) is a definite prediction from the Wheeler-DeWitt equation.

We now turn to the discussion of the second correction term in (26). It contributes an imaginary part ϵ_I to the energy density, which might be interpreted as an instability of the vacuum matter state due to the emission of gravitons. This unitarity violation can be understood from the fact that the Wheeler-DeWitt equation does not obey a conservation law for a Schrödinger current, but for a Klein-Gordon current [6]. The imaginary contribution to the energy reads

$$\epsilon_I = -\frac{2\pi G\hbar}{3a^3 V H_0^2}\left\langle\frac{\partial\mathcal{H}_m}{\partial t}\right\rangle. \tag{33}$$

This can be evaluated by using the explicit expression (14) and calculating expectation values with respect to the state (18) in the same manner as above. One finds that

$$\left\langle\frac{\partial\mathcal{H}_m}{\partial t}\right\rangle = 3H_0\langle\mathcal{H}_m\rangle,$$

leading to

$$\epsilon_I = -\frac{G\hbar^2 H_0^3}{720\pi V}. \tag{34}$$

The time scale t^* of this quantum gravitational instability (the sign of ϵ_I signals that it is a *decay*) is thus given by

$$t^* = \hbar|2\epsilon_I V|^{-1} = \frac{360\pi}{G\hbar H_0^3} \sim \left(\frac{H_0^{-1}}{t_P}\right)^3 t_P, \tag{35}$$

where t_P is the Planck time. This time scale is thus huge, except if H_0^{-1} is of the order of the Planck length. Nevertheless, this correction term might have some relevance for inflationary cosmology. The reason is that in the early universe, during inflation, H_0 is supposed to be large, so that the time scale t^* may be small enough to become relevant. Specifically, if

$$10^{-34}t_P^{-1} \leq H_0 \leq 10^{-6}t_P^{-1},$$

then

$$10^{18}t_P \leq t^* \leq 10^{102}t_P.$$

Thus, t^* may be small enough to enable a "quantum gravity induced" decay of the matter state, which, in turn, may produce a mechanism for a natural exit from the inflationary stage of the universe. We note that it has also been concluded from a two-loop calculation of pure gravity that infrared effects may be responsible for such a natural exit [11].

We finally mention that the back reaction of the matter state onto the gravitational background leads to a change in the definition of semiclassical time and thus to an additional contribution to the corrected Schrödinger equation (26) [6]. The net effect of this additional term is a *change of sign* in the energy shift (32) [6], and there is no change in the unitarity violating term (34).

In conclusion, we have calculated definite predictions of quantum gravity from the Wheeler-DeWitt equation. It should be straightforward to apply this approach to other situations where the matter state evolves adiabatically with respect to the background [2]. In the general situation, however, the corrections terms in (26) must be regularised carefully. We also note that the unitarity violating contribution becomes relevant in the final stages of black hole evaporation [12].

References

[1] R. Floreanini, C. Hill, and R. Jackiw, Ann. Phys. (N.Y.) **175**, 345 (1987).

[2] N. D. Birrell and P. C. W. Davies, *Quantum fields in curved space*, Cambridge University Press (Cambridge, 1982).

[3] L. H. Ford, Ann. Phys. (N.Y.) **144**, 238 (1982).

[4] T. Padmanabhan and T. P. Singh, Class. Quantum Grav. **7**, 411 (1990); S. Habib and R. Laflamme, Phys. Rev. D **42**, 4056 (1990); J. P. Paz and S. Sinha, Phys. Rev. D **45**, 2823 (1992).

[5] C. Kiefer, Phys. Rev. D **46**, 1658 (1992).

[6] C. Kiefer, in *Canonical Gravity: From Classical to Quantum*, edited by J. Ehlers and H. Friedrich, Springer (Berlin, 1994).

[7] C. Kiefer and T. P. Singh, Phys. Rev. D **44**, 1067 (1991).

[8] C. Kiefer, Phys. Lett. B **225**, 227 (1989).

[9] D. Giulini and C. Kiefer, *Consistency of semiclassical gravity*, to appear in Class. Quantum Grav.

[10] J. Guven, B. Lieberman, and C. Hill, Phys. Rev. D **39**, 438 (1989).

[11] R. P. Woodard, *A quantum gravitational mechanism for exiting inflation*, preprint UFIFT-HEP-94-11 (1994).

[12] C. Kiefer, R. Müller, and T. P. Singh, Mod. Phys. Lett. A **9**, 2661 (1994).

Gennadi A. Sardanashvily, Editor
New Frontiers in Gravitation
Hadronic Press, Palm Harbor, FL 34682-1577, U.S.A.
ISBN 0–911767–96–7, 1996, Pages 215-225

THE DE SITTER SPACE–TIME
AS ATTRACTOR SOLUTION IN
HIGHER ORDER GRAVITY

Sabine Kluske

Universität Potsdam, Mathematisch-naturwissensch. Fakultät
D-14415 Potsdam, Germany

1. Introduction

Hermann Weyl [1] was the first to think about gravitational field equations of higher than second order: 1951 Buchdahl [2] gave a general method for deriving the field equation from a Lagrangian, written as an arbitrary invariant of the curvature tensor and its covariant derivatives up to an arbitrarily high order. He studied the example $R\Box R$. $\Box$ denotes the D'Alembertian. This example leads to a field equation of sixth order. Other generalisations of the Lagrangian are R^k, $R^k\Box R$, [3], $R\Box^k R$ and $R\frac{1}{1-\Box}R$. The example $R+aR^2 = +bR\Box R$ correspondents for finely tuned initial conditions to a cosmological solution with double inflation. The attempt to find more typical cosmological solutions with double inflations led to $R^k\Box R$ [4], [5].

This Lagrangian gives unfortunately a theory with unstable weak field behaviour. The effort to connect the gravitation theory with quantum theory leads to studies about the Lagrangian $R\frac{1}{1-\Box}R$, [6]. This Lagrangian can be approximat at the k-th step by the sum

$$\sum_{i=3D0}^{k} R\Box^i R .\tag{1.1}$$

This gives a $2k+4$-th order field equation. The Lagrangian $c_0 R + c_1 R\Box R + c_2 R\Box\Box R$ is discussed in [7]. In this paper we will ded uce the stability properties of the de Sitter solution for R^k, $R\Box^k R$

and $\sum_{i=3D0}^{k} c_i R\Box^i R.$

2. The field equation

The Lagrangian $L = 3DF(R, \Box R, \ldots, \Box^k R)$ leads to a field equation of $4k + 4$-th order in general:

$$0 = 3D \ GR^{ij} - \frac{1}{2}Fg^{ij} - G^{;ij} + g^{ij}\Box G +$$

$$+ \sum_{A=3D1}^{k} \frac{1}{2}g^{ij}\left[F_A(\Box^{A-1}R)^{;k}\right]_{;k} - F_A^{;(i}(\Box^{A-1}R)^{;j)}\tag{2.1}$$

The abbreviations are:

$$F_A := 3D \sum_{j=3DA}^{k} \Box^{j-A}\frac{\partial F}{\partial \Box^j R}\tag{2.2}$$

and

$$G := 3DF_0 .\tag{2.3}$$

The operator $\Box$ denotes the D'Alembertian, "," the partial derivation and ";" the covariant derivation. For the D-dimensional ($D = 3Dn + 1 \geq 2$) de Sitter space-time with ($H \neq 0$) we use

$$ds^2 = 3Ddt^2 - e^{2Ht}\sum_{i=3D1}^{n} (dx^i)^2.\tag{2.4}$$

The relation between H and R is

$$R = 3D - n(n+1)H^2. \tag{2.5}$$

We restrict R to the interval $R < 0$ subsequently. Other important relations are

$$R^{ij} = 3D \frac{R}{n+1} g^{ij} \tag{2.6}$$

and

$$\square^k R = 3D0 \quad \text{for} \quad k > 0. \tag{2.7}$$

We get the field equation:

$$
\begin{aligned}
0 &= 3D \ GR^{ij} - \frac{1}{2}Fg^{ij} \\
&= 3D \ g^{ij}\left(\frac{1}{n+1}RG - \frac{1}{2}F\right)
\end{aligned} \tag{2.8}
$$

for the de Sitter space-time.

If we choose the Lagrangian $(-R)^u$ with $u \in \mathbf{R}$ the D-dimensional de Sitter space-time satisfies the field equation iff $u = 3D\frac{n+1}{2} = 3D\frac{D}{2}$.
An other important Lagrangian is $R\square^k R$ for $k > 0$. For this we get

$$F = 3DR\square^k R, \qquad G = 3D2\square^k R \tag{2.9}$$

and the solubility condition

$$R\square^k R = 3D\frac{u}{n+1}R\square^k R \tag{2.10}$$

for the field equation. It is automatically satisfied because of equation (2.7)

The D-dimensional $(D > 2)$ de Sitter space-time is an exact solution of the field equation following from the Lagrangian $R\square^k R$ iff $D \neq 4$ and $k > 0$.

3. The attractor property of the de Sitter space-time

We will examine the attractor property of the de Sitter space-time in the set of the spatially flat Friedmann-Robertson-Walker model (FRW model). We use the metric

$$ds^2 = 3Ddt^2 - e^{2\alpha(t)} \sum_{i=3D1}^{n} (dx^i)^2 \tag{3.1}$$

for the spatial flat FRW model. For $\alpha(t) = 3DHt$, $H > 0$ we get the de Sitter space-time metric. To find the dynamically behaviour in the neighbourhood of the de Sitter space-time we make the ansatz

$$\dot{\alpha}(t) = 3DH + \beta(t) \tag{3.2}$$

for the linearisation of the field equation. This is justified, because the field equation does not depend on α itself, but on its derivatives only ..

We say, the de Sitter space-time is an attractor solution of the differential equation if the solutions $\alpha(t)$ of the around the de Sitter space-time linearized differential equation satisfies

$$\lim_{t \to \infty} \frac{\alpha(t)}{t} = 3D\widetilde{H} = 3D\text{const} . \tag{3.3}$$

It is enough to discuss the special de Sitter space-time with $H = 3D1$, because homothetic and coordinate transformations transfer de Sitter space-time of the same dimension into each other.

4. The Lagrangian F=3D(−R)ᵘ

We will examine the attractor property of the de Sitter space-time in the set of the FRW models for the Lagrangian $(-R)^u$ with $2u = 3DD = 3Dn + 1 > 2$. From this Lagrangian follows

$$F_A = 3D0 \tag{4.1}$$

and

$$G = 3D - u(-R)..\qquad(4.2)$$

We get the field equation

$$0 = 3D - u(-R)^{u-1}R^{ij} - \frac{1}{2}g^{ij}(-R)^u + u\left[(-R)^{u-1}\right]^{;ij} - g^{ij}u\Box\left[(-R)^{u-1}\right].\qquad(4.3)$$

It is enough to examine the 00-component of the field equation, because all the other components are fulfilled, if the 00-component is fulfilled. We make the ansatz

$$\dot{\alpha}(t) = 3D1 + \beta(t)\qquad(4.4)$$

and get

$$\begin{aligned}
R^{00} &= 3D \quad -n\dot{\beta} - 2n\beta - n \\
R &= 3D \quad -2n\dot{\beta} - 2(n^2 + n)\beta - (n^2 + n) \qquad(4.5)\\
(-R)^m &= 3D \quad 2nm(n^2 + n)^{m-1}\dot{\beta} + 2m(n^2 + n)^m\beta + (n^2 + n)^m .
\end{aligned}$$

It follows the field equation

$$0 = 3D - 2n^2u(u+1)(n^2+n)^{u-2}\ddot{\beta} - 2n^3u(u-1)(n^2+n)u - 2\dot{\beta} +$$
$$+nu(2u - n - 1)(n^2 + n)^{u-1}\beta + \left(nu - \frac{1}{2}(n^2 + n)\right)(n^2 + n)^{u-1}.\qquad(4.6)$$

Using the condition $2u = 3Dn + 1$ we get

$$0 = 3D\ddot{\beta} + n\dot{\beta} .\qquad(4.7)$$

All solutions of the linearized field equation are

$$\beta(t) = 3Dc_1 + c_2 e^{-nt} .\qquad(4.8)$$

It follows

$$\alpha(t) = 3Dt + \tilde{c}_1 t + \tilde{c}_2 e^{-nt} + \tilde{c}_3\qquad(4.9)$$

and

$$\lim_{t\to\infty}\frac{\alpha(t)}{t} = 3D1 + \tilde{c}_1 .\qquad(4.10)$$

The D-dimensional de Sitter space-time is for the Lagrangian $F = 3D(-R)^{\frac{D}{2}}$ an attractor solution.

5. The Lagrangian $F=3DR\square^kR$

The Lagrangian $(-R)^{\frac{D}{2}}$ leads only to a field equation of fourth order for $D > 2$. The Lagrangian $R\square^kR$ with $k > 0$ give a field equation of higher then fourth order.

For the 00-component of the field equation we need

$$F_A = 3D\square^{k-A}R \tag{5.1}$$

and

$$G = 3D2\square^kR \tag{5.2}$$

and get

$$0 = 3D\square^kR\left(2R^{00} - \frac{1}{2}R\right) + 2n\dot{\alpha}\square^kR_{,0} +$$
$$+ \sum_{A=3D1}^{k}(\square^{k-A}R)(\square^AR) - \frac{1}{2}(\square^{k-A}R)_{,0}(\square^{A-1}R)_{,0} . \tag{5.3}$$

The ansatz

$$\dot{\alpha}(t) = 3D1 + \beta(t) \tag{5.4}$$

leads to

$$\begin{aligned} R_{00} &= 3D \quad -n\dot{\beta} - 2n\beta - n \\ R &= 3D \quad -2n\dot{\beta} - 2(n^2+n)\beta - (n^2+n) , \end{aligned} \tag{5.5}$$

and

$$\square(\square^kR) = 3D(\square^kR)_{,00} + n(\square^kR)_{,0} . \tag{5.6}$$

We get the linearized field equation

$$\square^kR = 3D(\square^kR)_{,0} . \tag{5.7}$$

For $k = 3D1$ we have

$$0 = 3D\beta^{(4)} + 2n\dddot{\beta} + (n^2 - n - 1)\ddot{\beta} + (-n^2 - n)\dot{\beta} \tag{5.8}$$

with the characteristic polynomial

$$P(t) = 3Dx^4 + 2nx^3 + (n^2 - n - 1)x^2 + (-n^2 - n)x \qquad (5.9)$$

with the roots $x_1 = 3D1$, $x_2 = 3D0$, $x_3 = 3D - n$ and $x_4 = 3D - n - 1$. We get the solutions

$$\beta(t) = 3Dc_1 + c_2 e^t + c_3 e^{-nt} + c_4 e^{-(n+1)t} \qquad (5.10)$$

and

$$\alpha(t) = 3D\tilde{c}_1 t + \tilde{c}_2 e^t + \tilde{c}_3 e^{-nt} + \tilde{c}_4 e^{-(n+1)t} \qquad (5.11)$$

and

$$\lim_{t \to \infty} \frac{\alpha(t)}{t} = 3D\infty . \qquad (5.12)$$

The D-dimensional de Sitter space-time is for the Lagrangian $R\Box^k R$ not an attractor solution of the field equation. The formula

$$0 = 3D(\Box^{k+1} R)_{,0} - \Box^{k+1} R = 3D(\Box^k R_{,0} - \Box^k R)_{,00} + n((\Box^k R)_{,0} - \Box^k R)_{,0}$$
$$(5.13)$$

for the linearized field equation for $k+1$ leads to the recursive formula for the characteristic polynomial:

characteristic polynomial for $k + 1 =$

$3Dx(x + n) \cdot$ characteristic polynomial for k .

The characteristic polynomial for k has the roots:

$$
\begin{array}{llll}
x_1 & = 3D & 1 & \text{simple} \\
x_2 & = 3D & 0 & \text{k-fold} \\
x_3 & = 3D & -n & \text{k-fold} \\
x_4 & = 3D & -n-1 & \text{simple .}
\end{array}
\qquad (5.14)
$$

We get the solutions

$$\beta(t) = 3DS(t) + T(t)e^{-nt} + c_1 e^t + c_2 e^{(-n-1)t} \qquad (5.15)$$

and

$$a(t) = 3D\tilde{S}(t) + \tilde{T}(t)e^{-nt} + \tilde{c}_1 e^t + \tilde{c}_2 e^{(-n-1)t} \tag{5.16}$$

with $S, T, \tilde{T}$ polynomials at most k-th degree and $\tilde{S}$ polynomial at most $k + 1$-th degree. For the most solutions is

$$\lim_{t \to \infty} \frac{a(t)}{t} = 3D\infty \tag{5.17}$$

fulfilled and the de Sitter space-time is not an attractor solution for the the field equation derived from Lagrangian $R\Box^k R$.

6. The generalized Lagrangian

The results of the last section have shown, that for the Lagrangian $R\Box^k R$ with $k > 1$ the de Sitter space-time is not an attractor solution. The Lagrangian $(-R)^{\frac{D}{2}}$ gives only a fourth order differential equation. We will try to answer the following question:

Are there generalized Lagrangians so, that the de Sitter space-time is an attractor solution of the field equation?

First we make the ansatz

$$F = 3D \sum_{k=3D1}^{m} c_k R\Box^k R \quad \text{with} \quad c_m \neq 0 . \tag{6.1}$$

In this case is the de Sitter space-time not an attractor solution, because for each term is $+1$ a root of the characteristic polynomial of the linearized field equation.

Now we make the ansatz

$$F = 3Dc_0(-R)^{\frac{D}{2}} + \sum_{k=3D1}^{m} c_k R\Box^k R \quad \text{with} \quad c_m \neq 0 . \tag{6.2}$$

for the generalized Lagrangian. It follows the characteristic polynomial

$$P(x) = 3Dx(x+n)\left[c_0 + \sum_{k=3D1}^{m} c_k x^{k-1}(x+n)^{k-1}(x-1)(x+n-1)\right] \quad (6.3)$$

for the linearized field equation. The solutions $x_1 = 3D0$ and $x_2 = 3D - n$ do not depend on the coefficients c_i of the Lagrangian. It is sufficient to look for the roots of the polynomial

$$P(x) = 3Dc_0 + \sum_{k=3D1}^{m} c_k x^{k-1}(x+n)^{k-1}(x-1)(x+n-1) . \quad (6.4)$$

If the above polynomial only has solutions with negative real part, then is the de Sitter space-time an attractor solution for the field equation. The transformation

$$z = 3Dx^2 + nx + \frac{n^2}{4} \quad (6.5)$$

gives

$$P(x) = 3DQ(z) = 3D$$

$$= 3Dc_0 + \sum_{k=3D1}^{m} c_k \left(z - \frac{n^2}{4}\right)^{k-1} \left(z - \frac{n^2}{4} - n - 1\right) = 3Dc_0 +$$

$$\sum_{k=3D1}^{m} c_k \left(\frac{n^2}{4}\right)^{k-1} \left(\frac{n^2}{4} - n - 1\right) + \sum_{l=3D1}^{m-1}\left[c_l + \sum_{k=3Dl+1}^{m} c_k \left(-\frac{n^2}{4}\right)^{k-l-1}\right.$$

$$\left. \cdot \left[\binom{k-1}{l-1}\left(-\frac{n^2}{4}\right) - \binom{k-1}{l}\left(\frac{n^2}{4} + n + 1\right)\right]\right] z^l + c_m z^m$$

$$= 3Dd_0 + d_1 z + \ldots + d_m z^m . \quad (6.6)$$

Now let be

$$a_{ll} = 3D\ 1 \qquad\qquad\qquad\qquad\qquad\qquad l = 3D0,\dots,m$$

$$a_{0k} = 3D\ -\left(-\frac{n^2}{4}\right)^{k-1}\left(\frac{n^2}{4}+n+1\right) \qquad k = 3D1,\dots,m$$

$$a_{lk} = 3D\ \left(-\frac{n^2}{4}\right)^{k-l-1}[\binom{k-1}{l-1}\left(-\frac{n^2}{4}\right) \tag{6.7}$$

$$\qquad\qquad -\binom{k-1}{l}\left(\frac{n^2}{4}+n+1\right)] \qquad l < k \le m$$

$$a_{kl} = 3D\ 0 \qquad\qquad\qquad\qquad\qquad\qquad \text{else .}$$

This gives the equation

$$\begin{pmatrix} d_0 \\ \vdots \\ d_m \end{pmatrix} = 3DA \begin{pmatrix} c_0 \\ \vdots \\ c_m \end{pmatrix} \qquad \text{with} \quad A \quad \text{regular .} \tag{6.8}$$

The roots of $P(x)$ have a negative real part iff the roots of $Q(z)$ are from the set

$$M := 3D\left\{ x - iy : x < \frac{n^2}{4} \wedge |y| < n\sqrt{x - \frac{n^2}{4}} \right\}. \tag{6.9}$$

If the roots z_k of the polynomial $Q(z)$ are elements of M, then the coefficients d_k are determined by

$$Q(z) = 3D \sum_{k=3D0}^{m} d_k z^k = 3D \prod_{k=3D1}^{m} (z - z_k). \tag{6.10}$$

The coefficients

$$\begin{pmatrix} c_0 \\ \vdots \\ c_m \end{pmatrix} = 3DA^{-1} \begin{pmatrix} d_0 \\ \vdots \\ d_m \end{pmatrix} \tag{6.11}$$

belongs to a Lagrangian, that gives a field equation with a de Sitter attractor solution. The above considerations have shown that for every m

there exists an example for coefficients c_k, so that the de Sitter space-time is an attractor solution for the field equation derived from the Lagrangian

$$c_0(-R)^{\frac{D}{2}} + \sum_{k=3D1}^{m} c_k R \Box^k R \quad \text{with} \quad c_m \neq 0.$$

Acknowledgements

The author would like to thank H.-J. Schmidt and K. Peters for discussions and valuable comments.

References

[1] Weyl, H.: *Sitz. Ber. Akad. Wiss. Berlin* (1918) 465

[2] Buchdahl, H.: *Acta Math.* **85** (1951) 63

[3] Amendola, L., Mayer, A. B., Cappoziello, S., Gottlöber, S., Müller, V., Occhionero, F. and Schmidt, H.-J.: *Class. Quantum Grav.* **10** (1993) L43

[4] Gottlöber, S., Müller, V. and Schmidt, H.-J.: *Astron. Nachr.* **312** (1991) 291

[5] Gottlöber, S., Schmidt, H.-J. and Starobinsky, A. A.: *Class. Quantum Grav.* **7** (1990) 893

[6] Schwarz, D. J. and Kummer, W.: *Class. Quantum Grav.* **10** (1993) 235

[7] Mayer, A. B. and Schmidt, H.-J.: *Class. Quantum Grav.* **10** (1993) 2441

Gennadi A. Sardanashvily, Editor
New Frontiers in Gravitation
Hadronic Press, Palm Harbor, FL 34682-1577, U.S.A.
ISBN 0–911767–96–7, 1996, Pages 227–242

GRAVITATIONAL–GEOMETRIC PHASES AND TRANSLATIONS

**Alfredo Macías, Eckehard W. Mielke
and Hugo A. Morales–Técotl**

Departmento de Física
Universidad Autónoma Metropolitana–Iztapalapa
P.O. Box 55-534, 09340 México D.F., MEXICO

Abstract

Recently, Anandan has pointed out that the gravitational analog of the Aharonov–Bohm effect does not work as for Yang–Mills fields because the — by definition non-degenerate — soldering form is a fake potential for spacetime translations. We show that for metric-affine gravity (MAG) theory, a true Yang–Mills like potential can be defined that does the job; it can be gauged locally to zero — in contrast to the coframe. A cosmic string is given as an example here. Furthermore, this framework seems to be helpful in the study of the loop variables of the Einstein–Cartan–Dirac theory.

1   Introduction

It was put forward by Aharonov and Bohm in the late fifties [1] that the electromagnetic potential could be the basic physically meaningful quantity needed to account for the quantum features of the electromagnetic interactions. Several different aspects of their proposal were confirmed by experiments later on (see, e.g., Ref. [19]). The phase shift in the interference pattern of matter waves now known as the *Aharonov–Bohm phase* was even measured. It is a particular case of a more general phase shift due to a *geometric phase* which is usually associated with the name of Berry, who first discussed it thoroughly [6], cf. also [9].

Along these lines much success has been achieved, not only for electromagnetism, but for the non–gravitational gauge interactions formulated a la Yang–Mills, among others, because of their renormalizability at the quantum level. This leads one to wonder whether a theory for gravity can be built up so that it admits a description in terms of Yang–Mills like potentials. Such a theory might inherit desirable properties of the Yang–Mills scheme as it is renormalizability, and, perhaps, would pave the way towards a consistent quantum theory of gravity.

In order to devise a theory of gravity resembling the Yang–Mills structure, one slightly departs from general relativity (GR). It was shown by Hehl et al. [10] that a very general framework for classical gravitation, that can be given the above structure, is the metric–affine gravity (MAG) one; GR is contained as a particular case having zero nonmetricity and torsion.

On the other hand, Anandan [2] and others [8, 17] have investigated the gravitational analog of the geometric phase both in GR and in Einstein–Cartan (EC) theory [4]. These approaches, however, involve the soldering form as a potential for translations [3, 4]. This is inconsistent with the fact that true gauge potentials can locally be gauged to zero, whereas the soldering form, by its very definition, is nondegenerate and therefore cannot. This problem can be tackled by adopting MAG as the theory for gravity. A true connection for translations, i.e. one which can locally be gauged to zero, naturally enters here [13]. We exemplify the above ideas by an exact cosmic string solution.

It is worth stressing that the approach considered here may also shed some light on the non-perturbative quantum gravity studies, mainly through the *loop variables*, where the role of self–dual connections (potentials) is crucial [5]. Furthermore, when spin-$\frac{1}{2}$ fields are coupled to gravity in the loop formulation, the classical counterpart is naturally the Einstein–Cartan–Dirac theory having non-zero torsion [15, 16]; this makes our methods potentially applicable also in that direction.

We organized our work as follows: In Sec.2, details in building up the Yang–Mills like potential for translations in the context of MAG are given. Sec.3 is concerned with Cartan's alternative point of view of forming circuits for parallel–transporting objects using a connection when there is non-zero torsion involved. The gravitational analog of the Aharonov–Bohm effect is described in Sec.4. In order to show explicitly how the ideas presented here work, we applied them to the case of a cosmic string in Sec.5. Finally, in Sec.6, a series of perspective comments is presented. Our notation is that of Ref. [10].

2 Yang–Mills potentials for local translations

We follow ideas of Cartan [7] and introduce the *generalized affine connection* $\widetilde{\widetilde{\Gamma}}$ as

$$\widetilde{\widetilde{\Gamma}} := \Gamma^{(T)\alpha} P_\alpha + \Gamma^{(L)\beta}_\alpha L^\alpha{}_\beta , \qquad (2.1)$$

which includes the true translational potential $\Gamma^{(T)\alpha}$, and the $GL(n,R)$– gauge connection $\Gamma^{(L)\beta}_\alpha$, cf.[12] and [13] for a Moebius type five–dimensional representation of the affine gauge group $A(n,R) := R^n \otimes GL(n,R)$. The operators P_α and $L^\alpha{}_\beta$ of four momentum and angular momentum, respectively, the latter including possible shear deformations, have the convential physical dimensions. The infinitesimal gauge transformations of the affine connection are of the standard Yang–Mills form

$$\delta\Gamma^{(T)\alpha} = D^{(L)}\varepsilon^\alpha + \omega_\beta{}^\alpha \Gamma^{(T)\beta} , \qquad (2.2)$$

and

$$\delta\Gamma_\alpha^{(L)\beta} = D^{(L)}\omega_\alpha{}^\beta, \qquad \cdot \ (2.3)$$

with $D^{(L)}$ as the covariant derivative constructed with the $GL(n,R)$–gauge connection and ε^α and $\omega_\alpha{}^\beta$ the infinitesimal parameters of the local affine group $A(n,R)$.

In a new nonlinear realization [11] which however, involves already a metric, the nonlinear translational connection ϑ^α and the nonlinear $GL(4,R)$ connection $\Gamma_\alpha{}^\beta$, respectively, can be defined as

$$\vartheta^\alpha := r_\beta{}^\alpha \left(\Gamma^{(T)\beta} + D^{(L)}\xi^\beta \right), \qquad (2.4)$$

and

$$\Gamma_\alpha{}^\beta := \left(r^{-1}\right)_\alpha{}^\gamma \Gamma_\gamma^{(L)\lambda} r_\lambda{}^\beta - \left(r^{-1}\right)_\alpha{}^\gamma d\, r_\gamma{}^\beta, \qquad (2.5)$$

where $r_{\alpha\beta}$ is related to the coset parameter $h_{\alpha\beta}$ of $A(n,R)/SO(1,n-1)$ via $r_{\alpha\beta} = \exp h_{\alpha\beta}$. In the following, we will interpret (2.4) and (2.5) geometrically, identifying

$$\vartheta^\alpha = e_i{}^\alpha dx^i, \qquad \qquad \Gamma_\alpha{}^\beta = \Gamma_{i\alpha}{}^\beta dx^i \qquad (2.6)$$

with the coframe and the *geometrical* connection, respectively. Eqs. (2.4, 2.5) thus establish the correspondence between the *geometrical* objects on the l.h.s. and the original Lie algebra–valued objects on the r.h.s. As a consequence, see [11], we find that the usual coframe and the connection, respectively, transform as

$$\delta\vartheta^\alpha = -u_\beta{}^\alpha \vartheta^\beta \qquad (2.7)$$

and

$$\delta\Gamma_\alpha{}^\beta = D u_\alpha{}^\beta. \qquad (2.8)$$

Now D is constructed from the nonlinear connection (2.5). Eqs. (2.7, 2.8) show that the coframe transforms as a vector, with the nonlinear Lorentz parameter $u_{\alpha\beta}$ of Ref. [11], and the connection behaves as a linear connection.

In components, our key relation (2.4) takes the form

$$\Gamma_i^{(T)\alpha} = r_\beta{}^\alpha e_i{}^\beta - D_i\xi^\alpha . \tag{2.9}$$

The condition $D_i\xi^\alpha = \delta_i^\alpha$ would identify the coset space $A(n,R)/GL(n,R) \approx R^n$ with the *cotangent space* $T^*(M_n)$. Note that we do not have to put the "Poincaré coordinates" ξ^α to zero, in order to obtain the affine gauge transformation law (2.7) of the coframe. The reason is that the local translations are now "hidden" in the invariant transformation behavior of the exterior one–forms ϑ^α under (passive) diffeomorphisms. Moreover, our approach in Ref. [13] explicitly shows of how to avoid a degenerate coframe.

Since $\xi = \xi^\alpha P_\alpha$ aquires its values in the "orbit" (coset space)

$$A(n,R)/GL(n,R) \approx R^n,$$

it can be regarded as an affine vector field (or "generalized Higgs field" according to Trautman [22]) which "hides" the action of the local translational "symmetry" $T(n,R)$. If we require, however, the condition

$$D\xi^\alpha = 0, \tag{2.10}$$

then the translational connection $\Gamma^{(T)\alpha}$, together with the coframe ϑ^α is soldered to the spacetime manifold, and the translational part of the affine gauge group is "spontaneously broken", see also [18]. We may even postulate the stronger constraint of a "zero section" vector field $\xi = 0$. Then the generalized affine connection $\tilde{\tilde{\Gamma}}$ on the affine bundle $A(M)$ reduces to the *Cartan connection* [7]

$$\bar{\bar{\Gamma}} = \vartheta^\alpha P_\alpha + \Gamma_\alpha^{(L)\beta} L^\alpha{}_\beta , \tag{2.11}$$

on the bundle $L(M)$ of linear frames. This is not anymore a connection in the usual sense.

3 Cartan circuits and their geometric interpretation

Let us first recapitulate the parallel–transport of a vector in a flat linearly connected space — that is an L_n with $R_\alpha{}^\beta = 0$. A *parallel* vector field $\zeta = \zeta^\alpha e_\alpha$ is one that satisfies the equation

$$D\zeta^\alpha = 0. \tag{3.1}$$

In an *arbitrary* linearly connected space L_n, the integrability condition for (3.1) is

$$DD\,\zeta^\alpha = R_\beta{}^\alpha\,\zeta^\beta = 0. \tag{3.2}$$

If the linear *curvature*

$$R_\alpha{}^\beta := d\Gamma_\alpha{}^\beta - \Gamma_\alpha{}^\gamma \wedge \Gamma_\gamma{}^\beta = \frac{1}{2}\,R_{\mu\nu\alpha}{}^\beta\,\vartheta^\mu \wedge \vartheta^\nu, \tag{3.3}$$

a tensor–valued two–form, does *not* vanish, we may still integrate (3.1) along a curve in order to get a vector which is parallelly transported along this curve. A standard calculation shows that if a vector ζ is parallelly transported around an *infinitesimal closed loop*, it is linearly deformed by an amount proportional to the curvature $\times$ area enclosed by the loop. The *torsion* two–form

$$T^\alpha := D\vartheta^\alpha = d\vartheta^\alpha + \Gamma_\beta{}^\alpha \wedge \vartheta^\beta = \frac{1}{2}\,T_{\mu\nu}{}^\alpha\,\vartheta^\mu \wedge \vartheta^\nu, \tag{3.4}$$

plays no role here.

In a true gauge approach to translations, the torsion does enter, however. Following [10], we generalize the parallel–transport law (3.1) along the lines of Cartan [7]. Returning to the flat L_n, we may define a *radius vector* field (or position vector field) ξ as one that satisfies the equation

$$D\xi^\alpha = \vartheta^\alpha, \tag{3.5}$$

compare with (2.4). Let us refer to (3.5) as the equation of a *Cartan transport* ('rolling without sliding', since it corresponds to $\Gamma^{(T)\alpha} = 0$). In terms of a Cartesian coordinate basis ∂_i with $\xi = \xi^i \partial_i$, Eq.(3.5) is simply $\partial_j \xi^i = \delta^i_j$. Then a solution is $\xi^i = x^i + c^i$, with c^i as a constant vector, so that ξ^i is the radius (or position) vector of x^i with respect to the shifted origin $x^i = -c^i$. In an L_n, the integrability condition for (3.5) is

$$DD\xi^\alpha - D\vartheta^\alpha = R_\beta{}^\alpha \xi^\beta - T^\alpha = 0. \tag{3.6}$$

Hence a necessary condition for the existence of global radius vector fields ξ is vanishing *translational* curvature

$$R^{(T)\alpha} := D\Gamma^{(T)\alpha} = T^\alpha - R_\beta{}^\alpha \xi^\beta. \tag{3.7}$$

Sufficient for this is zero torsion and zero linear curvature. Note that a *metric* is *not* yet involved in these considerations.

Suppose now that the torsion and curvature are non–zero and we integrate (3.5) around a closed infinitesimal curve C, with tangent vector v, beginning and ending at a point P having coordinates x^i. Let Q be any point on the curve with coordinates $x^i + y^i$ and Q' a neighboring point with coordinates $x^i + y^i + dy^i$. The equation of the curve is of the form $y^i = y^i(t)$ and the tangent vector field is $v = (dy^i/dt) \partial_i$. Then (3.5) becomes

$$\frac{d\xi^\alpha}{dt} = e_i{}^\alpha \frac{dy^i}{dt} - \Gamma_{i\beta}{}^\alpha \xi^\beta \frac{dy^i}{dt}. \tag{3.8}$$

Thus the change in ξ^α in the displacement from Q to Q' becomes

$$d\xi^\alpha = (e_i{}^\alpha dy^i - \Gamma_{i\beta}{}^\alpha \xi^\beta dy^i)|_{(x^i + y^i)}. \tag{3.9}$$

Following Cartan [7], we may interpret this equation by looking upon the tangent spaces at Q and Q' as affine spaces. Eq. (3.9) tells us that the mapping bringing the point ξ^α in the tangent space at Q to $\xi^\alpha + d\xi^\alpha$ at Q' consists of a soldered translation $e_i{}^\alpha dy^i$ and a linear deformation $-\Gamma_{i\beta}{}^\alpha dy^i \xi^\beta$.

If we now make a Taylor expansion about x^i of the functions $e_i{}^\alpha(x+y)$ and $\Gamma_{i\beta}{}^\alpha(x+y)$ and apply (3.9) to the infinitesimal displacement $x^i \to x^i + y^i$ to get $\xi^\beta(x+y) = \xi^\beta(x) + e_j{}^\beta\, y^j - \Gamma_{j\mu}{}^\beta(x)\,\xi^\mu(x)\,y^j$, then (3.9) becomes

$$d\xi^\alpha = d(e_i{}^\alpha\, y^i - \Gamma_{i\beta}{}^\alpha\, \xi^\beta\, y^i) + (T_{ij}{}^\alpha - R_{ij\beta}{}^\alpha \xi^\beta)\, y^{[i}\, dy^{j]}, \qquad (3.10)$$

where $[ij] := (ij - ji)/2$. Hence, on integrating around C, it is found that the total change in ξ^α is

$$\Delta\xi^\alpha \simeq (T_{ij}{}^\alpha - R_{ij\beta}{}^\alpha \xi^\beta)\oint_C y^{[i}\, dy^{j]}$$

$$= \frac{1}{2}(T_{ij}{}^\alpha - R_{ij\beta}{}^\alpha \xi^\beta)\int_S dy^i \wedge dy^j, \qquad (3.11)$$

where S is the two–dimensional surface element enclosed by C. The $\simeq$ sign indicates that the surface S is assumed to be so small that the components of curvature and torsion are constant in this area and can be taken in front of the surface integral. Thus, in going around the infinitesimal closed loop C, the vector ξ undergoes a translation and a linear deformation of the same order of magnitude as the area of S, the *Cartan displacement* being determined by the *torsion* and the *linear deformation* by the *curvature*. In the limiting case of vanishing curvature, our result (3.11) completely agrees with that of Ref. [14], p. 281, taking the opposite sign convention for the Riemannian curvature into account.

The Cartan transport may also be understood rather directly from the affine point of view. The affine connection $\tilde{\tilde{\Gamma}}$ and the affine curvature $\tilde{\tilde{R}}$ are defined in the standard Yang–Mills manner. If, by means of $\tilde{\tilde{\Gamma}}$, an affine vector $\tilde{\tilde{v}}$ is parallelly transported around a small closed loop, an affine transformation of $\tilde{\tilde{v}}$ is induced, the linear piece of which is determined by the linear curvature $R^{(L)}$ and the translational piece by the translational curvature $R^{(T)}$.

The affine version of (3.1) reads

$$\tilde{\tilde{D}}\tilde{\tilde{\xi}}^\alpha = d\xi^\alpha + \Gamma_\beta^{(L)\alpha} \wedge \xi^\beta + \Gamma^{(T)\alpha}$$

$$= D\xi^\alpha + \Gamma^{(T)\alpha} = 0. \qquad (3.12)$$

Parallel–transport of (3.12) along an affine tangent vector $\tilde{\tilde{y}} := \begin{pmatrix} y \\ 1 \end{pmatrix}$ of the Cartan circuit yields

$$
\begin{aligned}
\tilde{\tilde{L}}_{\tilde{\tilde{y}}} \tilde{\tilde{D}} \tilde{\tilde{\xi}}^\alpha &= \tilde{\tilde{y}} \rfloor (\tilde{\tilde{D}} \tilde{\tilde{D}} \tilde{\tilde{\xi}}^\alpha) + \tilde{\tilde{D}} (\tilde{\tilde{y}} \rfloor \tilde{\tilde{D}} \tilde{\tilde{\xi}}^\alpha) \\
&= y \rfloor (DD\xi^\alpha + R^{(T)\alpha}) = 0 ,
\end{aligned}
\tag{3.13}
$$

where $L_y := y \rfloor D + D y \rfloor$ denotes the gauge–covariant Lie derivative. Integration of the first one–form in (3.13) along a closed loop parametrized by y yields

$$
\begin{aligned}
\Delta \xi^\alpha &= -\oint_C y \rfloor (DD\xi^\alpha) = \oint_C y \rfloor R^{(T)\alpha} = \int_S R^{(T)\alpha} \\
&\simeq \frac{1}{2} (T_{ij}{}^\alpha - R_{ij\beta}{}^\alpha \xi^\beta) \int_S dy^i \wedge dy^j .
\end{aligned}
\tag{3.14}
$$

This more concise derivation yields the same result as (3.11).

4   Gravitational Aharonov–Bohm effect

This affects also the measurability of a connection. Quantum interference measurements depend on the *non–integrable phase factor*

$$
\Phi(A, \gamma) = P \, \exp[(i/\hbar) \oint A] ,
\tag{4.1}
$$

where $A = A_i^J \lambda_J dx^i$ is a Yang–Mills type connection. and P the principal value. If the loop γ lies in a field–free region, i.e., one with Yang–Mills curvature $F = dA + A \wedge A = 0$, but encloses a region with "magnetic" flux $F \neq 0$, the potential A can still be measured via the amount of phase shift for closed loops. In a nut–shell this is the meaning of the Aharonov–Bohm effect. The same would hold true for a gravitationally induced phase factor

$$
\Phi(\tilde{\tilde{\Gamma}}, \gamma) = P \, \exp[(i/\hbar) \oint (\Gamma^{(T)\alpha} P_\alpha + \Gamma^{(L)\beta}_\alpha L^\alpha{}_\beta)] ,
\tag{4.2}
$$

arising from a gauge theory of the affine group $A(4, R)$.

For a closed loop enclosing an infinitesimally small surface area S the *total phase shift* induced by the generalized affine connection $\tilde{\tilde{\Gamma}}$ is given by

$$\Delta\Phi(\tilde{\tilde{\Gamma}}, \gamma) = \frac{i}{\hbar} \int_S (R^{(T)\alpha} P_\alpha + R_\alpha^{(L)\beta} L^\alpha{}_\beta) \tag{4.3}$$

This total phase shift has the same contribution from the translational curvature as in the result (3.14) obtained from the Cartan circuit.

For a manifield Ψ carrying no $GL(4, R)$–excitations, i.e. no spin, no shear, and no dilation, we need a *closed loop* γ to detect the gravitational analog of the Aharonov–Bohm effect in a conical space, since outside the (rounded) apex of the cone there is $\Gamma^{(T)\alpha} \doteq 0$ locally. This analogy to Yang–Mills theory would break down, however, if one considered, instead of the true translational potential $\Gamma^{(T)\alpha}$, the coframe ϑ^α soldered to the spacetime manifold, as, for instance, Anandan does [3, 4]. Because the coframe is non–degenerate by definition, it could be measured even by a non–closed loop, showing its essential classical character.

Since the dimension of P_α is $2\pi\hbar/\ell$, the gravitational analog of Dirac's quantization condition would be $\Phi(\tilde{\tilde{\Gamma}}, \gamma) = (2\pi\hbar\mathcal{M}_n G/\hbar\ell c^2) = 2\pi n$, i.e. the mass would turn out to be a multiple $\mathcal{M}_n = n M_{\text{Planck}}$ of the Planck mass.

5 Cosmic string in Einstein–Cartan theory

Let us consider a cosmic string solution within the Einstein–Cartan (EC) theory. The Lagrangian four–form reads

$$V_{EC} = -\frac{1}{2\ell^2} R^{\alpha\beta} \wedge \eta_{\alpha\beta}, \tag{5.1}$$

where $\ell := \sqrt{8\pi G_N \hbar/c^3}$ is the Planck length and natural units with $\hbar = c = 1$ are used.

Variation of (5.1) plus a matter Lagrangian L with repect to the gauge potentials ϑ^α and $\Gamma^{\alpha\beta}$ yields the two Einstein–Cartan (EC) equations

$$\frac{1}{2}\eta_{\alpha\beta\gamma}\wedge R^{\beta\gamma}=\ell^2\,\Sigma_\alpha\,,\tag{5.2}$$

$$\frac{1}{2}\eta_{\alpha\beta\gamma}\wedge T^\gamma=\ell^2\,\tau_{\alpha\beta}\,,\tag{5.3}$$

where the three–forms Σ_α and $\tau_{\alpha\beta}$ are the energy–momentum and spin current of external sources.

Let us adopt the convention that x^α together with y^α are spacelike orthogonal vectors which span the (x,y)–plane orthogonal to the (t,z)–plane, the world sheet of the string. The corresponding one–forms are denoted by capital letters, i.e.

$$X:=x_\alpha\,\vartheta^\alpha\,,\qquad Y:=y_\alpha\,\vartheta^\alpha\,.\tag{5.4}$$

Moreover, the vector n^α is a timelike unit vector normal to the hypersurface with $n^\alpha\,n_\alpha=s$, the signature s of spacetime.

Following Soleng [20], we assume that the energy and spin currents "inside" the string are *constant*, i.e.

$$\Sigma_\alpha=\epsilon\,\vartheta_\alpha\wedge X\wedge Y\,,\tag{5.5}$$

$$\tau_{\alpha\beta}=\tau\eta_{\alpha\beta\gamma}\,n^\gamma\wedge X\wedge Y\,.\tag{5.6}$$

The constant parameters ϵ and τ of this *spinning string* have to be related to the exterior vacuum solution by appropriate matching conditions, see Ref. [20] for details. For the related *conical singularities* with torsion of Tod [21], ϵ and τ are *delta distributions* at the location of the string. From the specification (5.4) of the one–forms X and Y it can easily be infered that the only nonzero components are $\Sigma_{\hat0}\neq0$, $\Sigma_{\hat3}\neq0$ and $\tau_{\hat1\hat2}=-\tau_{\hat2\hat1}\neq0$, cf. Anandan [4].

The first EC field equation converts into the following condition on the *Lie dual* of the Riemann–Cartan (RC) curvature:

$$R_\alpha^\star:=\frac{1}{2}\eta_{\alpha\beta\gamma}\wedge R^{\beta\gamma}=\epsilon\ell^2\,\vartheta_\alpha\wedge X\wedge Y\quad\Rightarrow\quad R^\star:=\vartheta^\alpha\wedge R_\alpha^\star=0\,.\tag{5.7}$$

Thus the pseudo–scalar R^* vanishes. Moreover, contractions with x^α and y^α reveal that $x^{[\alpha} y^{\beta]} R_{\alpha\beta} = R_{\hat{1}\hat{2}} = -R_{\hat{2}\hat{1}} \neq 0$ are the only nonvanishing components. Consequently, a covariant expression for the solution reads

$$R^{\alpha\beta} = -\epsilon\ell^2\, x^{[\alpha} y^{\beta]}\, X \wedge Y. \tag{5.8}$$

¿From the second field equation we find for the torsion

$$T^\alpha = 2\tau\ell^2\, n^\alpha\, X \wedge Y \quad \Rightarrow \quad n_\alpha\, T^\alpha = 2s\tau\ell^2\, X \wedge Y. \tag{5.9}$$

Thus, only $T^{\hat{0}} \neq 0$ is nonvanishing, cf. Ref. [4]. Since n^α is orthogonal to x^α and y^α, the spinning string solution has the property that

$$DX = x_\alpha\, T^\alpha = 0 \quad \text{and} \quad DY = y_\alpha\, T^\alpha = 0. \tag{5.10}$$

Let us check the validity of the first and second Bianchi identity

$$DT^\alpha \equiv R_\beta{}^\alpha \wedge \vartheta^\beta \quad \text{and} \quad DR_\alpha{}^\beta \equiv 0, \tag{5.11}$$

of RC spacetimes. For the curvature we find

$$R_\beta{}^\alpha \wedge \vartheta^\beta = -\frac{\epsilon\ell^2}{2}(x^\alpha Y \wedge X \wedge Y - y^\alpha X \wedge X \wedge Y) = 0. \tag{5.12}$$

Due to (5.10) the second Bianchi identity is identically satisfied, whereas the first identity provides us with a condition for the normal vector field:

$$DT^\alpha = 2\tau\ell^2\, Dn^\alpha \wedge X \wedge Y = 0, \tag{5.13}$$

cf. Eq. (4.9) of Ref. [21].

Remembering that $N^\alpha = n \rfloor \vartheta^\alpha$ is the ADM lapse and shift vector in the (3+1)–decomposition of the ADM formalism, the metric and the corresponding coframe can now explicitly be obtained by applying a finite boost to the usual conical metric of the cosmic string, cf.[4]

$$\begin{aligned} \vartheta^{\hat{0}} &= dt + 8\pi Gs\rho^{*2}[1 - \cos(\rho/\rho^*)]d\phi \\ \vartheta^{\hat{1}} &= d\rho, \qquad \vartheta^{\hat{2}} = \rho^* \sin(\rho/\rho^*)d\phi, \qquad \vartheta^{\hat{3}} = dz. \end{aligned} \tag{5.14}$$

Since $R_{\hat{1}\hat{2}} = -R_{\hat{2}\hat{1}} \neq 0$ are the only nonvanishing curvature components, we can make the ansatz

$$\Gamma := x^\alpha y^\beta \Gamma_{\alpha\beta} = f(\rho)Y \qquad (5.15)$$

for the RC connection and find from (5.8) the condition

$$x^\alpha y^\beta R_{\alpha\beta} = d\Gamma = -\epsilon \ell^2 X \wedge Y = f'(\rho)X \wedge Y + f(\rho)dY = -\epsilon \ell^2 X \wedge Y . \qquad (5.16)$$

The term nonlinear in the connection vanishes for this ansatz. Since the torsion of the string has only a component in the normal direction, we can use

$$y^\alpha T_\alpha = dY + \Gamma \wedge X = 0 . \qquad (5.17)$$

in order to substitute dY. Thereby we obtain the nonlinear differential equation

$$f'(\rho) + f^2(\rho) = -\epsilon \ell^2 \qquad (5.18)$$

which has the solution

$$f(\rho) = \rho^* \cot(\rho/\rho^*) \qquad (5.19)$$

where $\rho^* := \ell\sqrt{\epsilon}$. For $Y = \rho^* \sin(\rho/\rho^*)d\phi$, cf. (5.14), the ansatz (5.15) yields explicitly

$$\Gamma^{\hat{1}\hat{2}} = \cos(\rho/\rho^*)d\phi = -\Gamma^{\hat{2}\hat{1}} , \qquad (5.20)$$

cf. Eq. (26) of Ref. [4].

In order to obtain another RC string solution, we alternatively tried the ansatz

$$T^\alpha = \frac{2\tau}{\epsilon} R_\beta{}^\alpha \xi^\beta \qquad (5.21)$$

for the torsion, cf. Ref. [13] and [10]. Due to the EC equations, the spin current is now determined by the RC curvature via

$$\tau_{\alpha\beta} = \frac{\tau}{\epsilon \ell^2} \eta_{\alpha\beta\gamma} R_\mu{}^\gamma \xi^\mu . \qquad (5.22)$$

¿From the first and second Bianchi identity (5.11) we find

$$DT^\alpha = \frac{2\tau}{\epsilon} R_\beta{}^\alpha D\xi^\beta \equiv R_\beta{}^\alpha \wedge \vartheta^\beta . \qquad (5.23)$$

Provided the curvature of the solution is non–degenerate, this relation can be solved for the coframe as

$$\vartheta^\alpha = \frac{2\tau}{\epsilon} D\xi^\alpha = \frac{2\tau}{\epsilon} r_\beta{}^\alpha Dx^\beta . \qquad (5.24)$$

Thus for $\epsilon = 2\tau$ the translational connection $\Gamma^{(T)\alpha} = \vartheta^{(T)\alpha} - D\xi^\alpha$ together with its translational curvature $R^{(T)\alpha}$, see (3.7), will vanish and thus give no contribution to a Cartan circuit or the translational part of the gravitationally induced phase factor (4.3).

6 Discussion

We have shown a way out to the problem arising when considering, as Anandan did [3, 4], the coframe as the potential for translations in spacetime. Adopting MAG, our approach neatly provides a true translational potential. It remains to be proved what is the precise relation between Anandan's results [4] and ours. Since Anandan's are approximate, we expect our analysis to be rather powerful.

As in the case of the cosmic string worked out here in Sec.5 and by Anandan [4], the loops we looked at were spacelike even though the analysis enables one to take arbitrary curves (Sec.3). Future research should clarfy whether the description given here allows a better understanding of the loop variables for the non–perturbative quantum gravity program of Ref. [5, 15, 16].

Acknowledgments

We cordially thank Friedrich W. Hehl for very useful hints to the literature. This work was partially supported by CONACyT Grant No. 3544–E9311.

References

[1] Y. Aharonov and D. Bohm, *Phys. Rev.* (1959) 485.

[2] J. Anandan, *Nature* **360** (1992) 307.

[3] J. Anandan: "Remarks concerning the geometries of gravity and gauge fields", in: *Directions in General Relativity*, Proc. of the 1993 Intern. Symp., Maryland, Vol. 1, Papers in honor of Charles Misner. B.L. Hu, M.P. Ryan Jr., and C.V. Vishveshwara, eds. (Cambridge University Press, Cambridge 1993) p. 10.

[4] J. Anandan, *Phys. Lett.* **A195** (1994) 284.

[5] A. Ashtekar: *Lectures on Non-perturbative Canonical Gravity* (World Scientific, Singapore 1991).

[6] M.V. Berry, *Proc. R. Soc.* (London) **A392** (1984) 45.

[7] É. Cartan: *On Manifolds with an Affine Connection and the Theory of General Relativity*, English translation of the French original (Bibliopolis, Napoli 1986); for a book review, see F.W. Hehl, *Gen. Rel. Grav.* **21** (1989) 315.

[8] A. Corichi and M. Pierri: "Gravity and geometric phases", University of Pennsylvania preprint 1994.

[9] R. Dandoloff, *Phys. Lett.* **A139** (1989) 19.

[10] F.W. Hehl, J.D. McCrea, E.W. Mielke, and Y. Ne'eman, *Phys. Rep.* (1995, in press).

[11] A. López–Pinto, A. Tiemblo and R. Tresguerres: "Ordinary matter in nonlinear affine gauge theories" preprint IAMFF 94/4.

[12] E.W. Mielke: *Geometrodynamics of Gauge Fields* — On the geometry of Yang-Mills and gravitational gauge theories (Akademie–Verlag, Berlin 1987).

[13] E.W. Mielke, J.D. McCrea, Y. Ne'eman, and F.W. Hehl, *Phys. Rev.* D48 (1993) 673–679,

[14] C.W. Misner, K.S. Thorne, and J.A. Wheeler: *Gravitation* (W.H. Freeman & Co., San Francisco 1973).

[15] H.A. Morales–Técotl and G. Esposito, *Nuovo Cim.* B109 (1994) 973.

[16] H.A. Morales–Técotl and C. Rovelli, *Phys. Rev. Lett.* 72 (1994) 3642.

[17] B. Reznik: "Gravitational analog of the Aharonov–Casher effect", Vancouver preprint TP-94-0009.

[18] G. Sardanashvily and M. Gogbersvily, *Mod. Phys. Lett.* A2 (1987) 609.

[19] A. Shapere and F. Wilczek, eds.: *Geometric Phases in Physics* (World Scientific, Singapore 1989).

[20] H.H. Soleng, *Gen. Rel. Grav.* 24 (1992) 111.

[21] K.P. Tod, Class. *Quantum Grav.* 11 (1994) 1331.

[22] A. Trautman: "On the structure of the Einstein–Cartan equations", in *Symposia Mathematica*, Vol. 12 (Academic Press, London 1973), p. 139.

Gennadi A. Sardanashvily, Editor
New Frontiers in Gravitation
Hadronic Press, Palm Harbor, FL 34682-1577, U.S.A.
ISBN 0–911767–96–7, 1996, Pages 243–255

PROJECTIVELY INVARIANT METRIC–AFFINE MODELS OF GRAVITY

**Alfredo Macías, Eckehard W. Mielke
Hugo A. Morales–Técotl**

Departmento de Física
Universidad Autónoma Metropolitana–Iztapalapa
P.O. Box 55-534, 09340 México D.F., MEXICO

and Romualdo Tresguerres

IMAFF, Consejo Superior de Investigaciones Científicas
Serrano 123, Madrid 28006, Spain

Abstract

The projective transformations of nonlinear curvature scalar Lagrangians are analyzed within the metric–affine framework. It is shown that only the Weyl covector piece of the nonmetricity and the vector part of the torsion are affected by this transformations, but in an opposite manner. As an application, we consider a generalized topological 3D gravity by supplementing a *translational* Chern–Simons term. We obtain an exact solution, which implies that, for very large times, Poincaré invariance becomes exact.

1 Introduction

In this paper, we consider the relation between torsion and nonmetricity in the framework of the scalar–tensor theories of gravity, in particular of the Jordan–Brans–Dicke (JBD) one [2]. We analyze in detail the projective transformations of the linear connection and show that only the vector part of the torsion and the Weyl covector piece of the nonmetricity are affected by this projective transformations. It turns out that there is a relation only between this two irreducible pieces of the torsion and of the nonmetricity fields, respectively, but not between the total fields. For nonlinear curvature scalar Lagrangians, this relation represents only a particular solution of the field equations, but not a general one.

Moreover, we look at a generalized topological 3D gravity constructed by means of a translational Chern-Simons term added to the curvature scalar Lagrangian of the theory. An exact solution of the field equations, with an exponentially decaying term in the conformal factor, see Eq. (6.2), is obtained. This implies that, without breaking the affine symmetry, Poincaré invariance turns to be an approximate symmetry of the solution. For very large times it even becomes exact.

The plan of the paper is as follows: Sec.2 deals with projective transformation of torsion and of the Weyl covector. Purely curvature scalar Lagrangians in the metric-affine gravity (MAG) are considered in Sec.3. In Sec.4 we derive a formal solution of the second field equation. Within this projective framework, the generalized topological 3D gravity is considered in Sec.5 as an application . In Sec.6 we present a solution to the corresponding field equations and discuss its properties. In an outlook (Sec.7) possible relations to a Higgsless standard model of elementary particle interactions are pointed out. We will use the notation of Ref. [6].

2 Projectively deformed torsion and Weyl covector

Let us consider a *projective* transformation of the linear $GL(n, R)$–valued connection

$$\Gamma_\alpha{}^\beta \quad \rightarrow \quad \Gamma_\alpha{}^\beta = \Gamma_\alpha{}^\beta + \delta_\alpha^\beta \, P \tag{2.1}$$

where P is a one–form. Under a projective transformation the torsion $T^\alpha :=$ $d\vartheta^\alpha + \Gamma_\beta{}^\alpha \wedge \vartheta^\beta$ changes as follows

$$\overline{T}^\alpha = T^\alpha + P\delta_\beta^\alpha \wedge \vartheta^\beta = T^\alpha + P \wedge \vartheta^\alpha. \tag{2.2}$$

Then the torsion one–form $T := e_\alpha \rfloor T^\alpha$ transforms as

$$\overline{T} = T + (1-n)P, \tag{2.3}$$

whereas the *axial torsion* $(n-3)$–form

$$A := e_\alpha \rfloor {}^*T^\alpha = {}^*(T^\alpha \wedge \vartheta_\alpha) \tag{2.4}$$

is projectively invariant, i.e. $\overline{A} = A$, due to $\vartheta^\alpha \wedge \vartheta_\alpha = 0$.

The *Weyl one-form* $Q := (1/n)g^{\alpha\beta} Q_{\alpha\beta}$, where $Q_{\alpha\beta} := -Dg_{\alpha\beta}$ is the *nonmetricity*, transforms as

$$\overline{Q} = Q + 2P. \tag{2.5}$$

With these formulas it is straightforward to show that the combination $2T +$ $(n-1) Q$, which will arise in our field equations, is a *projective invariant*.

There are two special cases for which torsion or the Weyl covector can be projectively deform to zero:

$$P = \frac{1}{(n-1)}T : \quad \begin{cases} \overline{Q} = Q + \frac{2}{n-1}T, \\[2mm] \overline{T} = 0, \end{cases} \tag{2.6}$$

and

$$P = -\frac{1}{2}Q : \quad \begin{cases} \overline{Q} = 0, \\[2mm] \overline{T} = T + \frac{n-1}{2}Q. \end{cases} \tag{2.7}$$

From Eqs. (2.6) and (2.7) it can be seen that for these particular choices the vector piece of the torsion and the Weyl covector piece of the nonmetricity transform opposite to each other.

The so-called λ-transformations of Einstein are special projective transformation for which $P = d\lambda$ is an exact form. Moreover, for the generalized conformal change of the metric $g \to \tilde{g} = \Omega^L g$, the connection contains a projective transformation $P = -Cd\ln\Omega$ of similar nature, cf. Smalley [14] and Ref. [6] for details.

3 Truncated metric–affine gravity

In this section we study curvature scalar Lagrangians in the framework of MAG. The curvature scalar is given by the zero–form

$$R := e_\alpha \rfloor e_\beta \rfloor R^{\alpha\beta} \,, \tag{3.1}$$

where $R_\alpha{}^\beta := d\Gamma_\alpha{}^\beta + \Gamma_\gamma{}^\beta \wedge \Gamma_\alpha{}^\gamma$ is the curvature two–form. Since it involves only *the antisymmetric part* of the linear curvature, it is a projective invariant, i.e. $\bar{R} = R$, as was already known to Einstein. We use the notation $\eta := (1/n!)\,\eta_{\alpha_1\cdots\alpha_n}\,\vartheta^{\alpha_1} \wedge \cdots \wedge \vartheta^{\alpha_n}$, $\eta_\alpha := e_\alpha \rfloor \eta$, $\eta_{\alpha\beta} := e_\beta \rfloor \eta_\alpha$, with $\rfloor = interior\ \ product$ and $\eta_{\alpha_1\cdots\alpha_n} := \sqrt{|\det g_{\mu\nu}|}\,\epsilon_{\alpha_1\cdots\alpha_n}$.

For the variational proceedure it is more convenient to use the n–form

$$
\begin{aligned}
\mathcal{R} := R\eta &= e_\beta \rfloor R^{\alpha\beta} \wedge \eta_\alpha + e_\alpha \rfloor (e_\beta \rfloor R^{\alpha\beta} \wedge \eta) \\
&= -R^{\alpha\beta} \wedge \eta_{\alpha\beta} \,.
\end{aligned}
\tag{3.2}
$$

Let us consider a gravitational model, which depends only via an arbitrary function on the scalar curvature, or on the n–form $\mathcal{R}$, for later convenience:

$$V = V(\mathcal{R}) \,. \tag{3.3}$$

Then the gravitational field momenta, cf.[6], read

$$M^{\alpha\beta} := -2\frac{\partial V}{\partial Q_{\alpha\beta}} = 0 \ , \qquad H_\alpha := -\frac{\partial V}{\partial T^\alpha} = 0, \tag{3.4}$$

$$H^\alpha{}_\beta := -\frac{\partial V}{\partial R_\alpha{}^\beta} = -\frac{\partial V}{\partial \mathcal{R}}\frac{\partial \mathcal{R}}{R_\alpha{}^\beta} = \frac{\partial V}{\partial \mathcal{R}}\,\eta^\alpha{}_\beta \,. \tag{3.5}$$

Since in our Lagrangian (3.3) we have no *explicit* dependence on torsion and nonmetricity, we have obtained a *truncated* MAG model of gravity.

The Noether identities show that the zeroth–field equation, which follows from the variation of the metric, is redundant. Using the nonlinear realization [9], one can see that the metric does not contain dynamical degrees of freedom.

Since $H_\alpha = 0$ and $M^{\alpha\beta} = 0$, the *first field equation* takes the form

$$E_\alpha = e_\alpha \rfloor V + (e_\alpha \rfloor R_\beta{}^\gamma) \wedge V' \eta^\beta{}_\gamma = \Sigma_\alpha, \tag{3.6}$$

where Σ_α is the energy-momentum current of matter fields. We use the abbreviation $V' = (\partial V/\partial R)$. It is interesting to note that the zero–form V' will simulate a Brans–Dicke type scalar in the solutions.

For the trace we find in vacuum

$$\vartheta^\alpha \wedge E_\alpha = nV + 2R_\beta{}^\gamma \wedge \eta^\beta{}_\gamma V' = nV - 2RV' = 0. \tag{3.7}$$

This is an Euler type equation for homogeneous functions which, for $R \neq 0$, has the solution

$$V = R^{n/2} \, \eta. \tag{3.8}$$

For all other Lagrangians including Einstein's, the trace (3.7) is not automatically satisfied but amounts to a constraint on the space of solutions.

4 Formal solution of the second Yang–Mills type equation

The second Yang–Mills type field equation takes the form

$$DH^\alpha{}_\beta = \Delta^\alpha{}_\beta, \tag{4.1}$$

where $\Delta^\alpha{}_\beta$ is the hypermomentum of matter fields. Insertion of the field momentum (3.4), (3.5) and employing the identity $D\eta_{\alpha\beta} = -(n/2)\, Q \wedge \eta_{\alpha\beta} +$

$T^\gamma \wedge \eta_{\alpha\beta\gamma}$, cf.[6], yields

$$DH^\alpha{}_\beta = DV' \wedge \eta^\alpha{}_\beta + V' \left(Q^{\mu\alpha} \wedge \eta_{\mu\beta} - \frac{n}{2} Q \wedge \eta^\alpha{}_\beta + T^\gamma \wedge \eta^\alpha{}_{\beta\gamma} \right) = \Delta^\alpha{}_\beta .$$

(4.2)

The symmetric part of this equation reads

$$^\dagger Q^\mu{}_{(\alpha} \wedge \eta_{\mu|\beta)} V' = \Delta_{(\alpha\beta)} ,$$

(4.3)

which in vacuum can be satisfied by a vanishing tracefree nonmetricity $^\dagger Q_{\alpha\beta} := Q_{\alpha\beta} - g_{\alpha\beta} Q = 0$.

Note that the tracefree nonmetricity is projectively invariant. In order to solve of the antisymmetric part of this field equation, we employ the following identities:

$$Q^\gamma{}_\delta \wedge \vartheta^\delta \wedge \eta_{\alpha\beta\gamma} = n \, Q \wedge \eta_{\alpha\beta} + 2 Q^\gamma{}_{[\alpha} \wedge \eta_{\beta]\gamma} ,$$

(4.4)

$$\vartheta^\gamma \wedge \eta_{\alpha\beta\gamma} = \vartheta^\gamma \wedge e_\gamma \rfloor \eta_{\alpha\beta} = (n-2)\eta_{\alpha\beta} .$$

(4.5)

For $n \neq 2$, the antisymmetric part of (4.2) reads

$$\left[\frac{1}{n-2} DV' \wedge \vartheta^\gamma + V' \left(T^\gamma - \frac{1}{2} Q^\gamma{}_\delta \wedge \vartheta^\delta \right) \right] \wedge \eta_{\alpha\beta\gamma} = \Delta_{[\alpha\beta]} .$$

(4.6)

In the following we will associate with the zero–form V', the dilaton weight $\omega_{V'} = 0$ in order to have $DV' = dV' - (n\omega_{V'}/2)QV' = dV'$.

For tracefree nonmetricity and in vacuum, Eq. (4.6) is necessarily fulfilled by

$$T^\gamma - \frac{1}{2} Q \wedge \vartheta^\gamma = \frac{1}{n-2} \vartheta^\gamma \wedge d\ln V' \quad .$$

(4.7)

This relation implies that $T^\alpha \wedge \vartheta_\alpha = 0$ which means that the axial torsion (2.4) is zero, whereas for the vector torsion one-form $T := e_\alpha \rfloor T^\alpha$ we find the relation

$$T + \frac{n-1}{2} Q = \frac{n-1}{n-2} d\ln V' .$$

(4.8)

In two dimensions our model degenerates. Due to (4.6) we have $d\ln V' = 0$ and, after multiplication with $(n-2)$, Eq. (4.8) leaves torsion and Weyl covector undetermined.

Not only the axial torsion ${}^{(3)}T^\alpha := (-1)^s \frac{1}{3} *(\vartheta^\alpha \wedge {}^*A)$ is vanishing in our model, but also the irreducible tensor torsion ${}^{(1)}T^\alpha := T^\alpha - {}^{(2)}T^\alpha - {}^{(3)}T^\alpha = T^\alpha - \frac{1}{n-1}\vartheta^\alpha \wedge T$. Since the righthand side of (4.8) is projectively invariant, we can apply the results of the previous section and find

$$T + \frac{n-1}{2}Q = T + \frac{n-1}{2}Q = \frac{n-1}{n-2}d\ln V', \qquad (4.9)$$

i.e. that the lefthand side is also projective invariant. It is easily to be seen that, also in this case, the torsion or Weyl covector can be projectively deformed to zero, cf. (2.6) and (2.7). Actually, the same results would arise, if we had set torsion or Weyl covector to zero by hand in (4.8). The projective method, however, utilizes the invariance of the Lagrangian. Observe that in three dimensions, the projectively deformed torsion or Weyl covector is given by exactly the same expression, namely $2d\ln V'$.

5   3D topological MAG

In three dimensions, let us add to (3.3) the translational Chern-Simons [4] term

$$C_T = \frac{1}{2\ell^2}\,\vartheta_\alpha \wedge T^\alpha = \frac{1}{2\ell^2}\,g_{\alpha\beta}\,\vartheta^\alpha \wedge T^\beta, \qquad (5.1)$$

which together with $C_{RR}^\dagger$, cf. Ref. [6], is also projectively invariant. Thus we will consider the Lagrangian

$$V_\infty = V(\mathcal{R}) + \Theta_T\,C_T, \qquad (5.2)$$

where ℓ is the Plank length and Θ_T is a constant. It generalizes the model of Ref. [1] and [15] by admitting nonlinear curvature scalar Lagrangians. Since C_T will simulate a cosmological term in the solutions, we do not need to include an explicit cosmological term $\Lambda\eta$ in the Lagrangian. By variation with respect to ϑ^α and $\Gamma_\alpha{}^\beta$, we obtain as 3D field equations

$$E_\alpha - \frac{\Theta_T}{\ell^2}\left(g_{\alpha\beta}T^\beta + \frac{1}{2}\vartheta^\beta \wedge Q_{\alpha\beta}\right) = \Sigma_\alpha, \qquad (5.3)$$

$$DH^\alpha{}_\beta - \frac{\Theta_T}{2\ell^2} g_{\beta\gamma} \vartheta^\alpha \wedge \vartheta^\gamma = \Delta^\alpha{}_\beta. \qquad (5.4)$$

From (5.4) we can infer again (4.3), whereas (4.7) converts into

$$T^\alpha = \frac{1}{2} Q \wedge \vartheta^\alpha + \vartheta^\alpha \wedge d\ln V' - (-1)^s \frac{\Theta_T}{2\ell^2 V'} \eta^\alpha, \qquad (5.5)$$

where we have used the normalization $\eta_{\mu\nu\gamma} \eta^{\alpha\beta\gamma} = (-1)^s 2\delta^\alpha_{[\mu}\delta^\beta_{\nu]}$, where s is the signature of the space–time, see the Appendix of Ref.[1].

Thus the axial torsion term reads $A = {}^*(T^\alpha \wedge \vartheta_\alpha) = (3\Theta_T/2\ell^2 V')$, whereas the vector torsion obeys the same relation as in (4.7).

Inserting (5.5) into (5.3) yields

$$E_\alpha - \frac{\Theta_T}{\ell^2} \vartheta_\alpha \wedge d\ln V' - (-1)^s \frac{\Theta_T^2}{2\ell^4 V'} \eta_\alpha = \Sigma_\alpha + (-1)^s \frac{\Theta_T}{2\ell^2 V'} \eta_{\alpha\beta\gamma} \Delta^{\beta\gamma}, \qquad (5.6)$$

which is the 3D generalization of Einstein's equation. As already stressed, the translational Chern–Simons terms is sufficient for inducing an effective cosmological term in this equation, which is proportional to Θ_T^2. Observe that the energy–momentum current Σ_α is not the only source for the first field equation but that also the Lie–dual hypermomentum, i.e. the spin current $\tau^{*\alpha} := (1/2)\, \eta^{\alpha\beta\gamma} \Delta_{[\beta\gamma]} = (1/2)\, \eta^{\alpha\beta\gamma} \tau_{\beta\gamma}$, contributes in a Belinfante–Rosenfeld type fashion.

In particular, let us consider the quadratic vacuum Lagrangian

$$V = \frac{1}{2\ell} \mathcal{R} + a_6 \, {}^{(6)}W_\alpha{}^\beta \wedge {}^*R_\beta{}^\alpha + \Theta_T C_T, \qquad (5.7)$$

which consist of the Einstein-Cartan term $\mathcal{R}$, the translational Chern-Simons term C_T, and a quadratic curvature term involving the scalar piece ${}^{(6)}W_\alpha{}^\beta$ in the irreducible decomposition of the curvature, cf.[11]. In (5.4) we have

$$H^\alpha{}_\beta := -\frac{\partial V}{\partial R_\alpha{}^\beta} = \frac{1}{2\ell} \eta^\alpha{}_\beta - 2a_6 \, {}^{*(6)}W^\alpha{}_\beta, \qquad (5.8)$$

which means that $V' = 1/2\ell$ is a constant in the following.

6 Exact 3D solution

The metric part of the solution of (5.3), and (5.4) cum (5.8) describes a *conformal de Sitter* spacetime. In terms of the anholonomic metric tensor $g_{\alpha\beta} = diag(- + +)$, i.e. $s = 1$, and the one–form basis is given by

$$\vartheta^{\hat{0}} = \Omega\sqrt{1 - \Lambda_{\text{eff}} \, r^2} \, d\tau \,, \qquad \vartheta^{\hat{1}} = \frac{\Omega}{\sqrt{1 - \Lambda_{\text{eff}} \, r^2}} \, dr \,, \qquad \vartheta^{\hat{2}} = \Omega \, r \, d\phi \,. \quad (6.1)$$

The conformal factor reads

$$\Omega = \left[1 + \lambda\sqrt{1 - \Lambda_{\text{eff}} \, r^2} \, \exp\left(-\sqrt{\Lambda_{\text{eff}}}\,\tau\right)\right]^{-1} \,, \qquad (6.2)$$

where λ is a dimensionless parameter. The solution is well defined in the domain
$$-\infty < \tau < \infty, \quad 0 < r < (1/\sqrt{\Lambda_{\text{eff}}}), \quad 0 < \phi \le 2\pi.$$
The effective cosmological constant reads

$$\Lambda_{\text{eff}} := \frac{3k^2 \left(k\ell - 3\Theta_T\right)}{4\left(\Theta_T - 3k\ell\right)} \,. \qquad (6.3)$$

It is induced by the axial part of the torsion, since

$$T^\alpha = \frac{1}{2} Q \wedge \vartheta^\alpha - k\eta^\alpha \,. \qquad (6.4)$$

Consequently, the tensor part of the torsion vanishes, whereas the vector piece is proportional to the Weyl covector, and a constant axial torsion remains, respectively,

$$^{(1)}T^\alpha = 0, \qquad ^{(2)}T^\alpha = \frac{1}{2} Q \wedge \vartheta^\alpha, \qquad ^{(3)}T^\alpha = -k\eta^\alpha \,. \qquad (6.5)$$

The constant a_6 relates to the axial torsion constant k as follows:

$$a_6 = \frac{3k^2\ell^2 - 4k\ell\Theta_T + \Theta_T^2}{8k^3\ell^2\Theta_T} \,. \qquad (6.6)$$

The nonmetricity reduces to the Weyl covector Q which is not determined by the field equations, i.e. $Q_{\alpha\beta} = {}^{(4)}Q_{\alpha\beta} = g_{\alpha\beta}\,Q$.

If we decompose the whole curvature into irreducible pieces [11], we find that the only nonvanishing contribution to the antisymmetric part $R_{[\alpha\beta]}$ is the scalar piece ${}^{(6)}W_{\alpha\beta}$. It has the form

$$R_{[\alpha\beta]} = {}^{(6)}W_{\alpha\beta} = -\left(\Lambda_{\text{eff}} + \frac{k^2}{4}\right)\vartheta_\alpha \wedge \vartheta_\beta\,. \tag{6.7}$$

Furthermore, only one irreducible piece of the symmetric part is nonzero, namely

$$R_{(\alpha\beta)} = {}^{(4)}Z_{(\alpha\beta)} = \frac{1}{3}g_{\alpha\beta}\,R_\gamma{}^\gamma = \frac{1}{2}g_{\alpha\beta}\,dQ\,. \tag{6.8}$$

In the particular case when $a_6 = 0$, Eq. (6.6) admits two values, namely $k = \Theta_T/\ell$ and $k = \Theta_T/3\ell$ for the axial tensor constant. In the first case, the effective cosmological constant reduces to

$$\Lambda_{\text{eff}} := \frac{3\Theta_T^2}{4\ell^2}\,. \tag{6.9}$$

In the second case, the theory trivializes, since Θ_T, and thus k and Λ_{eff} have to be put equal to zero. The solution has been tested with REDUCE 3.5 by applying the EXCALC package.

As can be seen from Eq. (6.2), there is an exponential decay with time such that the conformal field Ω is tending to one very rapidly. It is whorthwhile to note that although this solution is not the most general solution, it makes sense due to the fact that in a theory with broken projective invariance [15], the Weyl vector and the vector piece of the torsion are proportional to the gradient of the conformal factor and as it evolves with time to a constant value, the nonmetricity tends very rapidly to zero. This means that without breaking the affine symmetry, the Poincaré one turns to be an approximate symmetry of the solution. Moreover, as time goes to infinity, the time dependence disappears and the Poincaré symmetry becomes exact. This mechanism seems to be an alternative to the explicit breaking of the affine symmetry.

7 Outlook

Besides the projectively invariant Lagrangian (3.3), the relation (4.9) suggest to consider also the n–form

$$V_{\text{trQT}} := [(2T + (n-1)Q)] \wedge^* [(2T + (n-1)Q)] \qquad (7.1)$$

as a further projectively invariant gravitational Lagrangian in n dimensions. The mixed term $Q \wedge {}^*T$ could be viewed as that piece in (7.1) which breaks the projective symmetry *minimally*. The same would hold for the subcase of conformally invariant Lagrangian. Its breaking by a related term was preliminarily entertained in Ref.[4] and [6].

The fact that $V' = \partial V / \partial \mathcal{R}$ simulates a Brans–Dicke scalar may pave the way for constructing a Higgsless version of the standard model of strong and elektroweak interactions with a conformally invariant gravitational sector, cf.[13].

Since the projectively deformed torsion or nonmetricity, are of the pure gauge type, they can be made to vanish by a conformal transformation. Thereby one can possibly convert the Higgsless standard model of Cheng et al. [3] with a Weyl vector coupling to a related one with an "invisible" vector torsion coupling to the fermions. If one identifies the conformal factor via $\Omega^L = V'$, this amount to a *field redefinition*, cf.[12], of the metric which in Riemannian space–time maps [10] the nonlinear Lagrangian $V(\mathcal{R})$ into the self–gravitating scalar field $\varphi = \sqrt{3/2} \ln V'$ in conventional general relativity. In our more general geometrical framework with torsion and Weyl covector, the projective transformation seems to take over this role.

Moreover, the influence of the projective transformation (2.1) on the renormalizability of the metric–affine models of gravity has recently been analyzed [7]. Some quadratic torsion terms in the Lagrangian break projective invariance on the tree level, but according to [8] do not contribute to one–loop counterterms.

On the other hand, it is important to stress, that an electron in the gravitational field of Riemann–Cartan spacetime feels only the axial torsion, which is, however, not affected by projective transformationes. In the framework of MAG, we would have to go beyond the covariant Dirac equation [5] and consider field equations for the spinor manifields, cf. Ref. [6].

Acknowledgment

This work was partially supported by CONACyT Grant No. 3544–E9311.

References

[1] P. Baekler, E.W. Mielke, and F.W. Hehl, *Nuovo Cimento* **107B** (1992) 91.

[2] C. Brans and R.H. Dicke, *Phys. Rev.* **124** (1961) 925.

[3] H. Cheng, *Phys. Rev. Lett.* **61** (1988) 2182; H. Cheng and W.F. Kao: "Consequences of scale invariance", MIT preprint (1988).

[4] F.W. Hehl, W. Kopczyński, J.D. McCrea, and E.W. Mielke, *J. Math. Phys.* **32** (1991) 2169.

[5] F.W. Hehl, J. Lemke, and E.W. Mielke: "Two lectures on fermions and gravity", in: Proc. of the School on *Geometry and Theoretical Physics*, Bad Honnef, 12 – 16 Feb. 1990, J. Debrus and A.C. Hirshfeld, eds. (Springer, Berlin 1991), p. 56.

[6] F.W. Hehl, J.D. McCrea, E.W. Mielke and Y. Ne'eman, *Found. Phys.* **19** (1989) 1075; *Phys. Rep.* (1995, in press.).

[7] M.Yu. Kalmykov, P.I. Pronin, and K.V. Stepansky, *Class. Quantum Grav.* **11** (1994) 2645.

[8] M.Yu. Kalmykov and P.I. Pronin: "The one–loop divergences and renormalizability of the minimal gauge theory of gravity", Dubna preprint (1994).

[9] A. López–Pinto, A. Tiemblo, and R. Tresguerres: "Ordinary matter in nonlinear affine gauge theories", preprint IAMFF94/4.

[10] G. Magnano and L.M. Sokolowski, *Phys. Rev.* **D50** (1994) 5039.

[11] J.D. McCrea, *Class. Quantum Grav.* **9** (1992) 553.

[12] E.W. Mielke and F.W. Hehl, *Phys. Rev. Lett.* **67** (1991) 1370.

[13] M. Pawlowski and R. Rączka: "A unified conformal model for fundamental interactions without dynamical Higgs field", preprint ILAS4/94.

[14] L.L. Smalley, *Phys. Rev.* **D33** (1986) 3590.

[15] R. Tresguerres, *Phys. Lett.* **A168** (1992) 174.

Gennadi A. Sardanashvily, Editor
New Frontiers in Gravitation
Hadronic Press, Palm Harbor, FL 34682-1577, U.S.A.
ISBN 0–911767–96–7, 1996, Pages 257–268

TELEPARALLELISM
AND GEOMETRODYNAMICS

José W. Maluf

International Centre for Condensed Matter Physics
Universidade de Brasília
70.919-910 Brasília, DF
Brazil

Abstract

The teleparallel equivalent of general relativity (TEGR) is considered. This formulation is structuraly different from Einstein's general relativity, but the dynamical content is the same. It displays features that may lead to a more consistent picture of the canonical, non-perturbative quantization of the gravitational field. We show initially that the Hamiltonian formulation of the TEGR may be carried out under a particular gauge fixing, which ammounts to the fixation of a *global* reference frame. As a consequence, the Hamiltonian is written in terms of first class constraints and therefore the time evolution of the field quantities is well defined. The two major properties of the Hamiltonian formulation are: (i) the integral form of the Hamiltonian constraint contains in an explicit way the ADM energy. Thus the corresponding quantum constraint operator may be written as an energy eigenvalue equation, a feature that is not shared by the standard Wheeler-DeWitt equation; (ii) an unambiguous definition of *localized* gravitational energy density is naturally obtained from the Hamiltonian constraint. This energy density also appears as a surface term in the Hamiltonian density. Therefore this definition has canonical significance.

I. Introduction

A Riemannian manifold admits an absolute parallelism if it is possible to define the parallelism of two directions in two different points in a manner that independs of the choice of the coordinates and satisfies: (i) a geodesic is in all her points self-parallel; (ii) the angle between two different directions in an arbitrary point P is equal to the angle between the two parallel directions in another point Q. As a consequence of these conditions a connection arises such that it has zero curvature.

Theories that possess the above geometrical properties were considered long ago by Einstein[1] in his attempt to construct a unified theory of gravitation and electromagnetism. Nowadays teleparallel theories have been reconsidered in the literature as *alternative* theories of gravity[2, 3, 4, 5, 6]. The idea was that such models could provide a better description of the gravitational interaction at the *microscopic* level, retaining at the same time the phenomenological features of Einstein's general relativity. Teleparallel theories were understood as gauge theories of the space-time translational group; the tetrad field $e^a{}_\mu$ and the spin affine connection $\omega_{\mu ab}$ were viewed as the translational and rotational gauge potentials, respectively.

Manifolds with vanishing curvature tensor exhibit many interesting features. Recently it has been shown that in such manifolds it is possible to carry out a simple construction of BRST-type operators[7], which are constructed by means of the torsion tensor. This fact constitutes a bridge between a specific geometrical framework and a well known quatization procedure, which may eventually provide new ideas on how to quantize gravity.

Among the infinite class of teleparallel theories constructed out of invariants of the torsion tensor[5], there is one which is precisely equivalent to Einstein's general relativity. The teleparallel equivalent of general relativity[8] (TEGR) displays a very interesting canonical structure, as we will show below. The two major properties are: (i) the ADM energy appears explicitly in the integral form of the Hamiltonian constraint. Therefore the former can be written in terms of canonical field quantities; (ii) The Hamiltonian contains a surface term that can be naturally and unambiguously identified as the gravitational energy *density*. This surface term transforms covariantly under reparametrizations of the three-dimensional space-like hypersurface, and yields the ADM energy when integrated over the whole three-dimensional space. These properties hold in asymptotically flat space-times.

The above properties suggest that the geometrodynamics of the (TEGR) may be suitable to the canonical quantization of the gravitational field, at least from the conceptual point of view. The appearance of the ADM energy in the Hamiltonian constraint allows us to interpret this equation as an energy eigenvalue equation, a feature that is not shared by the Wheeler-DeWitt equation[9]. Unlike the latter, the Hamiltonian constraint in the present case naturally leads to a straightfoward construction of a Schrödinger equation for time dependent physical states. This equation will be written down in section II. Although the construction is purely formal, the indications are that the canonical quantization based on the TEGR may lead to concrete and consistent achievements[10].

The canonical description of the spherically symmetric geometry in the framework of the TEGR will be carried out in section III. One is naturally lead to the Schwarzschild solution. The surface term that corresponds to the energy density of this solution will be explicitly obtained. We will find out that the expression of the energy density for the Schwarzschild solution is precisely the same obtained by Brown and York[12], who developed the analysis of *quasilocal* energy in the framework of the Hilbert-Einstein action integral. Finally we will mention that for the standard spherically symmetric line element there corresponds two inequivalent set of tetrad fields, one of which is not appropriate for our considerations, as it yields infinite total energy when the integration is carried out over the whole three-dimensional *flat* space.

Notation: spacetime indices $\{\mu, \nu, ...\}$ and local Lorentz indices $\{a, b, ...\}$ run from 0 to 3. In the canonical 3+1 decomposition latin indices from the middle of the alphabet indicate space indices according to $\{\mu = 0, i\}$, $\{a =$

$(0), (i)\}$. The tetrad field $e^a{}_\mu$ and the (arbitrary) spin affine connection $\omega_{\mu ab}$ yield the usual definitions of the curvature and torsion tensors: $R^a{}_{b\mu\nu} = \partial_\mu \omega_\nu{}^a{}_b + \omega_\mu{}^a{}_c \omega_\nu{}^c{}_b - ...., \ T^a{}_{\mu\nu} = \partial_\mu e^a{}_\nu + \omega_\mu{}^a{}_b e^b{}_\nu - .....$ The flat spacetime metric is fixed by $\eta_{(0)(0)} = -1$. The tetrad field will be used to convert spacetime indices into Lorentz indices and vice-versa.

II. Canonical Structure of the TEGR

The Lagrangian density of the TEGR[8] in empty spacetime, assuming that the gravitational field is asymptoticaly flat, is given by

$$L(e, \omega, \lambda) = -ke\Sigma^{abc}T_{abc} + e\lambda^{ab\mu\nu}R_{ab\mu\nu}(\omega) . \tag{1}$$

where $k = \frac{1}{16\pi G}$, G is the gravitational constant, and $e = det(e^a{}_\mu)$. The field quantities $\{\lambda^{ab\mu\nu}\}$ are Lagrange multipliers. The tensor Σ^{abc} is defined as

$$\Sigma^{abc} = \frac{1}{4}(T^{abc} + T^{bac} - T^{cab}) + \frac{1}{2}(\eta^{ac}T^b - \eta^{ab}T^c),$$

which yields

$$\Sigma^{abc}T_{abc} = \frac{1}{4}T^{abc}T_{abc} + \frac{1}{2}T^{abc}T_{bac} - T^aT_a ,$$

where $T_a = T^b{}_{ba}$.

An arbitrary spin affine connection $\omega_{\mu ab} = -\omega_{\mu ba}$ may be written in terms of the Levi-Civita connection $^0\omega_{\mu ab}$, which is a function of $e^a{}_\mu$ only, and of the contorsion tensor $K_{\mu ab} = \frac{1}{2}e_a{}^\lambda e_b{}^\nu(T_{\lambda\mu\nu} + T_{\nu\lambda\mu} - T_{\mu\nu\lambda})$ according to

$$\omega_{\mu ab} = {}^0\omega_{\mu ab} + K_{\mu ab} . \tag{2}$$

Such decomposition of $\omega_{\mu ab}$ allows us to obtain the identity

$$eR(e, \omega) = eR(e) + e\Sigma^{abc}T_{abc} - 2\partial_\mu(eT^\mu) , \tag{3}$$

by just substituting $\omega_{\mu ab}$ for $^o\omega_{\mu ab} + K_{\mu ab}$ on the left hand side (LHS) of (3). We observe then that the vanishing of $R^a{}_{b\mu\nu}(\omega)$ implies the equivalence between the scalar curvature tensor $R(e)$, constructed out of $e^a{}_\mu$ only, and the quadratic combination of the torsion tensor. For asymptotically flat spacetimes the divergence in (3) does not contribute to the action integral.

Variation of L with respect to $\lambda^{ab\mu\nu}$ yields

$$R^a{}_{b\mu\nu}(\omega) = 0. \tag{4}$$

Let $\frac{\delta L}{\delta e^{a\mu}} = 0$ denote the field equation satisfied by $e_{a\mu}$. With the help of (4) it can be shown by explicit and lengthy calculations that

$$\frac{\delta L}{\delta e^{a\mu}} = \frac{1}{2}\{R_{a\mu}(e) - \frac{1}{2}e_{a\mu}R(e)\}, \tag{5}$$

The expression above can be verified by just substituting $\omega_{\mu ab}$ for $^o\omega_{\mu ab}(e) + K_{\mu ab}$ on the LHS of (5). Therefore $e_{a\mu}$ satisfies Einstein's equations.

The field equations arising from variations of L with respect to $\omega_{\mu ab}$ can be best analysed in the Hamiltonian formulation. The latter has been presented in ref.[8], with the gauge ω_{0ab} being fixed from the outset. Here we will likewise maintain this gauge fixing, as it can be shown that in this context the constraints of the theory constitute a *first class* set. The condition $\omega_{0ab} = 0$ is fixed by breaking the local Lorentz symmetry of (1). We still make use of the residual time independent gauge symmetry to fix the usual time gauge condition $e_{(k)}{}^0 = e_{(0)i} = 0$.

The Hamiltonian density H can be constructed out of (1) in terms of canonical field variables and Lagrange multipliers. Because of the gauge fixing $\omega_{0ab} = 0$, H does not depend on P^{kab}, the momentum canonically conjugated to ω_{kab}. Thus arbitrary variations of $L = p\dot{q} - H$ with respect to P^{kab} yields $\dot{\omega}_{kab} = 0$ (see expression (21) of the Lagrangian density in [8]; had we not fixed $\omega_{0ab} = 0$ the corresponding equation would be $\dot{\omega}_{kab} - D_k\omega_{0ab} = 0$, which is equivalent to the Lagrangian field equation $R_{ab0k} = 0$). Therefore in view of $\omega_{0ab} = 0$, ω_{kab} drops out from our considerations.

The above gauge fixing can be understood as the fixation of a *global* reference frame.

As a consequence of the fixation of both gauges the Hamiltonian density becomes

$$A_{TL} = \int d^4x \{\Pi^{(j)k}\dot{e}_{(j)k} - H\} , \qquad (6)$$

$$H = NC + N^iC_i + \Sigma_{mn}\Pi^{[mn]} + \frac{1}{8\pi G}\partial_k(NeT^k) + \partial_k(\Pi^{jk}N_j). \qquad (7)$$

N and N^i are the lapse and shift functions, and $\Sigma_{mn} = -\Sigma_{nm}$ are Lagrange multipliers. The constraints are defined by

$$C = \partial_j(2keT^j) - ke\Sigma^{kij}T_{kij} - \frac{1}{4ke}(\Pi^{ij}\Pi_{ji} - \frac{1}{2}\Pi^2) , \qquad (8)$$

$$C_k = -e_{(j)k}\partial_i\Pi^{(j)i} - \Pi^{(j)i}T_{(j)ik} , \qquad (9)$$

with $e = det(e_{(j)k})$ and $T^i = g^{ik}e^{(j)l}T_{(j)ik}$. We remark that (6) is invariant under global SO(3) and general coordinate transformations. An important feature of this framework is that although we are considering asymptoticaly flat gravitational fields, the action integral determined by (1) does *not* require any additional surface term, as it is invariant under coordinate transformations that preserve the asymptotic structure of the field quantities. A clear discussion of the necessity of the addition of a surface term to the Hilbert-Einstein action, in the case of asymptoticaly flat gravitational fields, is given by Faddeev[11].

We assume now that for $r \to \infty$ we have $e_{(j)k} \approx \eta_{jk} + \frac{1}{2}h_{jk}(\frac{1}{r})$. Because of this asymptotic behaviour we have

$$\frac{1}{8\pi G}\int d^3x\partial_j(eT^j) = \frac{1}{16\pi G}\int_S dS_k(\partial_i h_{ik} - \partial_k h_{ii}) \equiv E_{ADM} , \qquad (10)$$

where the surface term is evaluated for $r \to \infty$. Therefore we observe that the integral form of the Hamiltonian constraint $C = O$ may be rewritten as

$$\int d^3x \left\{ ke\Sigma^{kij} T_{kij} + \frac{1}{4ke}(\Pi^{ij}\Pi_{ji} - \frac{1}{2}\Pi^2) \right\} = E_{ADM} . \tag{11}$$

Defining the LHS of (11) by $\mathbf{H}$, we are naturally led to establish a Schrödinger equation

$$\hat{\mathbf{H}}\Psi = i\frac{\delta\Psi}{\delta\tau} , \tag{12}$$

with

$$\Psi(\tau) = \int dE\, \rho(E)\Psi_E(e_{(k)i})e^{-iE\tau} . \tag{13}$$

$\hat{\mathbf{H}}$ is formally understood as a quantum operator and $E \equiv E_{ADM}$. The function $\rho(E)$ determines the superposition of states corresponding to different values of E_{ADM}. It is not evident at once which is the probabilistic interpretation can one draw from (13). In classical physics time corresponds to a foliation of three dimensional space-like hypersurfaces Σ. It is not clear that τ plays such a role here, but it is not clear as well that the concepts of time in classical and quantum gravity ought to be the same.

Given that $\partial_j(eT^j)$ is a scalar density, in view of (10) we define the *gravitational energy density* enclosed by a volume V of the space as[13]

$$E_g = \frac{1}{8\pi G}\int_V d^3x\, \partial_j(eT^j) . \tag{14}$$

The surprising feature is that the expression above is manifestly invariant under general coordinate transformations of the three dimensional space-like hypersurfaces Σ. Let us note from (7) that $\int d^3xH$ evaluated from a set $(e_{(j)k}, \Pi^{(k)l})$ that satisfy the field equations, in a coordinate system such that for $r \to \infty$ we have $N = 1$, $N_j = 0$, also yields E_{ADM}. Therefore definition (14) has a canonical significance.

III. The Spherically Symmetric Geometry

We will now specialize the Hamiltonian formulation to the spherically symmetric geometry in order to compute the expression of the energy density for the Schwarzschild black hole. The triads $e_{(k)i}$ will be fixed as

$$e_{(k)i} = \begin{pmatrix} e^\lambda \sin\theta\cos\phi & r\cos\theta\cos\phi & -r\sin\theta\sin\phi \\ e^\lambda \sin\theta\sin\phi & r\cos\theta\sin\phi & r\sin\theta\cos\phi \\ e^\lambda \cos\theta & -r\sin\theta & 0 \end{pmatrix} \quad (15)$$

where $\lambda = \lambda(r,t)$; (k) is the line index and i is the column index. The one form $e^{(k)}$ is defined as

$$e^{(k)} = e^{(k)}{}_r dr + e^{(k)}{}_\theta d\theta + e^{(k)}{}_\phi d\phi ,$$

from what follows

$$e^{(k)}e_{(k)} = e^{2\lambda}dr^2 + r^2 d\theta^2 + r^2 \sin^2\theta d\phi^2 .$$

We also obtain $e = det(e_{(k)i}) = r^2 \sin\theta e^\lambda$. For $r \to \infty$ we require $\lambda(r) \sim O(\frac{1}{r})$.

The reduction to spherical symmetry is performed directly in the Hamiltonian. We first determine the Killing vectors ξ of $g_{ij} = e^{(k)}{}_i e_{(k)j}$. Then we require the vanishing of the Lie derivative $L_\xi(e^{-1}\Pi_{ij}) = 0$, where $\Pi_{ij} = g_{jk}e_{(l)i}\Pi^{(l)k}$. We obtain

$$e^{-1}\Pi_{ij} = diag(A(r,t), B(r,t), B(r,t)\sin^2\theta) ; \quad (16)$$

$A(r,t)$ and $B(r,t)$ are arbitrary functions. From (16) we can calculate all $\{\Pi^{(k)j}\}$. Upon substitution of the latter and (15) into (6) we find out, as expected, that there is no canonical field quantity conjugated to $B(r,t)$. Thus we enforce $B(r,t) = 0$, which implies in $\Pi^{(k)2} = \Pi^{(k)3} = 0$. Defining Π by $\Pi = kr^2e^{-\lambda}A$ and integrating over angles we finally obtain the action integral

$$A = 4\pi \int dt\, dr \left\{ \Pi \dot{\lambda} - NC - N^1 C_1 \right\},\tag{17}$$

$$C = 2ke^{\lambda}(1 - e^{-\lambda})^2 - \frac{1}{8kr^2} e^{-\lambda}\Pi^2 + \frac{1}{4\pi}\varepsilon,\tag{18}$$

$$C_1 = -e^{\lambda}\frac{\partial}{\partial r}(e^{-\lambda}\Pi),\tag{19}$$

$$\varepsilon = 16\pi k \frac{\partial}{\partial r}[r(1 - e^{-\lambda})].\tag{20}$$

The constraints $C_2 = C_\theta$ and $C_3 = C_\phi$ vanish identically.

The Hamiltonian formulation of the spherically symmetric geometry has been carried out already in the framework of the ADM formulation[14]. The present construction is completely equivalent to the latter, as it can be shown that the Hamiltonian and vector constraints are equivalent in both cases. If we choose a coordinate system such that $N^1 = 0$, then the constraints and the evolution equations for λ and Π yield the Schwarzschild solution,

$$e^{-2\lambda} = 1 - \frac{2mG}{r},\tag{21}$$

together with $N^2 = e^{-2\lambda}$.

The energy density (20) can be easily integrated over the whole three dimensional space. It yields $E_g = E_{ADM} = m$, as expected. We can, in addition, evaluate the gravitational energy inside a spherical surface of arbitrary radius R. We find

$$E_g = R\left\{ 1 - (1 - \frac{2m}{R})^{\frac{1}{2}} \right\}\tag{22}$$

This is exactly the expression found by Brown and York[12] in their analysis of *quasilocal* gravitational energy of the Schwarzschild solution. However, the method developed by Brown and York does not seem to be applicable to an arbitrary metric field. Problems already appear in the calculation of the quasilocal energy in the framework of the Kerr metric[15]. On the contrary, given the triad components restricted to a three dimensional hypersurface of the Kerr type we can easily calculate E_g by means of (14).

We would like to mention finally that special attention has to be paid to the construction of the tetrad fields out of the usual metric components. The reason is that one can occasionally write down two (or more) inequivalent sets of tetrad fields that yield the the same metric field, one of which yields unclear results when inserted in (14). In the case of the spherically symmetric geometry this fact can be easily observed. One usually takes as triad one forms the quantities

$$e^{(r)} = e^{\lambda(r)}dr \ , \ e^{(\theta)} = rd\theta \ , \ e^{(\phi)} = r\sin\theta d\phi \tag{23}$$

Imposing the same boundary conditions on $\lambda(r)$ as before, we find that E_g calculated out of the triads above yields an infinite value. This feature is maintained even in the simple case of $\lambda = 0$. Although the curvature tensor constructed out of (23) vanishes if we make $\lambda = 0$, some components of the torsion tensor $T_{(k)ij} = \partial_i e_{(k)j} - \partial_j e_{(k)i}$ do not vanish, e.g., $T_{(2)12} = 1$, $T_{(3)13} = \sin\theta$. We can easily verify that $\partial_k(eT^k) = -2\sin\theta$, from what we conclude that E_g diverges if we integrate over the whole spacetime. The triads given by (15) yield vanishing curvature and torsion tensor for $\lambda = 0$. Moreover, ε defined by (20) vanishes for $\lambda = 0$.

IV. Conclusion

The vanishing of the curvature tensor is a a basic feature of teleparallel theories of gravity. The particular structure of the Lagrangian density (1) makes it equivalent to Einstein's general relativity. Therefore we have considered a theory that is structurally different from Einstein's general relativity, but whose dynamical content is the same. Under a suitable gauge fixing the Hamiltonian formulation corresponding to (1) can be carried out.

We have shown that the latter displays at least two significant advantages over the standard ADM formulation. First, because of the appearance of the ADM energy in the integral form of the quantum Hamiltonian constraint, the canonical quantization program may be carried out in a way more similar to the quantization of other field theories, as the Hamiltonian constraint may be written as an energy eigenvalue equation. We understand this to be a conceptual advantage over attempts based on the Wheeler-DeWitt equation. Second, a natural and unambiguous definition of *localized* gravitational energy density (of wheight $+1$) arises from the canonical formulation of the theory. In the case of the spherically symmetric geometry the energy density, expression (20), yields the ADM energy when the integration is performed over the whole spacetime.

In summary, we expect this reformulation of general relativity to be suitable to address questions regarding the canonical quantization of the gravitational field.

Acknowledgements
This work was supported in part by CNPQ-Brazil.

References

[1] A. Einstein, Sitzungsber. Preuss. Akad. Wiss. Phys.-Math. Kl. **224** (1928); Math. Ann. **102**, 685 (1930)

[2] K. Hayashi and T. Shirafuji, Phys. Rev. **D19**, 3524 (1979)

[3] F. W. Hehl, in *Cosmology and Gravitation*, edited by P. G. Bergmann and V. de Sabbata (Plenum, NY, 1980)

[4] W. Kopczynski, J. Phys. **A15**, 493 (1982)

[5] F. Muller-Hoissen and J. Nitsch, Phys. Rev. **D28**, 718 (1983); Gen. Rel. Grav. **17**, 747 (1985)

[6] H. Goenner and F. Muller-Hoissen, Class. and Quantum Grav. **1**, 651 (1984)

[7] S. Okubo, Gen. Rel. Grav. **23**, 599 (1991); J. Math. Phys. **33**, 895 (1992); J. Math. Phys. **33**, 2148 (1992)

[8] J. W. Maluf, J. Math. Phys. **35**, 335 (1994)

[9] B. S. DeWitt, Phys. Rev. **160**, 1113 (1967)

[10] J. W. Maluf, *The Hamiltonian Constraint in the Teleparallel Equivalent of General Relativity*, Universidade de Brasília preprint (1994)

[11] L. D. Faddeev, Sov. Phys. Usp. **25**, 130 (1982)

[12] J. David Brown and J. W. York, Jr., Phys. Rev. **D47** 1407 (1993)

[13] J. W. Maluf, *Localization of Energy in General Relativity*, Universidade de Brasília preprint (1994)

[14] B. K. Berguer, D. M. Chitre, V. E. Moncrief and and Y. Nutku, Phys. Rev. **D5**, 2467 (1972); W. G. Unruh, Phys. Rev. **D14**, 870 (1976); F. Lund, Phys. Rev. **D8**, 3247 (1973)

[15] E. A. Martinez, Phys. Rev. **D50**, 4290 (1994)

Gennadi A. Sardanashvily, Editor
New Frontiers in Gravitation
Hadronic Press, Palm Harbor, FL 34682-1577, U.S.A.
ISBN 0–911767–96–7, 1996, Pages 269–297

CONNECTION FORMS
IN GRAVITY MODELS

Yuri N.Obukhov

Institute for Theoretical Physics
University of Cologne, D-50923 Köln, Germany[1]

Abstract

The theory of connections on principal fiber bundles is discussed, and a generalisation of the connection 1-forms is suggested. This is shown to be useful in providing a natural unified approach to a number of gravitational models in which non-Riemannian linear connections appear. The relevance of the developed formalism to the conformal (Weyl) symmetry is demonstrated in these applications.

---

[1]Permanent address: Department of Theoretical Physics, Moscow State University, 117234 Moscow, Russia

1. Introduction

The notion of connection is crucial in the gauge theories of a Yang-Mills type [1-2], including the theory of gravity [3-4]. The basic object is the connection on a principal fiber bundle [5] for the corresponding gauge group. Secondary objects and notions are that of the parallel transport, covariant derivatives and connections in associated bundles which usually provide a geometrical description of various matter fields.

Some non-standard parallel transports and relevant linear connections are discussed in the literature [6-8] devoted to the generalisations of the gravitational theory. In this paper we introduce the natural geometrical framework for such generalisations.

It is well known that the connection on a principal bundle is a prescription of how to split the vectors into horizontal and vertical parts. We will not attempt in generalising the very concept of connection on a principal bundle. However, as soon as the vector fields play an essential role in defining a connection, we discuss the possibility of introduction of additional structure on the tangent bundle over a principal bundle. We then find that connection, in its standard definition, can be defined by a *generalised* Lie-algebra valued connection one-forms which depend on this additional structure.

We show how some of the recently discussed non-standard linear connections could be recovered in this framework, and discuss the introduction of the conformal symmetry in the Poincaré gauge gravity.

2. Geometry: the generalised connection forms

Let us consider the principal fiber bundle $P(M, G)$ over the smooth manifold M with the structure group G (which is the Lie group but not necessarily semisimple). As usually [5], the definition of P includes the assumption of the free smooth action of G on P from the right:

$$P \times G \to P : g \in G, \quad R_g : P \to P.$$

The bundle projection is denoted as $\pi : P \to M$, on the fibers $\pi^{-1}(x), x \in M$, the group G acts simply transitively, and the base M is the quotient of P with respect to the right action of G.

Let us introduce a new structure on P: the smooth *linear map*

$$\phi : T(P) \to T(P),$$

defined by its action on the tangent vectors

$$u \in P, \quad X \in T_u P, \quad \phi_u(X) = X' \in T_u P, \tag{1}$$

such that
$$\phi_u(aX_1 + bX_2) = a\phi_u(X_1) + b\phi_u(X_2),$$

and this action differentiably depends on u. This map is assumed to be:
(a) compatible with the right group action, in the sense that

$$(R_g)_*(\phi_u(X)) = \phi_{ug}((R_g)_*(X)), \tag{2}$$

for all $X \in T_u P, \quad g \in G$, and
(b) nondegenerate, i.e. $\phi_u(X) = 0 \to X = 0$ for all $u \in P$.

In general, for a vector X tangent to a fiber at u the vector $\phi_u(X)$ is not tangent to the fiber. Let us, however, restrict ourselves to the case when this is true. Namely, we call ϕ a *linear vertical map* if at any u

$$\phi_u(V_u) = V_u,$$

where

$$V_u = \{X \in T_u P | \pi_*(X) = 0\}$$

is the subspace of vertical vectors (tangent to a fiber) at u.

Linear vertical maps are distinguished among all the other linear maps $\{\phi\}$ by the possibility of defining two *associated maps* on $T(M)$ and $T(G)$. Namely, let us consider the point $x \in M$ and a vector $\bar{X} \in T_x M$. At a point $u \in \pi^{-1}(x)$ in the fiber over x there exists a vector $X \in T_u P$ which is projected into $\bar{X}$, that is $\pi_*(X) = \bar{X}$. Then, by definition,

$$\hat{\varphi}_u(\bar{X}) = \pi_*(\phi_u(X)). \tag{3}$$

This new map $\hat{\varphi}_u$ evidently acts linearly at $x = \pi(u)$. Easy to see that provided ϕ_u is vertical, definition (3) is meaningful. Indeed, one can choose another vector $X' \in T_u P$, which also is projected to $\bar{X}$, i.e. $\pi_*(X') = \bar{X}$. But then clearly the difference is a vertical vector $X' - X \in V_u$, and

$$\pi_*(\phi_u(X')) - \pi_*(\phi_u(X)) = \pi_*(\phi_u(X' - X)) = 0,$$

since ϕ is vertical.

In view of (2) the associated map $\hat{\varphi}$ actually depends only on x, in the sense that

$$\hat{\varphi}_u = \hat{\varphi}_{ug}. \tag{4}$$

The second associated map can be introduced on the Lie algebra $\mathcal{G} = T_e G$ with the help of the fundamental vector fields which are defined for every element $\xi \in \mathcal{G}$. Denote the fundamental vector fields by Σ_ξ. As is well known, at any point $u \in P$ these describe the isomorphism between $\mathcal{G}$ and the vertical tangent space V_u.

Hence, for the vertical ϕ_u one naturally defines the linear map φ on the Lie algebra by

$$\Sigma_{\varphi_u(\xi)} = \phi_u(\Sigma_\xi). \tag{5}$$

The fundamental vector field has a well known property under the right bundle action,

$$(R_g)_*(\Sigma_\xi) = \Sigma_{g^{-1}\xi g}.$$

Using this and (2), one can prove the analogue of (4). This reads

$$\varphi_u(g\xi g^{-1}) = g\varphi_{ug}(\xi)g^{-1}. \tag{6}$$

[Indeed:

$$\Sigma_{\varphi_{ug}(\xi)} = \phi_{ug}(\Sigma_\xi) = \phi_{ug}(\Sigma_{g^{-1}(g\xi g^{-1})g}) = \phi_{ug}((R_g)_*(\Sigma_{g\xi g^{-1}})) =$$

$$= (R_g)_*(\phi_u(\Sigma_{g\xi g^{-1}})) = (R_g)_*(\Sigma_{\varphi_u(g\xi g^{-1})}) = \Sigma_{g^{-1}\varphi_u(g\xi g^{-1})g}]$$

Let us denote the basis of the Lie algebra t_A, so that arbitrary element is $\xi = \xi^A t_A$. Then the associated linear map φ can be given in terms of components Λ^A_B such that

$$\varphi(\xi^A) = \Lambda^A_B \xi^B. \tag{7}$$

This quantity is a (matrix-valued) zero-form on $P(M,G)$, which we assume to be a smooth function $\Lambda^A_B(u)$ of u. One can construct a 1-form from it with a simple structure properties,

$$b^A_B := \Lambda^A_C d(\Lambda^{-1})^C_B, \qquad db = -\frac{1}{2}[b \wedge b], \tag{8}$$

where the last relation is the matrix one with indices suppressed ([ ] is the matrix commutator).

Looking at the linear map $\varphi_u(\xi)$ as the transformation of the Lie algebra basis, $t'_A = \Lambda^B_A t_B$, one can describe this as a "deformation" of algebra. Let us denote the algebra structure constants by f^A_{BC},

$$[t_B, t_C] = f^A_{BC} t_A.$$

Then the deformation is determined by the "structure functions"

$$\mathcal{F}^A_{BC} = \Lambda^A_K (\Lambda^{-1})^M_B (\Lambda^{-1})^N_C f^K_{MN}. \tag{9}$$

It is clear that these still satisfy the Jacobi identity, and define the same Cartan-Killing form for the algebra $\mathcal{G}$.

In a sense, by means of the linear map φ one constructs over P a "bundle" of deformed algebras $\mathcal{G}_u$ with $\mathcal{F}^A_{BC}(u)$ changing smoothly over P. Then the 1-form b is naturally interpeted as a connection which enables to define the "covariant derivative"

$$\mathcal{D}\xi^A = d\xi^A + b^A_B \xi^B.$$

Along these lines one easily verifies that

$$\mathcal{D}\mathcal{F}^A_{BC} = d\mathcal{F}^A_{BC} + b^A_D \mathcal{F}^D_{BC} - b^D_B \mathcal{F}^A_{DC} - b^D_C \mathcal{F}^A_{BD} = 0, \tag{10}$$

and recognises (8) as the "zero curvature" equation.

Now let us discuss the introduction of connection in a principal bundle P. To remind [5], a connection Γ in $P(M, G)$ is a rule which defines at each point $u \in P$ a *horizontal* subspace H_u of the tangent space $T_u P$ so that:

(i) $T_u P = H_u + V_u$,
(ii) $H_{ug} = (R_g)_* H_u$,
(iii) H_u differentiably depends on u.

There is the direct sum in (i), which means that projectors v, h exist which decompose any vector $X \in T_u P$ into a vertical and horizontal components,

$$X = v(X) + h(X), \qquad v(X) \in V_u, \qquad h(X) \in H_u.$$

Usually a connection Γ is determined by a Lie algebra-valued form on P.

Let us assume that on P a smooth ($\mathcal{G}$ -valued) 1-form ω exists with the properties:

(a) $\omega_u(\Sigma_\xi) = \varphi_u(\xi)$,

(b) $(R_g)^*(\omega) = g^{-1}\omega g$.

Proposition 1: for a given linear vertical map ϕ (and thus φ) this 1-form defines a connection on P. Indeed, the proof is standard: let ω have the properties $(a),(b)$. Then define at each $u \in P$ a subspace of a tangent space as $H_u = \{X \in T_uP | \omega(X) = 0\}$. This is the horizontal space with $(i) - (iii)$ easily verified. E.g., for X define the vertical part by $v(X) = \phi^{-1}(\Sigma_{\omega(X)})$, then clearly $X - v(X) \in H_u$, proving (i). By (b), $(R_g)^*(\omega(X)) = \omega((R_g)_*(X)) = g^{-1}\omega(X)g$, thus (ii) is also proved. Notice that (b) agrees with (6).

When $\phi = id$, one is left with the usual connection 1-form. We will call connection defined by ω with the properties $(a),(b)$ a ϕ-*connection*.

By definition, ϕ-connection is a (pseudo)tensorial 1-form on P of type $(adG, \mathcal{G})$ (using the standard terminology). Using the Lie algebra basis explicitly, we can write

$$\omega = \omega^A t_A.$$

For any pseudotensorial form on P one can define the *exterior covariant derivative* D by projecting the exterior differentiation to the horizontal subspaces defined by a connection.

We will call the exterior covariant derivative of the ϕ-connection a ϕ-*curvature* on P,

$$\Omega = D\omega = (d\omega)h. \tag{11}$$

This is also convenient to write as $\Omega = \Omega^A t_A$.

Proposition 2: *structure equation*. Let ω^A be the 1-form of a ϕ-connection on P, and Ω^A is its curvature 2-form. Then

$$d\omega^A = -b^A_B\omega^B - \frac{1}{2}\mathcal{F}^A{}_{BC}\omega^B \wedge \omega^C + \Omega^A. \tag{12}$$

The proof repeats the standard one with considering the values of (12) on different pairs of vectors $X, Y \in T_u P$ – horizontal and vertical.

Important information about the connection is contained in a collection of of $\mathcal{G}$-valued forms on the base manifold M. These are defined as usually, using the covering of M by open sets $\{U_\alpha\}$ with the corresponding family of isomorphic maps $\psi_\alpha : \pi^{-1}(U_\alpha) \to U_\alpha \times G$ and the transition functions $\psi_{\alpha\beta} : U_\alpha \cap U_\beta \to G$. Let us remind, that these define a set of standard local cross sections $\sigma_\alpha : U_\alpha \to P$ by $\sigma_\alpha(x) = \psi_\alpha^{-1}(x, e)$, where $M \ni x$, $G \ni e$ – the unity of the group. With the help of these in each U_α one introduces a $\mathcal{G}$-valued 1-form

$$\omega_\alpha = \sigma_\alpha^* \omega,$$

and a linear map

$$\varphi_\alpha = \varphi_{u=\sigma_\alpha}.$$

In non-empty intersections $U_\alpha \cap U_\beta$ as usually the $\mathcal{G}$-valued 1-form is defined

$$\theta_{\alpha\beta} = \psi_{\alpha\beta}^* \theta,$$

where θ is the left-invariant canonical 1-form on G.

Proposition 3: "gauge transformation". The forms and maps ω_α, $\theta_{\alpha\beta}$, φ_α satisfy in $U_\alpha \cap U_\beta$ the following conditions

$$\omega_\beta = ad(\psi_{\alpha\beta}^{-1})\omega_\alpha + \varphi_\beta(\theta_{\alpha\beta}), \tag{13}$$

$$\varphi_\beta \circ ad(\psi_{\alpha\beta}^{-1}) = ad(\psi_{\alpha\beta}^{-1}) \circ \varphi_\alpha. \tag{14}$$

Proof of (13) is straightforward, repeating the standard one with an account of the property (a) of the connection form. Equation (14) is a different form of (6).

These formulas will be the basis of the "physical" description of the ϕ-connection as a gauge field "potential" and its transformation.

Proposition 4: "*Bianchi identity*". The forms of the ϕ-connection and ϕ-curvature satisfy on P the following identity

$$d\Omega^A + b^A_B \wedge \Omega^B + \mathcal{F}^A{}_{BC}\omega^B \wedge \Omega^C = 0. \tag{15}$$

For the proof take the exterior derivative of (12), use (8),(10) and again substitute (12).

3. Physics: generalised gauge fields for arbitrary group G

The choice of a local section $\sigma : U \to P$, $U \subset M$ in physical terms is interpreted as a gauge, and the pullback $\sigma^*\omega$ is usually called the gauge field potential on the space-time M. We will denote this and other pullbacks by the same symbols $(\omega, \Omega, b, \mathcal{F}, \Lambda, \text{etc})$ understanding now that the relevant objects "live" on M, i.e. are the fields on the space-time in the usual physical sense.

The change of the gauge $\sigma \to \sigma'$ is called the gauge transformation, and this is described by an x-dependent element $g(x)$ of the group G. The transformed objects (i.e. the pullbacks for σ') will be denoted by primes. Let us derive explicitly the infinitesimal gauge transformations given by

$$g \approx 1 + \zeta^A t_A, \quad \zeta^A = \zeta^A(x). \tag{16}$$

Since $g^{-1} \approx 1 - \zeta^A t_A$, one easily obtains from (13) the gauge transformation of the generalised potential

$$\delta_\zeta \omega = \omega'^A - \omega^A = \Lambda^A_B d\zeta^B + f^A{}_{BC}\omega^B \zeta^C, \tag{17}$$

where the matrix $\Lambda^A_B = \Lambda^A_B(x)$, which is the spacetime description of the associated linear map φ, appears now as the new field in the gauge scheme.

Besides this, given the local spacetime coordinates x^μ, another associated linear map $\hat{\varphi}$ is represented by the type $(1,1)$ tensor field $\hat{\Lambda}^\mu_\nu$. It defines the local linear maps of tangent vectors,

$$X^\mu \to \hat{\Lambda}^\mu_\nu X^\nu.$$

In the standard gauge field theory both fields are trivial $\Lambda^A_B = \delta^A_B$, $\hat{\Lambda}^\mu_\nu = \delta^\mu_\nu$.

Under the gauge transformation these behave quite differently. While $\hat{\Lambda}^\mu_\nu$ is invariant, in view of (4), the algebra map (7) transforms as

$$\delta_\zeta \Lambda^A_B = \Lambda'^A_B - \Lambda^A_B = \zeta^D(f^A_{CD}\Lambda^C_B - \Lambda^A_C f^C_{BD}), \tag{18}$$

which is the consequence of (6),(14). It is also useful to notice that an explicit formula for the inverse reads analogously

$$\delta_\zeta(\Lambda^{-1})^A_B = (\Lambda'^{-1})^A_B - (\Lambda^{-1})^A_B = \zeta^D(f^A_{CD}(\Lambda^{-1})^C_B - (\Lambda^{-1})^A_C f^C_{BD}).$$

The pullback of the 1-form b (8) (which can be considered as the "field strength" for Λ) transforms as follows

$$\delta_\zeta b^A_B = b'^A_B - b^A_B = \zeta^D(f^A_{CD}b^C_B - b^A_C f^C_{BD}) + (\mathcal{F}^A_{BC}\Lambda^C_D - f^A_{BD})d\zeta^D, \tag{19}$$

where $\mathcal{F}^A_{BC} = \mathcal{F}^A_{BC}(x)$ is defined as in (9).

It is straighforward to derive the gauge transformation law for this quantity from (18),

$$\delta_\zeta \mathcal{F}^A_{BC} = \mathcal{F}'^A_{BC} - \mathcal{F}^A_{BC} = \zeta^D(f^A_{KD}\mathcal{F}^K_{BC} - f^K_{BD}\mathcal{F}^A_{KC} - f^K_{CD}\mathcal{F}^A_{BK}). \tag{20}$$

Equation (12) gives the the generalisation of the gauge field strength 2-form which is defined on M by the ϕ-connection ω. It involves explicitly the fields $\Lambda^A_B(x)$ and $b^A_B(x)$,

$$\Omega^A = \mathcal{D}\omega^A + \frac{1}{2}\mathcal{F}^A_{BC}\omega^B \wedge \omega^C = d\omega^A + b^A_B \wedge \omega^B + \frac{1}{2}\mathcal{F}^A_{BC}\omega^B \wedge \omega^C. \tag{21}$$

One can prove directly by using (17)-(20) that this quantity transforms covariantly under (16),

$$\delta_\zeta \Omega^A = \Omega'^A - \Omega^A = f^A_{BC} \Omega^B \zeta^C. \tag{22}$$

Let $\Psi = \Psi^A(x)t_A$ be an arbitrary $\mathcal{G}$-valued p-form on M, which
transforms covariantly under the adjoint transformation,

$$\Psi \to \Psi' = g^{-1}(x)\Psi g(x).$$

In the infinitesimal case (16) this reads

$$\delta_\zeta \Psi^A = \Psi'^A - \Psi^A = f^A_{BC} \Psi^B \zeta^C. \tag{23}$$

The ordinary derivative clearly does not transform as (23) and should be
replaced by the covariant one. Its definition is naturally suggested by (15),
so the generalised covariant derivative is given by

$$D\Psi^A := \mathcal{D}\Psi^A + \mathcal{F}^A_{BC}\omega^B \wedge \Psi^C = d\Psi^A + b^A_B \wedge \Psi^B + \mathcal{F}^A_{BC}\omega^B \wedge \Psi^C. \tag{24}$$

One can straighforwardly verify, that this is indeed a covariant quantity,
i.e. under (16),(23) it transforms as

$$\delta_\zeta D\Psi^A = D'\Psi'^A - D\Psi^A = f^A_{BC} D\Psi^B \zeta^C. \tag{25}$$

[Notice that in the proof one should take into account the behaviour of all
additional fields (17)-(20), since

$$D'\Psi'^A = d\Psi'^A + b'^A_B \wedge \Psi'^B + \mathcal{F}'^A_{BC}\omega'^B \wedge \Psi'^C]$$

Direct calculation shows also that

$$DD\Psi^A = \mathcal{F}^A_{BC}\Omega^B \wedge \Psi^C, \tag{26}$$

with Ω^A given by (21). This agrees with the usual definition of the curvature from the commutator of covariant derivatives.

4. Frame bundles and linear connections

Let us turn now to the discussion of the linear and affine connections, which is important for the applications to gravitational field models.

The principal bundle P will denote now the *frame bundle* $L(M)$, the elements of which are the linear frames, i.e. $P \ni u = (x, e_a)$, $x \in M$, $e_1, ..., e_n \in T_x M$ is an arbitrary set of linearly independent tangent vectors which form a basis at x $(n = dim M)$. As is well known, the structure group of $L(M)$ is the general linear group $G = GL(n, R)$ with the evidently defined right action, $g \in G : u \to R_g u = ug = (x, (eg)_a)$ (more explicitly, $(eg)_a = e_b g_a^b$ with an $n \times n$ matrix $g_b^a \in GL(n, R)$). It is useful to remind that the elements $u \in L(M)$ can be interpreted as the (linear) maps from R^n to tangent spaces $T_{\pi(u)} M$: $R^n \ni \chi^a \xrightarrow{u} \chi^a e_a = X \in T_x M$. Such a map we will denote also by u.

The connection in $L(M)$ is usually called a *linear connection*. Let us assume that a vertical linear map ϕ is defined on the frame bundle (and hence, the associated maps $\hat{\varphi}, \varphi$ are given on the tangent vectors over M and on the Lie algebra $\mathcal{G} = gl(n, R)$). Then the linear connection is introduced with the help of the ϕ-connection 1-form, $\omega = \omega^a{}_b E_a^b$ (with respect to the natural basis in $gl(n, R)$).

The principal bundle $P = L(M)$ of linear frames is distinguished among the other principal bundles over M by the possibility of defining one more fundamental object: the canonical (or soldering) 1-form. Given the vertical linear map ϕ one can generalise this concept, and introduce a *ϕ-canonical form* ϑ as the R^n valued 1-form on $L(M)$ by

$$\vartheta^a(X)e_a = \pi_*(\phi_u(X)), \text{ for } u = (x, e_a), X \in T_u P. \tag{27}$$

Easy to see, that the equivalent definition is provided by the above mentioned interpretation of frames u as the linear maps from R^n to $T_x M$:

$$\vartheta_u(X) := u^{-1}(\pi_*(\phi_u(X))). \qquad (28)$$

In view of the property (2) one can prove the equivariance of the generalised canonical form,

$$(R_g^* \vartheta)_u(X) = \vartheta_{ug}(R_g {}_* X) = (ug)^{-1}(\pi_*(\phi_{ug}(R_g {}_* X))) =$$

$$= g^{-1} u^{-1}(\pi_*(\phi_u(X))) = g^{-1}\vartheta_u(X).$$

Since for vertical vectors $\vartheta(vX) = 0$, the canonical form is thus the tensorial 1-form on $L(M)$ of the type $(GL(n, R), R^n)$:

$$(R_g)^*(\vartheta^a) = (g^{-1})_b^a \vartheta^b. \qquad (29)$$

Given the ϕ-connection and ϕ-canonical forms, one can introduce an important notion of the *standard horizontal field* on $L(M)$. This is in a sense a dual object to the fundamental (vertical) field Σ_ξ defined for any element of the algebra $\xi \in \mathcal{G}$. Let $\chi = \{\chi^a\}$ be an arbitrary element in R^n, then the corresponding standard horizontal field $B(\chi)$ at a point $u \in P$ is by definition a unique horizontal vector, such that $\pi_*(B(\chi)_u) = u(\chi) = \chi^a e_a$. It is easy to see that the value of the ϕ-canonical form on the standard horizontal fields is given by

$$\vartheta_u(B(\chi)) = (u^{-1}\hat{\varphi}_u u)(\chi), \qquad (30)$$

compare to the property (a) of the ϕ-connection 1-form.

With the help of the fundamental vertical vector fields and the standard horizontal vector fields one can introduce a convenient parallelization of the frame bundle, defining a basis at an arbitrary point $u \in L(M)$.

Let us call the covariant derivative of the generalised canonical form the *generalised torsion* 2-form,

$$\Theta := D\vartheta = (d\vartheta)h.$$

It is straightforward to derive a corresponding (1st) structure equation.

5. Local coordinates

Let us describe now the new notions and structures in terms of the coordinates and transformation laws.

Introducing the local coordinates $\{x^\mu\}$ on a base manifold M, one finds also a natural local coordinate system in the frame bundle $L(M)$:

$$\{x^\mu, \quad h_a^\mu\}, \tag{31}$$

where an element $L(M) \ni u = (x, e_a)$ is evidently described by a pair $(x^\mu, h_a^\mu \partial_\mu)$. Since $\{e_a\}$ are linearly independent, the matrix h_a^μ is non-degenerate. We denote its inverse by h_μ^a.

The coordinate basis in $T(P)$ is thus given by the partial derivatives,

$$\left\{ \frac{\partial}{\partial x^\mu}, \quad \frac{\partial}{\partial h_a^\mu} \right\},$$

so that arbitrary vector $X \in T_u P$ is described by its components, X^μ, X_a^μ, both being functions of x^μ and h_a^μ,

$$X = X^\mu \frac{\partial}{\partial x^\mu} + X_a^\mu \frac{\partial}{\partial h_a^\mu}.$$

A vertical vector is evidently

$$X = X_a^\mu \frac{\partial}{\partial h_a^\mu},$$

and the fundamental vector field, corresponding to an element ξ_b^a of the Lie algebra $gl(n, R)$ (arbitrary $n \times n$ matrix, so that $g_b^a = (\exp \xi)_b^a$), is represented by

$$\Sigma_\xi = h_b^\mu \xi_a^b \frac{\partial}{\partial h_a^\mu}. \tag{32}$$

The linear map ϕ in $T(P)$ is straightforwardly described in the local coordinates as follows,

$$\phi_u(\frac{\partial}{\partial x^\mu}) = \hat{\Lambda}_\mu^\nu(u)\frac{\partial}{\partial x^\nu} + \bar{\Lambda}_{a\mu}^\nu(u)\frac{\partial}{\partial h_a^\nu},$$

$$\phi_u(\frac{\partial}{\partial h_a^\mu}) = \tilde{\Lambda}_\mu^{a\nu}(u)\frac{\partial}{\partial x^\nu} + \Lambda_{\mu b}^{a\nu}(u)\frac{\partial}{\partial h_b^\nu}.$$

In general case, $\hat{\Lambda}, \bar{\Lambda}, \tilde{\Lambda}, \Lambda$ are arbitrary functions of the local coordinates (x^μ, h_a^μ) which we assume to be smooth. *Vertical* linear maps are given by the particular case

$$\tilde{\Lambda}_\nu^{a\mu} = 0. \tag{33}$$

The condition (2) which expresses the compatibility of the linear map ϕ with the right action of the group specifies the transformation properties of the coefficient functions Λ. The coordinate description of the right action, $u \rightarrow ug$, is given by

$$h_a^\mu \rightarrow h_b^\mu g_a^b,$$

where $g_a^b \in GL(n, R)$. This immediately yields

$$\hat{\Lambda}_\mu^\nu(ug) = \hat{\Lambda}_\mu^\nu(u), \quad \Lambda_{\mu b}^{a\nu}(ug) = \Lambda_{\mu d}^{c\nu}(u)(g^{-1})_c^a g_b^d, \tag{34}$$

$$\bar{\Lambda}_{a\mu}^\nu(ug) = \bar{\Lambda}_{b\mu}^\nu(u)g_a^b, \quad \tilde{\Lambda}_\mu^{a\nu}(ug) = \tilde{\Lambda}_\mu^{b\nu}(u)(g^{-1})_b^a. \tag{35}$$

Now we are in a position to define the two associated maps in the local coordinates. According to (3) one easily finds, for an arbitrary vector $\bar{X}^\mu \partial_\mu$ on M,

$$(\hat{\varphi}(\bar{X}))^\mu = \hat{\Lambda}_\nu^\mu \bar{X}^\nu. \tag{36}$$

The associated linear map on the algebra $gl(n, R)$, as defined by (5), in the local coordinates reads

$$(\varphi_u(\xi))_b^a = \Lambda_{db}^{ca}(u)\xi_c^d, \tag{37}$$

where

$$\Lambda_{db}^{ca} = h_\nu^a \Lambda_{\mu b}^{c\nu} h_d^\mu. \tag{38}$$

The properties (4),(6) of the associated maps are evident.

Let us now study local coordinate representations of the ϕ-connection form and the ϕ-canonical form.

For arbitrary coordinates $\{x^\mu\}$ let us define the n^3 functions $\Gamma_{\beta\mu}^\alpha(x)$ which transform as follows under the change of the local coordinates $x^\mu \rightarrow x'^\mu(x^\nu)$

$$\Gamma_{\beta\mu}'^\alpha(x') = \frac{\partial x'^\alpha}{\partial x^\rho}\left[\Gamma_{\sigma\nu}^\rho(x)\frac{\partial x^\nu}{\partial x'^\mu} + \frac{\partial^2 x^\delta}{\partial x'^\mu \partial x'^\lambda}\frac{\partial x'^\lambda}{\partial x^\gamma}\Lambda_{\delta\sigma}^{\gamma\rho}(x)\right]\frac{\partial x^\sigma}{\partial x'^\beta}, \tag{39}$$

where

$$\Lambda_{\mu\beta}^{\alpha\nu} = h_a^\alpha \Lambda_{\mu b}^{a\nu} h_\beta^b$$

is (in view of (34)) the type (2,2) tensor field on M.

Proposition 5. Given the functions $\Gamma_{\beta\mu}^\alpha$ with the transformation law (39), the general expression of the ϕ-connection 1-form on $P = L(M)$ reads

$$\omega_b^a = h_\alpha^a(\Gamma_{\beta\mu}^\alpha h_b^\beta dx^\mu + \Lambda_{\mu b}^{c\alpha} dh_c^\mu). \tag{40}$$

Proof. One easily verifies the properties $(a), (b)$ of the ϕ-connection 1-form. Equation (39) guarantees the global definition of the form ω (i.e. independence of the local coordinates).

As usually, the functions $\Gamma_{\beta\mu}^\alpha$ are interpreted as the *components of connection* with respect to the local coordinate system x^μ. Indeed, these are nothing but the pullback of the ϕ-connection 1-form by the local section $\sigma : x \to u(x)$ naturally defined by the choice of the local coordinates $u(x) = (x^\mu, h_a^\mu = \delta_a^\mu)$.

When $\phi = id$ the standard local expressions are recovered, since $\hat{\Lambda}_\nu^\mu = \delta_\nu^\mu$, $\Lambda_{\mu b}^{a\nu} = \delta_\mu^\nu \delta_b^a$.

The ϕ-canonical form in the local coordinates (31) reads as follows

$$\vartheta^a = h_\mu^a \hat{\Lambda}_\nu^\mu dx^\nu. \tag{41}$$

In general case, the local coordinate components of curvature and torsion look rather complicated, so we will not give them explicitly. Instead, it seems to be more illuminative to consider some particular cases.

6. Applications to geometrical and physical models

6.1. Ōtsuki geometry

Recently in [6] the Ōtsuki geometry [9] has been discussed in connection with its possible relevance to the unified geometrical models including gravitation.

It is interesting to see that a regular case of this generalised geometry naturally arises within the framework of the theory of ϕ-connections. Let a linear map ϕ be given in the local coordinates (31) by

$$\hat{\Lambda}_\nu^\mu = \delta_\nu^\mu, \quad \bar{\Lambda}_{a\nu}^\mu = 0, \quad \tilde{\Lambda}_\nu^{a\mu} = 0, \quad \Lambda_{\nu b}^{a\mu} = P_\nu^\mu \delta_b^a, \tag{42}$$

with a type (1,1) tensor field $P_\nu^\mu(x)$.

The ϕ-connection 1-form and the canonical 1-form are then given by the following expressions

$$\omega^a{}_b = h^a_\alpha \Gamma^\alpha_{\beta\mu} h^\beta_b dx^\mu + h^a_\alpha P^\alpha_\beta dh^\beta_b, \tag{43}$$

$$\vartheta^a = h^a_\mu dx^\mu. \tag{44}$$

Let us denote the inverse of P^μ_ν by Q^μ_ν, and introduce

$$P^a_b = h^a_\mu h^\nu_b P^\mu_\nu, \quad Q^a_b = h^a_\mu h^\nu_b Q^\mu_\nu, \quad P^a_c Q^c_b = \delta^a_b. \tag{45}$$

With the help of these the first and the second (12) structure equations for the torsion Θ^a and the curvature $\Omega^a{}_b$ 2-forms (defined on P as the covariant derivatives of canonical form and connection form (44), (43)) are easily calculated,

$$\Theta^a = d\vartheta^a + Q^a_c \omega^c{}_d \wedge \vartheta^d, \tag{46}$$

$$\Omega^a{}_b = d\omega^a{}_b + P^a_c dQ^c_d \wedge \omega^d{}_b + \omega^a{}_c \wedge Q^c_d \omega^d{}_b. \tag{47}$$

Comparing with [9], one finds that (43)-(47) describe a regular Ōtsuki geometry with coinciding covariant and contravariant parts of the generalised Ōtsuki connection. Notice, that like in the standard geometry, the torsion (46) is related to the antisymmetric part of the generalised connection components,

$$\Gamma^\mu_{\alpha\beta} - \Gamma^\mu_{\beta\alpha} = -P^\mu_\nu h^\nu_a \Theta^a_{\alpha\beta}. \tag{48}$$

The transformation law (39) for the Ōtsuki connection coefficients reduces to

$$\Gamma'^\alpha_{\beta\mu}(x') = \frac{\partial x'^\alpha}{\partial x^\rho} \frac{\partial x^\sigma}{\partial x'^\beta} \Gamma^\rho_{\sigma\nu}(x) \frac{\partial x^\nu}{\partial x'^\mu} + \frac{\partial x'^\alpha}{\partial x^\rho} P^\rho_\sigma \frac{\partial^2 x^\sigma}{\partial x'^\mu \partial x'^\beta}. \tag{49}$$

The corresponding generalised curvature tensor components are given explicitly by

$$R^\alpha{}_{\beta\mu\nu} =$$

$$= \partial_\mu \Gamma^\alpha_{\beta\nu} - \partial_\nu \Gamma^\alpha_{\beta\mu} + P^\alpha_\rho (\partial_\mu Q^\rho_\sigma \delta^\lambda_\nu - \partial_\nu Q^\rho_\sigma \delta^\lambda_\mu) \Gamma^\sigma_{\beta\lambda} + \Gamma^\alpha_{\rho\mu} Q^\rho_\sigma \Gamma^\sigma_{\beta\nu} - \Gamma^\alpha_{\rho\nu} Q^\rho_\sigma \Gamma^\sigma_{\beta\mu}.$$

$$(50)$$

In the next subsection a gravitational model based on such a regular Ōtsuki geometry is analysed.

6.2. Einstein-Ōtsuki gravitational model

In order to see, which physics could be related to the above regular Ōtsuki geometry, let us consider a simple model of a gravitational theory. We will assume, that in addition to the above described connection structure a space-time manifold M (let us consider the standard $n = 4$ case) has also a metric. It means that the symmetric scalar product is defined for the vectors, which in the local coordinates is decribed as usually by the metric tensor components $g_{\mu\nu} = (\partial_\mu, \partial_\nu)$. As it is, the metric structure is defined completely independently from the connection, however different relations could arise from the field equations.

In this section we will consider the minimal generalisation of the Einstein gravitational theory, by choosing the action in the Hilbert type form

$$S = \int d^4x \sqrt{-g} R, \qquad (51)$$

where $R_{\mu\nu} = R^\alpha_{\mu\alpha\nu}$, $R = g^{\mu\nu} R_{\mu\nu}$ are the generalised Ricci tensor and the curvature scalar constructed from components of the curvature tensor (50). This model was discussed also in [7], but a more general case of the Ōtsuki connection was considered there.

Let us furthermore restrict ourselves to the case

$$P^\mu_\nu = P\delta^\mu_\nu, \qquad (52)$$

where $P = P(x)$ is a scalar function on M.

The Palatini type variational principle, with $g_{\mu\nu}$, $\Gamma^\alpha_{\beta\mu}$, P^μ_ν treated as independent variables, gives for the action (51) the field equations (in absence of matter):

$$R_{(\mu\nu)} - \frac{1}{2}Rg_{\mu\nu} = 0, \tag{53.1}$$

$$N_\alpha{}^{\mu\alpha}\delta^\nu_\lambda - N_\lambda{}^{\mu\nu} + g^{\mu\nu}U^\alpha_{\lambda\alpha} - g^{\mu\alpha}U^\nu_{\lambda\alpha} + g^{\mu\alpha}\Theta^\nu_{\lambda\alpha} = 0, \tag{53.2}$$

$$g^{\mu\nu}Q^\alpha_\lambda R^\lambda{}_{\mu\beta\nu} = 0, \tag{53.3}$$

where

$$N_\lambda{}^{\mu\nu} = \frac{1}{\sqrt{-g}}\partial_\lambda(\sqrt{-g}g^{\mu\nu}) + \Gamma^\alpha_{\beta\lambda}(Q^\mu_\alpha g^{\beta\nu} + Q^\nu_\alpha g^{\beta\mu}) - Q^\beta_\alpha\Gamma^\alpha_{\lambda\beta}, \tag{54}$$

$$U^\alpha_{\beta\mu} = P^\alpha_\sigma\partial_\mu Q^\sigma_\beta + \Gamma^\alpha_{\sigma\mu}Q^\sigma_\beta - \Gamma^\sigma_{\beta\mu}Q^\alpha_\sigma. \tag{55}$$

Actually, eqs. (54)-(55) give the covariant derivatives of different geometrical quantities in the regular Ōtsuki geometry under consideration. In particular, (54) is the generalisation od the non-metricity tensor.

In vacuum the field equations (53) can be straightforwardly solved, giving the relation between the metric and connection. Let us illustrate this for the case of (52). Equation (53.3) is then a consequence of (53.1), while (53.2) is solved exactly (for detailes see ref. [9] with analogous calculations in the usual metric-affine framework) to give the connection in terms of metric

$$\Gamma^\alpha_{\beta\mu} = \frac{1}{2}g^{\alpha\nu}\left(\partial_\beta(Pg_{\mu\nu}) + \partial_\mu(Pg_{\beta\nu}) - \partial_\nu(Pg_{\beta\mu})\right) + \delta^\alpha_\beta K_\mu, \tag{56}$$

where the vector field K_μ is arbitrary due to the projective invariance of the Palatini-Hilbert action (50). Using this invariance, without loosing the generality we can put $K_\mu = 0$.

As we see, in general neither torsion, nor non-metricity are zero in vacuum. In presence of matter the solutions look more complicated but in essence they describe some sort of superposition of the Einstein-Cartan model (with spin coupled to the torsion) with the Weyl type non-metricity. In general case (for $P_\nu^\mu \neq \delta_\nu^\mu P$) the crucial role is played by the tensor (55) in terms of which both the torsion and the non-metricity are expressed.

Imposing from the beginning an additional assumption of zero non-metricity (e.g. with the help of the Lagrange multipliers) one finds further simplification. However, only for the particular case (53), in agreement with the results of [6-7], one is left with the torsion-less standard Einstein field equations. In general, torsion is non-zero and is determined in terms of $U_{\beta\mu}^\alpha$.

The results obtained (see equation (56)) suggest using the Ōtsuki geometry for the construction of alternative Weyl type gravitational theories. This is however typical also for the other choices of the linear map ϕ, as shown below.

6.3. Lyra geometry

Let us now demonstrate that the Lyra geometry [11] also can be treated as a particular case of the scheme under consideration. The gravitational models based on the Lyra spaces were suggested earlier to provide a different framework for the conformal (Weyl) symmetry (with possible applications to the problem of variability of fundamental constants), see e.g. [8].

Instead of (42) the fundamental linear map is now characterised by the following non-trivial components,

$$\hat{\Lambda}_\nu^\mu = \Lambda \delta_\nu^\mu, \quad \bar{\Lambda}_{a\nu}^\mu = 0, \quad \tilde{\Lambda}_\nu^{a\mu} = 0, \quad \Lambda_{\nu b}^{a\mu} = \delta_\nu^\mu \delta_b^a, \tag{57}$$

where $\Lambda = \Lambda(x)$ is a scalar function on M.

With (57) the ϕ-connection form (40) reduces to the usual linear connection on $L(M)$, however the canonical form (41) reduces to

$$\vartheta^a = \Lambda h^a_\mu dx^\mu. \tag{58}$$

This object plays the important role in the Lyra geometry, although the original formulation uses a different language and notations.

The 1-st generalised structure equation for (57)-(58) reads

$$\Theta^a = d\vartheta^a + \omega^a_{\ b} \wedge \vartheta^b - d\log\Lambda \wedge \vartheta^a,$$

and this suggests the specific ansatz for the torsion $\Theta^a = \Phi \wedge \vartheta^a$ with a 1-form Φ.

The most peculiar feature of the Lyra geometry is the explicit formulation of the whole theory with respect to the *conformally holonomic* frames. These are called the local reference systems in [8,11] and in terms of the of the bundle language their usage means the reduction of the frame bundle $L(M)$ to the subbundle (denoted $H_c(M)$) of conformally holonomic frames, $(x, \hat{e}_a) \in H_c(M) \subset L(M)$. The structure group $GL(n, R)$ reduces to the subgroup of conformal transformations, $W \subset GL(n, R)$, which are described by the diagonal $n \times n$ matrices $g^a_b = \lambda \delta^a_b \in W$ (thus W is isomorphic to R). For any open covering of M one can define the local coordinates on $H_c(M)$ by

$$\{x^\mu, \ h^\mu_a = (\chi^0)^{-1}\delta^\mu_a\}, \tag{59}$$

where x^μ are the local coordinates in an open set of M and an element $H_c(M) \ni \hat{u} = (x, \hat{e}_a)$ is described by a pair $(x^\mu, (\chi^0)^{-1}\delta^\mu_a \partial_\mu) = (x^\mu, (\chi^0)^{-1}\partial_\mu)$. In view of the δ in (59) there is no need in the two types of indices for the components of different objects in $H_c(M)$.

Let us remind the basic points of the Lyra geometry. The metric is introduced on M via the smooth scalar product of the conformally holonomic frames, $\hat{g}_{\mu\nu} = (\hat{e}_\mu, \hat{e}_\nu) = (\chi^0)^{-2}(\partial_\mu, \partial_\nu)$. The physically observable infinitesimal space-time interval is defined as $ds^2 = (\chi^0)^2 \hat{g}_{\mu\nu} dx^\mu dx^\nu$. It is thus independent on the internal conformal coordinate χ^0, and this is the main diffrenece with the Weyl geometry. The latter is formulated in terms of the holonomic frames and the *conformal equivalence classes* of metrics, and interval is subject to conformal changes.

This assumption of invariance of ds^2 justifies the introduction of the metricity condition in the Lyra geometry: the metric $\hat{g}_{\mu\nu}$ is postulated to be compatible with the linear connection, in that the covariant derivative (non-metricity form) vanishes $D\hat{g}_{\mu\nu} = 0$. Another basic postulate is about the torsion: this is assumed to be of the form $\Theta^a = \Phi \wedge \vartheta^a$, and the 1-form Φ is in fact a quantity which plays a role of the Weyl form in the Lyra geometry.

We will not discuss the physical models based on the Lyra geometry, see e.g. references [8].

6.4. The Riemann-Cartan geometry and conformal symmetry in the Poincaré gauge gravity

The geometrical arena for the Poincaré gauge theory of gravity [3, 4, 12, 13, 14] is another subbundle of $L(M)$ — the bundle of orthonormal frames, denoted by $O(M)$ hereafter. The orthonormality means that the metric (scalar product for the vectors) is defined on M by

$$(\bar{e}_a, \bar{e}_b) = \eta_{ab} = diag(+1, -1, -1, -1). \tag{60}$$

The structure group of the bundle is thus reduced to the Lorentz subgroup of the general linear group $GL(4, R)$.

Gauging the Poincaré group (an in particular, its translation subgroup) can be most conveniently understood in terms of the affine frame bundles [13,14,4], and the gravitational field potentials are then described by the *generalised affine connection*. The latter can be shown to define the linear (Lorentz) connection 1-form on $O(M)$, and the generalised soldering 1-form, ϑ^a. The latter does not, in general, coincide with the co-frame form $\bar{\vartheta}^a = h^a_\mu dx^\mu$ (dual to a frame $\bar{e}_a = h^\mu_a \partial_\mu$), as first noticed in [14]. Easy to see, that in the local coordinates (31) it is given by the formula (41). Thus in the Poincaré gauge theory of gravity one is naturally led to the ϕ-scheme with the particular form of the linear map

$$\hat{\Lambda}^\mu_\nu = \Phi^\mu_\nu, \qquad \bar{\Lambda}^\mu_{a\nu} = 0, \qquad \tilde{\Lambda}^{a\mu}_\nu = 0, \qquad \Lambda^{a\mu}_{\nu b} = \delta^\mu_\nu \delta^a_b, \tag{61}$$

with the non-trivial tensor field Φ^μ_ν on M.

The linear Lorentz connection 1-form on $O(M)$ is given in the local coordinates (31) by the relevant simplification of (40), namely by the standard formula

$$\omega^a_b = h^a_\alpha (\Gamma^\alpha_{\beta\mu} h^\beta_b dx^\mu + dh^\alpha_b). \tag{62}$$

Hence the curvature and the torsion are given by the usual expressions,

$$\Omega^a_b = d\omega^a_b + \omega^a_c \wedge \omega^c_b, \tag{63}$$

$$\Theta^a = \Phi^a_b (d\bar{\vartheta}^b + \omega^b_c \wedge \bar{\vartheta}^c). \tag{64}$$

Both express the structure equation for the generalised affine connection, and in (64) we used the relation between the soldering and the co-frame forms,

$$\vartheta^a = \Phi^a_b \bar{\vartheta}^b, \qquad \Phi^a_b = h^a_\mu \Phi^\mu_\nu h^\nu_b.$$

Let us now discuss the conformal (Weyl) symmetry in the Poincaré gauge theory. At the first sight, there is no place for it, since the structure (or equivalently, the gauge) group does not contain the relevant dilatation transformations.

However, a closer look on (60) reveals the possibility of defining the "hidden" conformal transformations which *preserve the Riemann-Cartan geometry* (63)-(64) of the Poincaré gauge approach. Indeed, the space-time interval is as usually $ds^2 = \eta_{ab}\bar{\vartheta}^a\bar{\vartheta}^b = g_{\mu\nu}dx^\mu dx^\nu$ with the metric tensor $g_{\mu\nu} = \eta_{ab}h_\mu^a h_\nu^b$. Hence, if the conformal (Weyl) transformation of the interval

$$ds^2 \rightarrow ds'^2 = e^{2\sigma}ds^2, \quad \text{so that} \quad g_{\mu\nu} \rightarrow g'_{\mu\nu} = e^{2\sigma}g_{\mu\nu}, \qquad (65)$$

with a scalar function $\sigma = \sigma(x)$, is accompanied by the *scaling of the frame coordinates*

$$h_a^\mu \rightarrow h_a'^\mu = e^{-\sigma}h_a^\mu, \qquad (66)$$

the frames $\{\bar{e}_a\}$ remain orthonormal, i.e. (60) is invariant under (65)-(66).

The Poincaré gauge gravitational field potentials are the linear connection and the canonical 1-forms $\omega^a{}_b, \vartheta^a$. We demand that these are conformally invariant, i.e. do not change under (65)-(66).

This is easily achieved by specifying the behaviour of the functions $\Gamma^\alpha_{\beta\mu}(x)$ and Φ_ν^μ under the conformal transformations. Let

$$\Gamma^\alpha_{\beta\mu} \rightarrow \Gamma'^\alpha_{\beta\mu} = \Gamma^\alpha_{\beta\mu} + \delta^\alpha_\beta \partial_\mu\sigma, \quad \Phi_\nu^\mu \rightarrow \Phi_\nu'^\mu = e^{-\sigma}\Phi_\nu^\mu. \qquad (67)$$

Then clearly the *Poincaré gauge gravitational fields*

$$\omega^a{}_b, \quad \vartheta^a$$

are conformally invariant.

Since the curvature (63) also does not change, it is straightforward to construct the simplest conformal invariant Poincaré gauge gravitational model. This is given by the generalised Einstein-Hilbert Lagrangian

$$L = \varepsilon_{abcd}\Omega^{ab} \wedge \vartheta^c \wedge \vartheta^d, \qquad (68)$$

where ε_{abcd} is the totally skew-symmetric Levi-Civita symbol.

The particular case with the diagonal linear map $\Phi^\mu_\nu = \Phi(x)\delta^\mu_\nu$ was analysed in detail in [15]. The gravitational action (68) is then

$$S = \int L = -4 \int d^4x \sqrt{-g}\Phi^2 R, \qquad (69)$$

with R the Riemann-Cartan curvature scalar.

The gravitational field equations arise from the independent variation of h^a_μ, ω^a_b, Φ, or equivalently, of the metric, torsion and the scalar field Φ. In the absence of matter these equations read

$$R_{(\mu\nu)} - \frac{1}{2}Rg_{\mu\nu} = 0, \qquad (70.1)$$

$$\Gamma^\alpha_{\mu\nu} - \Gamma^\alpha_{\nu\mu} = \delta^\alpha_\nu \partial_\mu \log \Phi - \delta^\alpha_\mu \partial_\nu \log \Phi, \qquad (70.2)$$

$$R = 0. \qquad (70.3)$$

The conformal invariance of (70) is clear from (67). It is well known, that the connection coefficients $\Gamma^\alpha_{\beta\mu}$ can always be decomposed into a sum of the purely Riemannian part – the Christoffel symbols $\tilde{\Gamma}^\alpha_{\beta\mu} = \frac{1}{2}g^{\alpha\nu}(\partial_\beta g_{\mu\nu} + \partial_\mu g_{\beta\nu} - \partial_\nu g_{\beta\mu})$, and the non-Riemannian part which in general is determined by non-metricity and torsion. The non-metricity is zero here, while the torsion is given by (70.2). When substituting this decomposition into (70.1),(70.3) one finds (denoting by a tilde the objects constructed with the help of the Christoffel connection $\tilde{\Gamma}^\alpha_{\beta\mu}$)

$$\tilde{R}_{(\mu\nu)} - \frac{1}{2}\tilde{R}g_{\mu\nu} =$$

$$= -\frac{6}{\Phi^2}[\partial_\mu \Phi \partial_\nu \Phi - \frac{1}{2}g_{\mu\nu}\partial_\alpha \Phi \partial^\alpha \Phi - \frac{1}{6}(\tilde{\nabla}_\mu\tilde{\nabla}_\nu - g_{\mu\nu}g^{\alpha\beta}\tilde{\nabla}_\alpha\tilde{\nabla}_\beta)\Phi^2], \quad (71)$$

$$(g^{\alpha\beta}\tilde{\nabla}_\alpha\tilde{\nabla}_\beta - \frac{1}{6}\tilde{R})\Phi = 0. \qquad (72)$$

Notice that the right hand side of (71) is presicely the improved Callan-Coleman-Jackiw energy-momentum for a conformal scalar field, while (72) is the standard conformal invariant wave equation. The gravitational coupling is nonconstant and effectively described by $(\frac{6}{\Phi^2})$.

For a dicussion of more complicated conformal invariant Poincaré gauge models see [15].

7. Conclusion

The new structure – vertical linear map on a principal fiber bundle – yields a natural generalisation of the Lie algebra-valued 1-forms on P. Leaving aside (at the moment) possible purely mathematical developments, it is satisfatory to see that this scheme provides a unified framework for several generalised gravitational theories. A common feature of these models is the account of the conformal (Weyl) symmetry transformations. This aspect requires further investigation, in particular the non-gravitational matter should be included.

In this paper we restricted ourselves mainly to the applications in the gravity theory, and shown that a number of non-Riemannian geometries might be more deeply understood in this way. However, in the sect. 3 the ordinary gauge models (in flat space-time) were discussed, showing an additional perspective in constructing the relevant generalisations of the standard Yang-Mills theories. The gauge models of electromagnetic, weak and strong interactions can thus be extended and the new physical consequences obtained. The work is in progress in this direction. An interesting possibility of further development is opened when a single ϕ map on P is replaced by a *group* of vertical linear maps.

Acknowledgements

I am grateful to Friedrich W. Hehl for the warm hospitality at the University of Cologne, his encouragement and support. The shortened version of this paper was reported in my talk at the Conference of the German Physical Society (Mainz, March 1993), I thank the participants for attention and discussion. This research was supported by the Alexander von Humboldt Foundation (Bonn) during my stay in Cologne.

References

[1] Daniel M., and Viallet C.M., *Rev. Mod. Phys.*, **52** (1980) 175.

[2] Bleecker D.D., *Gauge Theory and Variational Principles* (Addison-Wesley: New York, 1981).

[3] Trautman A., in: *General Relativity and Gravitation: One Hundred Years after the Birth of Albert Einstein*, Ed. A.Held (Plenum: New York, 1980) vol. 1, 287.

[4] Mielke E.W., *Geometrodynamics of Gauge Fields: On the Geometry of Yang-Mills and gravitational gauge theories* (Akademie Verlag: Berlin, 1987).

[5] Kobayashi S., and Nomizu K., *Foundations of Differential Geometry* (Interscience: New York, 1963), vol. 1.

[6] Smrz P.K., *Gen. Relat. Grav.*, **24** (1992) 857.

[7] Smrz P.K., *Gen. Relat. Grav.*, **25** (1993) 33.

[8] Sen D.K., and Vanstone J.R., *J. Math. Phys.*, **13** (1972) 990; Sen D.K., *Fields and/or Particles* (Academic Press: London, 1968).

[9] Ōtsuki T., *Proc. Japan Acad. Sci.*, **34** (1958) 325; **37** (1961) 183.

[10] Ponomariev V.N., and Obukhov Yu.N., *Gen. Relat. Grav.*, **14** (1982) 309.

[11] Lyra G., *Math. Z.*, **54** (1951) 52.

[12] Hehl F.W., von der Heyde P., Kerlick G.D., and Nester J.M., *Rev. Mod. Phys.*, **48** (1976) 393; Hehl F.W., Nitsch J., and von der Heyde P., in: *General Relativity and Gravitation: One Hundred Years after the Birth of Albert Einstein*, Ed. A.Held (Plenum: New York, 1980) vol. 1, 329.

[13] Pilch K.A., *Lett. Math. Phys.*, **4** (1980) 49; Tseytlin A.A., *Phys. Rev.*, **D26** (1982) 3327; Hennig J., and Nitsch J., *Gen. Rel. Grav.*, **13** (1981) 947.

[14] Norris L.K., Fulp R.O., and Davis W.R., *Phys. Lett.*, **A79** (1980) 278.

[15] Obukhov Yu.N., *Phys. Lett.*, **A90** (1982) 13.

Gennadi A. Sardanashvily, Editor
New Frontiers in Gravitation
Hadronic Press, Palm Harbor, FL 34682-1577, U.S.A.
ISBN 0–911767–96–7, 1996, Pages 299–336

GRAVITY AS A HIGGS FIELD

Gennadi A Sardanashvily

Department of Theoretical Physics, Physics Faculty,
Moscow State University, 117234 Moscow, Russia
E-mail: sard@grav.phys.msu.su

Abstract

If gravity is a metric field by Einstein, it is a Higgs field. Gravitation theory meets spontaneous symmetry breaking in accordance with the equivalence principle reformulated in the spirit of the Klein-Chern geometries of invariants. In gravitation theory, the structure group of the principal linear frame bundle LX over a world manifold X^4 is reducible to the connected Lorentz group $SO(3,1)$. The physical underlying reason of this reduction is the Dirac fermion matter possessing only exact Lorentz symmetries. The associated Higgs field is a tetrad gravitational field h represented by a global section of the quotient Σ of LX by $SO(3,1)$. From the mathematical viewpoint, the feature of gravity as a Higgs field issues from the fact that different tetrad fields imply nonequivalent representations of cotangent vectors to X^4 by the Dirac's matrices. It follows that a fermion field must be regarded only in a pair with a certain tetrad field. These pairs are represented by sections of the composite spinor bundle $S \to \Sigma \to X^4$ where values of tetrad gravitational fields play the role of coordinate parameters, besides the familiar world coordinates. It is a constraint system to describe which we use the covariant multisymplectic Hamiltonian formalism when canonical momenta correspond to derivatives of fields with respect to all world coordinates, not only the temporal one. The feature of a tetrad gravitational field as a Higgs field lies in the fact that, on the constraint space, its canonical momenta are equal to zero, otherwise in the presence of fermion fields. Fermion fields deform the constraint space in the gravitation sector that leads to modification of the Einstein equations.

1 Introduction

Gravitation theory is theory with spontaneous symmetry breaking. Spontaneous symmetry breaking is quantum phenomenon modelled by a classical Higgs field. In the algebraic quantum field theory, Higgs fields characterize nonequivalent Gaussian states of algebras of quantum fields. They are *sui generis* fictitious fields describing collective phenomena. In gravitation theory, spontaneous symmetry breaking displays on the classical level. It is established by the equivalence principle reformulated in the terms of Klein-Chern geometries of invariants [6, 13, 15].

In Einstein's General Relativity, the equivalence principle is called to provide transition to Special Relativity with respect to some reference frames. In the spirit of F.Klein's Erlanger program, the Minkowski space geometry can be characterized as geometry of Lorentz invariants. The geometric equivalence principle then postulates that there exist reference frames with respect to wich Lorentz invariants can be defined everywhere on a world manifold X^4. This principle has the adequate mathematical formulation in terms of fibre bundles.

We follow the generally accepted geometric description of classical fields as sections of a fibred manifold

$$\pi : Y \to X$$

over a world manifold X^4. In gauge theory, $Y \to X$ is a bundle with a structure group. In gravitation theory, all bundles must be associated with the tangent bundle TX of a world manifold.

Remark. A fibred manifold $\pi : Y \to X$ is provided with fibred coordinates (x^λ, y^i) where x^λ are coordinates of the base X. A locally trivial fibred manifold is termed the bundle. We denote by VY and V^*Y the vertical tangent bundle and the vertical cotangent bundle of Y respectively. For the sake of simplicity, the pullbacks $Y \underset{X}{\times} TX$ and $Y \underset{X}{\times} T^*X$ are denoted by TX and T^*X respectively. $\square$

Let LX be the principal bundle of linear frames in tangent spaces to X^4. Its structure group is

$$GL_4 = GL^+(4, \mathbf{R}).$$

The geometric equivalence principle requires that this structure group is reduced to the connected Lorentz group

$$L = SO(3, 1).$$

It means that there is given a reduced subbundle L^hX of LX whose structure group is L. They are atlases of L^hX with respect to which Lorentz invariants can be defined.

In accordance with the well-known theorem, there is the 1:1 correspondence between the reduced L subbundles L^hX of LX and the tetrad gravitational fields h represented by global sections of the quotient bundle

$$\Sigma := LX/L \to X^4. \tag{1}$$

Its standard fibre is the quotient space GL_4/L. The bundle (1) is isomorphic to the 2-fold covering of the bundle Σ_g of pseudo-Riemannian forms in cotangent spaces to X^4. A global section of Σ_g is a pseudo-Riemannian metric on X^4.

Thereby, the geometric equivalence principle provides a world manifold with the so-called L-structure [20]. From the physical point of view, it singles out the Lorentz group as the exact symmetry subgroup of world symmetries broken spontaneously [6]. The associated classical Higgs field is a tetrad (or metric) gravitational field.

For the first time, the conception of a graviton as a Goldstone particle corresponding to violation of Lorentz symmetries in a curved space-time had been advanced in mid 60s by Heisenberg and Ivanenko in discussion on cosmological and vacuum asymmetries. This idea was revived in connection with constructing the induced representations of the group GL_4 [5, 9, 10] and then in the framework of the approach to gravitation theory as a nonlinear σ-model [11]. In geometric terms, the fact that a pseudo-Riemannian metric is similar a Higgs field has been pointed out by Trautman [21] and by us [12]. To justify it, the new geometric formulation of the equivalence principle has been suggested [6].

The underlying physical reason of the geometric equivalence principle is the Dirac fermion matter possesing only exact Lorentz symmetries. D.Ivanenko and V.Fock in 1929 had been the first to face the problem that the symmetry of fermion matter differed from that of geometric arena when they investigated the parallel displacement of spinors in Riemannian geometry.

Let us consider a bundle of complex Clifford algebras $C_{3,1}$ over X^4, its spinor subbundle $S_M \to X^4$ and the subbundle $Y_M \to X^4$ of Minkowski spaces of generating elements of $C_{3,1}$. There exists the bundle morphism

$$\gamma : Y_M \otimes S_M \to S_M$$

which is representation of elements of Y_M by the Dirac's γ-matrices on elements of the spinor bundle S_M.

To describe Dirac fermion fields on a world manifold, one must require that the bundle Y_M is isomorphic to the cotangent bundle T^*X of X^4. It takes place if Y_M is associated with some reduced L subbundle $L^h X$ of the linear frame bundle LX. Then, there exists the representation

$$\gamma_h : T^*X \otimes S_h \to S_h$$

of cotangent vectors to a world manifold X^4 by Dirac's γ-matrices on elements of the spinor bundle S_h associated with the lift of $L^h X$ to the $SL(2, \mathbf{C})$ principal bundle. Sections of S_h describe Dirac fermion fields in the presence of the tetrad gravitational field h.

It follows that, in the presence of Dirac fermion matter, we must handle two types of reference frames. They are holonomic atlases of LX and atlases of a reduced Lorentz subbundle $L^h X$ of LX. The corresponding gravitational field h determines transformations between these reference frames. The percularity of gravity thus is clarified. In contrast to other fields, a tetrad gravitationsl field itself sets up reference frames. The Higgs field character of gravity issues from the fact that the reference frames and other characteristics associated with different gravitational fields are not equivalent in a sense.

The key point consists in the fact that, for different tetrad fields h and h', the representations γ_h and $\gamma_{h'}$ fail to be equivalent [13, 15]. It follows that every Dirac fermion field must be regarded only in a pair with a certain tetrad gravitational field h. Therefore, gravitational fields and fermion fields can not be represented by sections of the familiar product $S \times \Sigma$ of the bundle Σ and some standard spinor bundle $S \to X^4$. Their pairs constitute the so-called fermion-gravitation complex [9]. There is the 1:1 correspondence between these pairs and the sections of the composite bundle

$$S \to \Sigma \to X^4 \tag{2}$$

where $S \to \Sigma$ is a spinor bundle associated with the L principal bundle $LX \to \Sigma$ [14, 15]. At the same time, every spinor bundle $S_h \to X^4$ is isomorphic to restriction of $S \to \Sigma$ to $h(X^4) \subset \Sigma$. The goal consists in modification of the standard gravitational equations for sections of the composite bundle (2).

By a composite fibred manifold is meant the composition

$$Y \to \Sigma \to X \tag{3}$$

where $Y \to \Sigma$ is a bundle denoted by Y_Σ and $\Sigma \to X$ is a fibred manifold. In gauge theory, composite manifolds

$$P \to P/K \to X$$

where P is a principal bundle whose structure group is reducible to its closed subgroup K describe spontaneous symmetry breaking [14]. Global sections of $P/K \to X$ are treated the Higgs fields.

Application of composite manifolds to field theory is founded on the following. Given a global section h of Σ, the restriction Y_h of Y_Σ to $h(X)$ is a fibred submanifold of $Y \to X$. There is the 1:1 correspondence between the global sections s_h of Y_h and the global sections of the composite manifold (3) which cover h. Therefore, one can think of sections s_h of Y_h as describing fields in the presence of a background parameter field h, whereas sections of the composite manifold Y describe all the pairs (s_h, h). It is important when the bundles Y_h and $Y_{h \neq h'}$ fail to be equivalent in a sense. The configuration space of these pairs is the first order jet manifold J^1Y of the composite manifold Y and their phase space is the Legendre bundle Π over Y.

Dynamics of fields represented by sections of a fibred manifold $Y \to X$ is phrased in terms of jet manifolds [2, 3, 7, 8, 17, 18]. In field theory, we can restrict our consideration to the first order Lagrangian formalism where the jet manifold J^1Y plays the role of a finite-dimensional configuration space of fields.

Remark. The k-order jet manifold J^kY of a fibred manifold Y comprises the equivalence classes $j_x^k s$, $x \in X$, of sections s of Y identified by the $(k+1)$ terms of their Taylor series at x. The first order jet manifold J^1Y of Y is both the fibred manifold $J^1Y \to X$ and the affine bundle $J^1Y \to Y$ modelled on the vector bundle $T^*X \underset{Y}{\otimes} VY$. It is endowed with the adapted coordinates $(x^\lambda, y^i, y^i_\lambda)$ where

$$y'^i_\lambda = (\frac{\partial y'^i}{\partial y^j} y^j_\mu + \frac{\partial y'^i}{\partial x^\mu}) \frac{\partial x^\mu}{\partial x'^\lambda}.$$

One identifies usually J^1Y to its image under the canonical bundle monomorphism

$$\lambda : J^1Y \xrightarrow[Y]{} T^*X \underset{Y}{\otimes} TY,$$
$$\lambda = dx^\lambda \otimes (\partial_\lambda + y^i_\lambda \partial_i). \tag{4}$$

Every fibred morphism of $\Phi : Y \to Y'$ over a diffeomorphism of X has the jet prolongation

$$J^1\Phi : J^1Y \to J^1Y',$$

$$y'^i_\mu \circ J^1\Phi = (\partial_\lambda\Phi^i + \partial_j\Phi^i y^j_\lambda)\frac{\partial x^\lambda}{\partial x'^\mu}.$$

A section $\bar{s}$ of the fibred jet manifold $J^1Y \to X$ is called holonomic if it is the jet prolongation

$$\bar{s} = J^1s, \qquad \bar{s}^i_\mu = \partial_\mu s^i,$$

of a section s of Y. $\square$

A Lagrangian density on the configuration space J^1Y is defined to be a morphism

$$L : J^1Y \to \overset{n}{\wedge} T^*X, \qquad n = \dim X,$$
$$L = \mathcal{L}\omega, \qquad \omega = dx^1 \wedge ... \wedge dx^n.$$

Note that since the jet bundle $J^1Y \to Y$ is affine, every polynomial Lagrangian density of field theory factors

$$L : J^1Y \to T^*X \underset{Y}{\otimes} VY \to \overset{n}{\wedge} T^*X. \tag{5}$$

Dynamics of field systems utilizes the language of differential geometry because of the 1:1 correspondence between the connections on $Y \to X$ and global sections

$$\Gamma = dx^\lambda \otimes (\partial_\lambda + \Gamma^i_\lambda \partial_i) \tag{6}$$

of the affine jet bundle $J^1Y \to Y$. These global sections form the affine space modelled on the linear space of soldering forms

$$\phi : Y \to T^*X \underset{Y}{\otimes} VY$$

on Y. Every connection Γ on $Y \to X$ yields the first order differential operator

$$D_\Gamma : J^1Y \underset{Y}{\to} T^*X \underset{Y}{\otimes} VY,$$

$$D_\Gamma = (y_\lambda^i - \Gamma_\lambda^i)dx^\lambda \otimes \partial_i, \tag{7}$$

on Y which is called the covariant differential relative to the connection Γ.

The feature of the dynamics of field systems on composite manifolds consists in the following.

Let Y be a composite manifold (3) provided with the fibred coordinates $(x^\lambda, \sigma^m, y^i)$ where (x^λ, σ^m) are fibred coordinates of Σ. Every connection

$$A_\Sigma = dx^\lambda \otimes (\partial_\lambda + \tilde{A}_\lambda^i \partial_i) + d\sigma^m \otimes (\partial_m + A_m^i \partial_i) \tag{8}$$

on $Y \to \Sigma$ yields the first order differential operator

$$\tilde{D} : J^1Y \to T^*X \underset{Y}{\otimes} VY_\Sigma,$$

$$\tilde{D} = dx^\lambda \otimes (y_\lambda^i - \tilde{A}_\lambda^i - A_m^i \sigma_\lambda^m)\partial_i,$$

on Y. Let h be a global section of Σ and Y_h the restriction of the bundle Y_Σ to $h(X)$. The restriction of $\tilde{D}$ to $J^1Y_h \subset J^1Y$ comes to the familiar covariant differential relative to a certain connection A_h on Y_h. Thus, it is $\tilde{D}$ that we may utilize in order to construct a Lagrangian density

$$L : J^1Y \overset{\tilde{D}}{\to} T^*X \underset{Y}{\otimes} VY_\Sigma \to \overset{n}{\wedge} T^*X \tag{9}$$

for sections of a composite manifold. It should be noted that such a Lagrangian density is never regular because of the constraint conditions

$$A_m^i \partial_i^\mu \mathcal{L} = \partial_m^\mu \mathcal{L}.$$

If a Lagrangian density is degenerate, the corresponding Euler-Lagrange equations are underdetermined. To describe constraint field systems, one can utilize the multimomentum Hamiltonian formalism where canonical momenta correspond to derivatives of fields with respect to all world coordinates, not only the temporal one [1, 4, 16, 17, 18]. In the framework of this approach, the phase space of fields is the Legendre bundle

$$\Pi = \overset{n}{\wedge} T^*X \underset{Y}{\otimes} TX \underset{Y}{\otimes} V^*Y \tag{10}$$

over Y coordinatized by $(x^\lambda, y^i, p_i^\lambda)$. Note that every Lagrangian density L on J^1Y determines the Legendre morphism

$$\hat{L} : J^1Y \to \Pi,$$
$$(x^\mu, y^i, p_i^\mu) \circ \hat{L} = (x^\mu, y^i, \partial_i^\mu \mathcal{L}). \tag{11}$$

The Legendre bundle (10) carries the multisymplectic form

$$\Omega = dp_i^\lambda \wedge dy^i \wedge \omega \otimes \partial_\lambda. \tag{12}$$

We say that a connection γ on the fibred Legendre manifold $\Pi \to X$ is a Hamiltonian connection if the form $\gamma \rfloor \Omega$ is closed. Then, a Hamiltonian form H on Π is defined to be an exterior form such that

$$dH = \gamma \rfloor \Omega \tag{13}$$

for some Hamiltonian connection γ. The key point consists in the fact that every Hamiltonian form admits splitting

$$H = p_i^\lambda dy^i \wedge \omega_\lambda - p_i^\lambda \Gamma_\lambda^i \omega - \widetilde{\mathcal{H}}_\Gamma \omega = p_i^\lambda dy^i \wedge \omega_\lambda - \mathcal{H}\omega, \qquad \omega_\lambda = \partial_\lambda \rfloor \omega, \tag{14}$$

where Γ is a connection on $Y \to X$ and $\widetilde{\mathcal{H}}_\Gamma \omega$ is a horizontal density on $\Pi \to X$. Given the Hamiltonian form (14), the equality (13) comes to the first order Hamilton equations

$$\partial_\lambda r^i = \partial_i^\lambda \mathcal{H}, \tag{15a}$$
$$\partial_\lambda r_i^\lambda = -\partial_i \mathcal{H} \tag{15b}$$

for sections r of the fibred Legendre manifold $\Pi \to X$.

If a Lagrangian density L is regular, there exists the unique Hamiltonian form H such that the first order Euler-Lagrange equations and the Hamilton equations are equivalent, otherwise in general case. One must consider a family of different Hamiltonian forms H associated with the same degenerate Lagrangian density L in order to exaust solutions of the Euler-Lagrange equations. Lagrangian densities of field models are almost always quadratic and affine in derivative coordinates y_μ^i. In this case, given an associated Hamiltonian form H, every solution of the corresponding Hamilton equations which lives on $\hat{L}(J^1Y) \subset \Pi$ yields a solution of the Euler-Lagrange equations. Conversely, for any solution of the Euler-Lagrange equations, there exists the corresponding solution of the Hamilton equations for some associated Hamiltonian form. All these solutions live on $\hat{L}(J^1Y)$ which makes the sense of the Lagrangian constraint space.

The feature of Hamiltonian systems on composite manifolds (3) lies in the facts that: (i) every connection A_Σ on $Y \to \Sigma$ yields splitting

$$\omega \otimes \partial_\lambda \otimes [p_i^\lambda(dy^i - A_m^i d\sigma^m) + (p_m^\lambda + A_m^i p_i^\lambda)d\sigma^m]$$

of the Legendre bundle Π over a composite manifold Y and (ii) the Lagrangian constraint space is

$$p_m^\lambda + A_m^i p_i^\lambda = 0. \tag{16}$$

Moreover, if h is a global section of $\Sigma \to X$, the submanifold Π_h of Π given by the coordinate relations

$$\sigma^m = h^m(x), \qquad p_m^\lambda + A_m^i p_i^\lambda = 0$$

is isomorphic to the Legendre bundle over the restriction Y_h of Y_Σ to $h(X)$. The Legendre bundle Π_h is the phase space of fields in the presence of the background parameter field h.

In the Hamiltonian gravitation theory, the constraint condition (16) takes the form

$$p_\mu^{c\lambda} + \frac{1}{8}\eta^{cb}\sigma_\mu^a(y^B[\gamma_a, \gamma_b]^A{}_B p_A^\lambda + p_+^{A\lambda}[\gamma_a, \gamma_b]^{+B}{}_A y_B^+) = 0 \tag{17}$$

where (σ_c^μ, y^A) are respectively tetrad and spinor coordinates of the composite spinor bundle (2), $p_\mu^{c\lambda}$ and p_A^λ are the corresponding momenta and η denotes the Minkowski metric. The condition (17) replaces the standard gravitational constraints

$$p_\mu^{c\lambda} = 0. \tag{18}$$

The crusial point is that, when restricted to the constraint space (18), the Hamilton equations of the gauge gravitation theory come to the familiar gravitational equations, otherwise on the constraint space (17).

2   Dirac fermion fields

By X^4 is further meant an oriented world manifold which satisfies the well-known global topological conditions in order that gravitational fields, space-time structure and spinor structure can exist. To summarize these conditions, we assume that X^4 is not compact and that the tangent bundle of X^4 is trivial.

We describe Dirac fermion fields as follows. Given a Minkowski space M, let $\mathbf{C}_{1,3}$ be the complex Clifford algebra generated by elements of M. A spinor space V is defined to be a minimal left ideal of $\mathbf{C}_{1,3}$ on which this algebra acts on the left. We have the representation

$$\gamma : M \otimes V \to V \tag{19}$$

of elements of the Minkowski space $M \subset \mathbf{C}_{1,3}$ by Dirac's matrices γ on V.

Let us consider the transformations preserving the representation (19). These are pairs (l, l_s) of Lorentz transformations l of the Minkowski space M and invertible elements l_s of $\mathbf{C}_{1,3}$ such that

$$\gamma(lM \otimes l_s V) = l_s \gamma(M \otimes V).$$

Elements l_s form the Clifford group whose action on M however is not effective. We restrict ourselves to its spinor subgroup $L_s = SL(2, \mathbf{C})$ whose generators act on V by the representation

$$I_{ab} = \frac{1}{4}[\gamma_a, \gamma_b].$$

Let us consider a bundle of complex Clifford algebras $\mathbf{C}_{3,1}$ over X^4. Its subbundles are both a spinor bundle $S_M \to X^4$ and the bundle $Y_M \to X^4$ of Minkowski spaces of generating elements of $\mathbf{C}_{3,1}$. To describe Dirac fermion fields on a world manifold, one must require of Y_M to be isomorphic to the cotangent bundle T^*X of a world manifold X^4. It takes place if the structure group of LX is reducible to the Lorentz group L and LX contains a reduced L subbundle $L^h X$ such that

$$Y_M = (L^h X \times M)/L.$$

In this case, the spinor bundle

$$S_M = S_h = (P_h \times V)/L_s \tag{20}$$

is associated with the L_s-lift P_h of $L^h X$.

There is the above-mentioned 1:1 correspondence between the reduced subbubdles $L^h X$ of LX and the tetrad gravitational fields h identified with global sections of the quotient bundle Σ (1).

Given a tetrad field h, let Ψ^h be an atlas of LX such that the corresponding local sections z_ξ^h of LX take their values into $L^h X$. With respect to Ψ^h and a holonomic atlas $\Psi^T = \{\psi_\xi^T\}$ of LX, a tetrad field h can be represented by a family of GL_4-valued tetrad functions

$$h_\xi = \psi_\xi^T \circ z_\xi^h, \qquad x^\lambda = h_a^\lambda(x)h^a. \tag{21}$$

Given a tetrad field h, one can define the representation

$$\gamma_h : T^*X \otimes S_h = (P_h \times (M \otimes V))/L_s \to (P_h \times \gamma(M \otimes V))/L_s = S_h \tag{22}$$

of cotangent vectors to a world manifold X^4 by Dirac's γ-matrices on elements of the spinor bundle S_h. With respect to an atlas $\{z_\xi\}$ of P_h and the associated atlas $\{z_\xi^h\}$ of LX, the morphism (22) reads

$$\gamma_h(h^a \otimes y^A v_A(x)) = \gamma^{aA}{}_B y^B v_A(x)$$

where $\{v_A(x)\}$ are the associated fibre bases for S_h. As a shorthand, one can write

$$\hat{dx}^\lambda = \gamma_h(dx^\lambda) = h_a^\lambda(x)\gamma^a.$$

We shall say that, given the representation (22), sections of the spinor bundle S_h describe Dirac fermion fields in the presence of the gravitational field h. Indeed, let A_h be a principal connection on S_h and

$$D: J^1 S_h \underset{S_h}{\to} T^*X \underset{S_h}{\otimes} V S_h,$$
$$D = (y_\lambda^A - A^{ab}{}_\lambda(x) I_{ab}{}^A{}_B y^B) dx^\lambda \otimes \partial_A,$$

the corresponding covariant differential. Given the representation (22), one can construct the Dirac operator

$$\mathcal{D}_h = \gamma_h \circ D : J^1 S_h \to T^*X \underset{S_h}{\otimes} V S_h \to V S_h, \tag{23}$$

$$\dot{y}^A \circ \mathcal{D}_h = h_a^\lambda(x)\gamma^{aA}{}_B(y_\lambda^B - A^{ab}{}_\lambda I_{ab}{}^A{}_B y^B).$$

We here use the fact that the vertical tangent bundle $V S_h$ admits the canonical splitting

$$V S_h = S_h \times S_h,$$

and γ_h in the expression (23) is the pullback

$$\gamma_h : T^*X \underset{S_h}{\otimes} V S_h \underset{S_h}{\to} V S_h,$$
$$\gamma_h(h^a \otimes \dot{y}^A \partial_A) = \gamma^{aA}{}_B \dot{y}^B \partial_B,$$

over S_h of the bundle morphism (22).

For different tetrad fields h and h', Dirac fermion fields are described by sections of the spinor bundles S_h and $S_{h'}$ associated with the L_s-lifts P_h and $P_{h'}$ of different reduced L-principal subbundles of LX. Therefore, the representations γ_h and $\gamma_{h'}$ (22) are not equivalent [13, 15]. It follows that a Dirac fermion field must be regarded only in a pair with a certain tetrad gravitational field. There is the 1:1 correspondence between these pairs and sections of the composite spinor bundle (2).

3 Composite manifolds

A composite manifold is defined to be composition of surjective submersions

$$\pi_{\Sigma X} \circ \pi_{Y\Sigma} : Y \to \Sigma \to X. \tag{24}$$

It is provided with the particular class of coordinate atlases $(x^\lambda, \sigma^m, y^i)$ where (x^μ, σ^m) are fibred coordinates of Σ and y^i are bundle coordinates of Y_Σ. We further propose that Σ has a global section.

Recall the following assertions [14, 17, 19].

(i) Let Y be the composite manifold (24). Given a section h of Σ and a section s_Σ of Y_Σ, their composition $s_\Sigma \circ h$ is a section of the composite manifold Y. Conversely, if the bundle Y_Σ has a global section, every global section s of the fibred manifold $Y \to X$ is represented by some composition $s_\Sigma \circ h$ where $h = \pi_{Y\Sigma} \circ s$ and s_Σ is an extension of the local section $h(X) \to s(X)$ of the bundle Y_Σ over the closed imbedded submanifold $h(X) \subset \Sigma$.

(ii) Given a global section h of Σ, the restriction $Y_h = h^* Y_\Sigma$ of the bundle Y_Σ to $h(X)$ is a fibred imbedded submanifold of Y.

(iii) There is the 1:1 correspondence between the sections s_h of Y_h and the sections s of the composite manifold Y which cover h.

(iv) Given fibred coordinates $(x^\lambda, \sigma^m, y^i)$ of the composite manifold Y, the jet manifolds $J^1\Sigma$, $J^1 Y_\Sigma$ and $J^1 Y$ are coordinatized respectively by

$$(x^\lambda, \sigma^m, \sigma^m_\lambda), \qquad (x^\lambda, \sigma^m, y^i, \widetilde{y}^i_\lambda, y^i_m), \qquad (x^\lambda, \sigma^m, y^i, \sigma^m_\lambda, y^i_\lambda).$$

There exists the canonical surjection

$$\rho : J^1\Sigma \underset{\Sigma}{\times} J^1 Y_\Sigma \to J^1 Y, \tag{25}$$

$$y^i_\lambda \circ \rho = y^i_m \sigma^m_\lambda + \tilde{y}^i_\lambda,$$

where s_Σ and h are sections of Y_Σ and Σ respectively.

The following assertions are concerned with connections on composite manifolds.

Let A_Σ be the connection (8) on the bundle Y_Σ and Γ the connection (6) on the fibred manifold Σ. Building on the morphism (25), one can construct the connection

$$A = dx^\lambda \otimes [\partial_\lambda + \Gamma^m_\lambda \partial_m + (A^i_m \Gamma^m_\lambda + \tilde{A}^i_\lambda)\partial_i] \tag{26}$$

on the composite manifold Y. We call it the composite connection.

Let a global section h of Σ be an integral section of the connection Γ on Σ, that is, $\Gamma \circ h = J^1 h$. Then, the composite connection (26) on Y is reducible to the connection

$$A_h = dx^\lambda \otimes [\partial_\lambda + (A^i_m \partial_\lambda h^m + \tilde{A}^i_\lambda)\partial_i] \tag{27}$$

on the fibred submanifold Y_h of $Y \to X$. In particular, every connection A_Σ (8) on Y_Σ, whenever h, is reducible to the connection (27) on Y_h.

Every connection (8) on the bundle Y_Σ determines the horizontal splitting

$$VY = VY_\Sigma \underset{Y}{\oplus} (Y \underset{\Sigma}{\times} V\Sigma), \tag{28}$$

$$\dot{y}^i \partial_i + \dot{\sigma}^m \partial_m = (\dot{y}^i - A^i_m \dot{\sigma}^m)\partial_i + \dot{\sigma}^m(\partial_m + A^i_m \partial_i),$$

and the dual horizontal splitting

$$V^*Y = V^*Y_\Sigma \underset{Y}{\oplus} (Y \underset{\Sigma}{\times} V^*\Sigma), \tag{29}$$

$$\dot{y}_i dy^i + \dot{\sigma}_m d\sigma^m = \dot{y}_i(dy^i - A^i_m d\sigma^m) + (\dot{\sigma}_m + A^i_m \dot{y}_i)d\sigma^m.$$

Building on the horizontal splitting (28), one can constract the following first order differential operator on the composite manifold Y:

$$\widetilde{D} = \mathrm{pr}_1 \circ D_A : J^1 Y \to T^* X \underset{Y}{\otimes} VY \to T^* X \underset{Y}{\otimes} VY_\Sigma,$$

$$\widetilde{D} = dx^\lambda \otimes [y^i_\lambda - A^i_\lambda - A^i_m(\sigma^m_\lambda - \Gamma^m_\lambda)]\partial_i =$$
$$dx^\lambda \otimes (y^i_\lambda - \widetilde{A}^i_\lambda - A^i_m \sigma^m_\lambda)\partial_i, \qquad (30)$$

where D_A is the covariant differential (7) relative to the composite connection A (26) which is composition of A_Σ and some connection Γ on Σ. We shall call $\widetilde{D}$ the vertical covariant differential. This possesses the following property.

Given a global section h of Σ, let Γ be a connection on Σ whose integral section is h, that is, $\Gamma \circ h = J^1 h$. It is readily observed that the vertical covariant differential (30) restricted to $J^1 Y_h \subset J^1 Y$ comes to the familiar covariant differential relative to the connection A_h (27) on Y_h. Thus, it is the vertical covariant differential (30) that one may utilize in order to construct a Lagrangian density (9) for sections of a composite manifold.

Now, we consider the composite structure of principal bundles. Let

$$\pi_P : P \to X$$

be a principal bundle with a structure Lie group G and K its closed subgroup. We have the composite manifold

$$\pi_{\Sigma X} \circ \pi_{P\Sigma} : P \to P/K \to X \qquad (31)$$

where

$$P_\Sigma := P \to P/K$$

is a principal bundle with the structure group K and

$$\Sigma = P/K = (P \times G/K)/G$$

is the P-associated bundle.

Let the structure group G be reducible to its closed subgroup K. By the well-known theorem, there is the 1:1 correspondence

$$\pi_{P\Sigma}(P_h) = (h \circ \pi_P)(P_h)$$

between global sections h of the bundle $P/K \to X$ and the reduced K-principal subbundles P_h of P which consist with restrictions of the principal bundle P_Σ to $h(X)$.

Recall the following facts. Every principal connection A_h on a reduced subbundle P_h gives rise to a principal connection on P. Conversely, a principal connection A on P is reducible to a principal connection on P_h iff h is an integral section of the connection A. Every principal connection A_Σ on the K-principal bundle P_Σ, whenever h, induces a principal connection on the reduced subbundle P_h of P.

Given the composite manifold (31), the canonical morphism (25) results in the surjection

$$J^1 P_\Sigma / K \underset{\Sigma}{\times} J^1 \Sigma \to J^1 P/K$$

over $J^1 \Sigma$. Let A_Σ be a principal connection on P_Σ and Γ a connection on Σ. The corresponding composite connection (26) on the composite manifold (31) is equivariant under the canonical action of K on P. If the connection Γ has an integral global section h of $P/K \to X$, the composite connection (26) is reducible to the connection (27) on P_h which consists with the principal connection on P_h induced by A_Σ.

Let us consider the composite manifold

$$Y = (P \times V)/K \to P/K \to X \tag{32}$$

where the bundle

$$Y_\Sigma := (P \times V)/K \to P/K$$

is associated with the K-principal bundle P_Σ. Given a reduced subbundle P_h of P, the associated bundle

$$Y_h = (P_h \times V)/K$$

is isomorphic to the restriction of Y_Σ to $h(X)$. The composite manifold (32) can be provided with the composite connection (26) where the connection A_Σ is associated with a principal connection on the K principal bundle P_Σ and the connection Γ on P/K is associated with a principal connection on some reduced subbundle P_h of P. This composite connection is reducible to the connection (27) on the bundle Y_h which appears to be some principal connection A_h on P.

4 Composite spinor bundles

In gravitation theory, we have the composite manifold

$$\pi_{\Sigma X} \circ \pi_{P\Sigma} : LX \to \Sigma \to X^4 \tag{33}$$

where Σ is the quotient bundle (1) and

$$LX_\Sigma := LX \to \Sigma$$

is the L-principal bundle.

Building on the double universal covering of the group GL_4, one can perform the L_s-principal lift P_Σ of LX_Σ such that

$$P_\Sigma/L_s = \Sigma, \qquad LX_\Sigma = r(P_\Sigma).$$

In particular, there is imbedding of the L_s-lift P_h of $L^h X$ onto the restriction of P_Σ to $h(X^4)$.

Let us consider the composite spinor bundle (2) where

$$S_\Sigma = (P_\Sigma \times V)/L_s$$

is associated with the L_s-principal bundle P_Σ. It is readily observed that, given a global section h of Σ, the restriction S_Σ to $h(X^4)$ is the spinor bundle S_h (20) whose sections describe Dirac fermion fields in the presence of the tetrad field h.

Let us provide the principal bundle LX with a holonomic atlas $\{\psi^t_\xi, U_\xi\}$ and the principal bundles P_Σ and LX_Σ with associated atlases $\{z^s_\epsilon, U_\epsilon\}$ and $\{z_\epsilon = r \circ z^s_\epsilon\}$. With respect to these atlases, the composite spinor bundle is endowed with the fibred coordinates $(x^\lambda, \sigma^\mu_a, y^A)$ where $(x^\lambda, \sigma^\mu_a)$ are fibred coordinates of the bundle Σ such that σ^μ_a are the matrix components of the group element

$$GL_4 \ni (\psi^T_\xi \circ z_\epsilon)(\sigma) : \mathbf{R}^4 \to \mathbf{R}^4, \qquad \sigma \in U_\epsilon, \qquad \pi_{\Sigma X}(\sigma) \in U_\xi.$$

Given a section h of Σ, we have

$$z^h_\xi(x) = (z_\epsilon \circ h)(x), \qquad h(x) \in U_\epsilon, \qquad x \in U_\xi,$$
$$(\sigma^\lambda_a \circ h)(x) = h^\lambda_a(x),$$

where $h^\lambda_a(x)$ are tetrad functions (21).

The jet manifolds $J^1\Sigma$, J^1S_Σ and J^1S are coordinatized respectively by

$$(x^\lambda, \sigma^\mu_a, \sigma^\mu_{a\lambda}), \qquad (x^\lambda, \sigma^\mu_a, y^A, \tilde{y}^A_\lambda, y^{Aa}_\mu), \qquad (x^\lambda, \sigma^\mu_a, y^A, \sigma^\mu_{a\lambda}, y^A_\lambda).$$

Note that, whenever h, the jet manifold J^1S_h is a fibred submanifold of $J^1S \to X^4$ given by the coordinate relations

$$\sigma^\mu_a = h^\mu_a(x), \qquad \sigma^\mu_{a\lambda} = \partial_\lambda h^\mu_a(x).$$

Let us consider the bundle of Minkowski spaces

$$(LX \times M)/L \to \Sigma$$

associated with the L-principal bundle LX_Σ. Since LX_Σ is trivial, it is isomorphic to the pullback $\Sigma \underset{X}{\times} T^*X$ which we denote by the same symbol T^*X. Building on the morphism (19), one can define the bundle morphism

$$\gamma_\Sigma : T^*X \underset{\Sigma}{\otimes} S_\Sigma = (P_\Sigma \times (M \otimes V))/L_s \to (P_\Sigma \times \gamma(M \otimes V))/L_s = S_\Sigma, \quad (34)$$

$$\hat{d}x^\lambda = \gamma_\Sigma(dx^\lambda) = \sigma^\lambda_a \gamma^a,$$

over Σ. When restricted to $h(X^4) \subset \Sigma$, the morphism (34) comes to the morphism γ_h (22). Because of the canonical vertical splitting

$$VS_\Sigma = S_\Sigma \underset{\Sigma}{\times} S_\Sigma,$$

the morphism (34) yields the corresponding morphism

$$\gamma_\Sigma : T^*X \underset{S}{\otimes} VS_\Sigma \to VS_\Sigma. \tag{35}$$

We use this morphism in order to construct the total Dirac operator on sections of the composite spinor bundle S (2). We are based on the following fact.

Let

$$\tilde{A} = dx^\lambda \otimes (\partial_\lambda + \tilde{A}^B_\lambda \partial_B) + d\sigma^\mu_a \otimes (\partial^a_\mu + A^{Ba}_\mu \partial_B)$$

be a connection on the bundle S_Σ. It determines the horizontal splitting (28) of the vertical tangent bundle VS and the vertical covariant differential (30). The composition of the morphisms (35) and (30) is the first order differential operator

$$\mathcal{D} = \gamma_\Sigma \circ \widetilde{D} : J^1S \to T^*X \underset{S}{\otimes} VS_\Sigma \to VS_\Sigma,$$

$$\dot{y}^A \circ \mathcal{D} = \sigma^\lambda_a \gamma^{aA}{}_B(y^B_\lambda - \tilde{A}^B_\lambda - A^{Ba}_\mu \sigma^\mu_{a\lambda}),$$

on S. One can think of it as being the total Dirac operator since, whenever a tetrad field h, the restriction of $\mathcal{D}$ to $J^1S_h \subset J^1S$ comes to the Dirac operator $\mathcal{D}_h$ (23) relative to the connection

$$A_h = dx^\lambda \otimes [\partial_\lambda + (\tilde{A}^B_\lambda + A^{Ba}_\mu \partial_\lambda h^\mu_a) \partial_B]$$

on S_h.

5   Multimomentum Hamiltonian formalism

Let Π be the Legendre bundle (10) over a fibred manifold $Y \to X$. This is the composite manifold

$$\pi_{\Pi X} = \pi \circ \pi_{\Pi Y} : \Pi \to Y \to X$$

provided with fibred coordinates $(x^\lambda, y^i, p_i^\lambda)$ where

$$p_i'^\lambda = J \frac{\partial y^j}{\partial y'^i} \frac{\partial x'^\lambda}{\partial x^\mu} p_j^\mu, \qquad J^{-1} = \det(\frac{\partial x'^\lambda}{\partial x^\mu}). \tag{36}$$

By $J^1\Pi$ is meant the first order jet manifold of $\Pi \to X$. It is coordinatized by

$$(x^\lambda, y^i, p_i^\lambda, y^i_{(\mu)}, p^\lambda_{i\mu}).$$

Remark. We call by a momentum morphism any bundle morphism $\Phi : \Pi \to J^1Y$ over Y. Given a momentum morphism Φ, its composition with the monomorphism (4) is represented by the horizontal pullback-valued 1-form

$$\Phi = dx^\lambda \otimes (\partial_\lambda + \Phi^i_\lambda \partial_i) \tag{37}$$

on $\Pi \to Y$. For instance, let Γ be a connection on Y. Then, the composition $\hat{\Gamma} = \Gamma \circ \pi_{\Pi Y}$ is a momentum morphism. The corresponding form (37) on Π is the pullback $\hat{\Gamma}$ of the form Γ (6) on Y. Conversely, every momentum morphism Φ defines the associated connection $\Gamma_\Phi = \Phi \circ \hat{0}_\Pi$ on $Y \to X$ where $\hat{0}_\Pi$ is the global zero section of $\Pi \to Y$. Every connection Γ on Y gives rise to the connection

$$\tilde{\Gamma} = dx^\lambda \otimes [\partial_\lambda + \Gamma^i_\lambda(y)\partial_i + (-\partial_j \Gamma^i_\lambda(y)p^\mu_i - K^\mu_{\nu\lambda}(x)p^\nu_j + K^\alpha_{\alpha\lambda}(x)p^\mu_j)\partial^j_\mu] \tag{38}$$

on $\Pi \to X$ where K is a linear symmetric connection on T^*X. $\square$

The Legendre manifold Π carries the multimomentum Liouville form

$$\theta = -p_i^\lambda dy^i \wedge \omega \otimes \partial_\lambda \tag{39}$$

and the multisymplectic form Ω (12).

The Hamiltonian formalism in fibred manifolds is formulated intrinsically in terms of Hamiltonian connections which play the role similar to that of Hamiltonian vector fields in the symplectic geometry [1, 4, 16, 17, 18].

We say that a connection γ on the fibred Legendre manifold $\Pi \to X$ is a Hamiltonian connection if the exterior form $\gamma\rfloor\Omega$ is closed. An exterior n-form H on the Legendre manifold Π is called a Hamiltonian form if there exists a Hamiltonian connection satisfying the equation (13).

Let H be a Hamiltonian form. For any exterior horizontal density $\widetilde{H} = \widetilde{\mathcal{H}}\omega$ on $\Pi \to X$, the form $H - \widetilde{H}$ is a Hamiltonian form. Conversely, if H and H' are Hamiltonian forms, their difference $H - H'$ is an exterior horizontal density on $\Pi \to X$. Thus, Hamiltonian forms constitute an affine space modelled on a linear space of the exterior horizontal densities on $\Pi \to X$.

In particular, let Γ be a connection on $Y \to X$ and $\widetilde{\Gamma}$ its lift (38) onto $\Pi \to X$. We have the equality

$$\widetilde{\Gamma}\rfloor\Omega = d(\widehat{\Gamma}\rfloor\theta).$$

A glance at this equality shows that $\widetilde{\Gamma}$ is a Hamiltonian connection and

$$H_\Gamma = \widehat{\Gamma}\rfloor\theta = p_i^\lambda dy^i \wedge \omega_\lambda - p_i^\lambda \Gamma_\lambda^i \omega$$

is a Hamiltonian form. It follows that every Hamiltonian form on Π can be given by the expression (14) where Γ is some connection on $Y \to X$. Moreover, a Hamiltonian form has the canonical splitting (14) as follows. Given a Hamiltonian form H, the vertical tangent morphism VH yields the momentum morphism

$$\widehat{H} : \Pi \to J^1 Y, \qquad y_\lambda^i \circ \widehat{H} = \partial_i^\lambda \mathcal{H},$$

and the associated connection $\Gamma_H = \widehat{H} \circ \widehat{0}$ on Y. As a consequence, we have the canonical splitting

$$H = H_{\Gamma_H} - \widetilde{H}. \tag{40}$$

The Hamilton operator $\mathcal{E}_H$ for a Hamiltonian form H is defined to be the first order differential operator

$$\mathcal{E}_H = dH - \hat{\Omega} = [(y^i_{(\lambda)} - \partial^i_\lambda \mathcal{H})dp^\lambda_i - (p^\lambda_{i\lambda} + \partial_i \mathcal{H})dy^i] \wedge \omega \qquad (41)$$

where $\hat{\Omega}$ is the pullback of the multisymplectic form Ω onto $J^1\Pi$.

For any connection γ on $\Pi \to X$, we have

$$\mathcal{E}_H \circ \gamma = dH - \gamma\rfloor\Omega.$$

It follows that γ is a Hamiltonian connection for a Hamiltonian form H iff it takes its values into $\mathrm{Ker}\,\mathcal{E}_H$, that is, satisfies the algebraic Hamilton equations

$$\gamma^i_\lambda = \partial^i_\lambda \mathcal{H}, \qquad \gamma^\lambda_{i\lambda} = -\partial_i \mathcal{H}. \qquad (42)$$

Let a Hamiltonian connection has an integral section r of $\Pi \to X$. Then, the Hamilton equations (42) are brought into the first order differential Hamilton equations (15a) and (15b).

6 Constraint field systems

This Section is devoted to relations between Lagrangian and Hamiltonian formalisms in fibred manifolds in case of degenerate Lagrangian densities.

Remark. The repeated jet manifold $J^1 J^1 Y$, by definition, is the first order jet manifold of $J^1 Y \to X$. It is provided with the adapted coordinates $(x^\lambda, y^i, y^i_\lambda, y^i_{(\mu)}, y^i_{\lambda\mu})$. Its subbundle $\hat{J}^2 Y$ with $y^i_{(\lambda)} = y^i_\lambda$ is called the sesquiholonomic jet manifold. The second order jet manifold $J^2 Y$ of Y is the subbundle of $\hat{J}^2 Y$ with $y^i_{\lambda\mu} = y^i_{\mu\lambda}$. $\square$

Let $Y \to X$ be a fibred manifold and $L = \mathcal{L}\omega$ a Lagrangian density on $J^1 Y$. One can construct the exterior form

$$\Lambda_L = [y^i_{(\lambda)} - y^i_\lambda)d\pi^\lambda_i + (\partial_i - \hat{\partial}_\lambda \partial^\lambda_i)\mathcal{L}dy^i] \wedge \omega, \qquad (43)$$

$$\lambda = dx^\lambda \otimes \partial_\lambda, \qquad \hat{\partial}_\lambda = \partial_\lambda + y^i_{(\lambda)}\partial_i + y^i_{\mu\lambda}\partial^\mu_i,$$

on the repeated jet manifold J^1J^1Y. Its restriction to the second order jet manifold J^2Y of Y reproduces the familiar variational Euler-Lagrange operator

$$\mathcal{E}_L = [\partial_i - (\partial_\lambda + y^i_\lambda\partial_i + y^i_{\mu\lambda}\partial^\mu_i)\partial^\lambda_i]\mathcal{L}dy^i \wedge \omega. \tag{44}$$

The restriction of the form (43) to the sesquiholonomic jet manifold $\hat{J}^2Y$ defines the sesquiholonomic extension $\mathcal{E}'_L$ of the Euler-Lagrange operator (44). It is given by the expression (44), but with nonsymmetric coordinates $y^i_{\mu\lambda}$.

Let $\bar{s}$ be a section of the fibred jet manifold $J^1Y \to X$ such that its first order jet prolongation $J^1\bar{s}$ takes its values into $\mathrm{Ker}\,\mathcal{E}'_L$. Then, $\bar{s}$ satisfies the first order differential Euler-Lagrange equations

$$\partial_\lambda\bar{s}^i = \bar{s}^i_\lambda,$$
$$\partial_i\mathcal{L} - (\partial_\lambda + \bar{s}^j_\lambda\partial_j + \partial_\lambda\bar{s}^j_\mu\partial^\mu_j)\partial^\lambda_i\mathcal{L} = 0. \tag{45}$$

They are equivalent to the second order Euler-Lagrange equations

$$\partial_i\mathcal{L} - (\partial_\lambda + \partial_\lambda s^j\partial_j + \partial_\lambda\partial_\mu s^j\partial^\mu_j)\partial^\lambda_i\mathcal{L} = 0. \tag{46}$$

for sections s of Y where $\bar{s} = J^1s$.

Given a Lagrangian density L, the vertical tangent morphism of L yields the Legendre morphism (11). We say that a Hamiltonian form H is associated with a Lagrangian density L if H satisfies the relations

$$\hat{L} \circ \hat{H}\,|_Q = \mathrm{Id}_Q, \qquad Q = \hat{L}(J^1Y), \tag{47a}$$
$$H = H_{\hat{H}} + L \circ \hat{H}, \tag{47b}$$

or in the coordinate form

$$\partial^\mu_i\mathcal{L}(x^\lambda, y^j, \partial^j_\lambda\mathcal{H}) = p^\mu_i, \qquad p^\mu_i \in Q,$$
$$\mathcal{L}(x^\lambda, y^j, \partial^j_\lambda\mathcal{H}) = p^\mu_i\partial^i_\mu\mathcal{H} - \mathcal{H}.$$

Note that different Hamiltonian forms can be associated with the same Lagrangian density.

Let us restrict our consideration to the semiregular Lagrangian densities L when the preimage $\hat{L}^{-1}(q)$ of each point of $q \in Q$ is the connected submanifold of J^1Y.

All Hamiltonian forms associated with a semiregular Lagrangian density L consist with each other on the Lagrangian constraint space Q, and the Hamilton operator $\mathcal{E}_H$ (41) satisfies the relation

$$\Lambda_L = \mathcal{E}_H \circ J^1\hat{L}.$$

Let a section r of $\Pi \to X$ be a solution of the Hamilton equations (15a) and (15b) for a Hamiltonian form H associated with a semiregular Lagrangian density L. If r lives on the constraint space Q, the section $\bar{s} = \widehat{H} \circ r$ of $J^1Y \to X$ satisfies the first order Euler-Lagrange equations (45). Conversely, given a semiregular Lagrangian density L, let $\bar{s}$ be a solution of the first order Euler-Lagrange equations (45). Let H be a Hamiltonian form associated with L so that

$$\widehat{H} \circ \hat{L} \circ \bar{s} = \bar{s}. \tag{48}$$

Then, the section $r = \hat{L} \circ \bar{s}$ of $\Pi \to X$ is a solution of the Hamilton equations (15a) and (15b) for H. For sections $\bar{s}$ and r, we have the relations

$$\bar{s} = J^1 s, \qquad s = \pi_{\Pi Y} \circ r$$

where s is a solution of the second order Euler-Lagrange equations (46).

We shall say that a family of Hamiltonian forms H associated with a semiregular Lagrangian density L is complete if, for each solution $\bar{s}$ of the first order Euler-Lagrange equations (45), there exists a solution r of the Hamilton equations (15a) and (15b) for some Hamiltonian form H from this family so that

$$r = \hat{L} \circ \bar{s}, \qquad \bar{s} = \widehat{H} \circ r, \qquad \bar{s} = J^1(\pi_{\Pi Y} \circ r).$$

Such a complete family exists iff, for each solution $\bar{s}$ of the Euler-Lagrange equations for L, there exists a Hamiltonian form H from this family so that the condition (48) holds.

The most of field models possesses affine and quadratic Lagrangian densities. Complete families of Hamiltonian forms associated with such Lagrangian densities always exist [17, 18].

As a test case, let us consider the gauge theory of principal connections.

In the rest of this Section, the manifold X is assumed to be oriented world manifold provided with a nondegenerate fibre metric $g_{\mu\nu}$ in the tangent bundle of X. We denote $g = \det(g_{\mu\nu})$.

Let $P \to X$ be a principal bundle with a structure Lie group G wich acts on P on the right. There is the 1:1 correspondence between the principal connections A on P and the global sections of the bundle $C = J^1P/G$. It is the affine bundle modelled on the vector bundle

$$\bar{C} = T^*X \otimes V^G P, \qquad V^G P = VP/G.$$

Given a bundle atlas Ψ^P of P, the bundle C is provided with the fibred coordinates (x^μ, k_μ^m) so that

$$(k_\mu^m \circ A)(x) = A_\mu^m(x)$$

are coefficients of the local connection 1-form of a principal connection A with respect to the atlas Ψ^P. The first order jet manifold J^1C of the bundle C is coordinatized by $(x^\mu, k_\mu^m, k_{\mu\lambda}^m)$.

There exists the canonical splitting

$$J^1C = C_+ \underset{C}{\oplus} C_- = (J^2P/G) \underset{C}{\oplus} (\overset{2}{\wedge} T^*X \underset{C}{\otimes} V^G P), \qquad (49)$$

$$k_{\mu\lambda}^m = \frac{1}{2}(k_{\mu\lambda}^m + k_{\lambda\mu}^m + c_{nl}^m k_\lambda^n k_\mu^l) + \frac{1}{2}(k_{\mu\lambda}^m - k_{\lambda\mu}^m - c_{nl}^m k_\lambda^n k_\mu^l),$$

over C with the corresponding surjections

$$\mathcal{S} : J^1C \to C_+, \qquad \mathcal{S}_{\lambda\mu}^m = k_{\mu\lambda}^m + k_{\lambda\mu}^m + c_{nl}^m k_\lambda^n k_\mu^l,$$
$$\mathcal{F} : J^1C \to C_-, \qquad \mathcal{F}_{\lambda\mu}^m = k_{\mu\lambda}^m - k_{\lambda\mu}^m - c_{nl}^m k_\lambda^n k_\mu^l.$$

The Legendre bundle over the bundle C is

$$\Pi = \overset{n}{\wedge} T^*X \otimes TX \underset{C}{\otimes} [C \times \overline{C}]^*.$$

It is coordinatized by $(x^\mu, k_\mu^m, p_m^{\mu\lambda})$.

On the configuration space (49), the conventional Yang-Mills Lagrangian density L_{YM} is given by the expression

$$L_{YM} = \frac{1}{4\varepsilon^2} a_{mn}^G g^{\lambda\mu} g^{\beta\nu} \mathcal{F}_{\lambda\beta}^m \mathcal{F}_{\mu\nu}^n \sqrt{|g|} \, \omega \tag{50}$$

where a^G is a nondegenerate G-invariant metric in the Lie algebra of G. The corresponding Legendre morphism takes the form

$$p_m^{(\mu\lambda)} \circ \widehat{L}_{YM} = 0, \tag{51a}$$

$$p_m^{[\mu\lambda]} \circ \widehat{L}_{YM} = \varepsilon^{-2} a_{mn}^G g^{\lambda\alpha} g^{\mu\beta} \mathcal{F}_{\alpha\beta}^n \sqrt{|g|}. \tag{51b}$$

Let us consider connections on the bundle C which take their values into $\text{Ker} \, \widehat{L}_{YM}$:

$$S : C \to C_+, \qquad S_{\mu\lambda}^m - S_{\lambda\mu}^m - c_{nl}^m k_\lambda^n k_\mu^l = 0. \tag{52}$$

For all these connections, the Hamiltonian forms

$$H = p_m^{\mu\lambda} dk_\mu^m \wedge \omega_\lambda - p_m^{\mu\lambda} S_{B\mu\lambda}^m \omega - \widetilde{\mathcal{H}}_{YM}\omega, \tag{53}$$

$$\widetilde{\mathcal{H}}_{YM} = \frac{\varepsilon^2}{4} a_G^{mn} g_{\mu\nu} g_{\lambda\beta} p_m^{[\mu\lambda]} p_n^{[\nu\beta]} |g|^{-1/2},$$

are associated with the Lagrangian density L_{YM} and constitute the complete family. Moreover, we can minimize this complete family if we restrict ourselves to connections (52) of the following type. Given a symmetric linear connection K on the cotangent bundle T^*X of X, every principal connection B on P gives rise to the connection S_B (52) such that

$$S_B \circ B = \mathcal{S} \circ J^1 B,$$

$$S_{B\mu\lambda}^m = \frac{1}{2}[c_{nl}^m k_\lambda^n k_\mu^l + \partial_\mu B_\lambda^m + \partial_\lambda B_\mu^m - c_{nl}^m(k_\mu^n B_\lambda^l + k_\lambda^n B_\mu^l)] - K^\beta{}_{\mu\lambda}(B_\beta^m - k_\beta^m).$$

The corresponding Hamilton equations for sections r of $\Pi \to X$ read

$$\partial_\lambda p_m^{\mu\lambda} = -c_{lm}^n k_\nu^l p_n^{[\mu\nu]} + c_{ml}^n B_\nu^l p_n^{(\mu\nu)} - K^\mu{}_{\lambda\nu} p_m^{(\lambda\nu)}, \tag{54}$$

$$\partial_\lambda k_\mu^m + \partial_\mu k_\lambda^m = 2S_{B(\mu\lambda)}^m \tag{55}$$

plus the equation (51b). When restricted to the constraint space (51a), the equations (51b) and (54) are the familiar Yang-Mills equations for $A = \pi_{\Pi C} \circ r$. Different Hamiltonian forms (53) lead to different equations (55) which play the role of the gauge-type conditions.

7 Hamiltonian systems on composite manifolds

The major feature of Hamiltonian systems on a composite manifold Y (24) lies in the following. The horizontal splitting (29) yields immediately the corresponding splitting of the Legendre bundle Π over the composite manifold Y. As a consequence, the Hamilton equations (15a) for sections h of the fibred manifold Σ reduce to the gauge-type conditions independent of momenta. Thereby, these sections play the role of parameter fields. Their momenta meet the constraint conditions (16).

Let Y be a composite manifold (24). The Legendre bundle Π over Y is coordinatized by

$$(x^\lambda, \sigma^m, y^i, p_m^\lambda, p_i^\lambda).$$

Let A_Σ be a connection (8) on the bundle Y_Σ. With a connection A_Σ, the splitting

$$\Pi = \overset{n}{\wedge} T^*X \underset{Y}{\otimes} TX \underset{Y}{\otimes} [V^*Y_\Sigma \underset{Y}{\oplus} (Y \underset{\Sigma}{\times} V^*\Sigma)] \tag{56}$$

of the Legendre bundle Π is performed as an immediate consequence of the splitting (29). Given the splitting (56), the Legendre bundle Π can be provided with the corresponding coordinates .

$$\overline{p}^\lambda_i = p^\lambda_i, \qquad \overline{p}^\lambda_m = p^\lambda_m + A^i_m p^\lambda_i. \tag{57}$$

Let h be a global section of the fibred manifold Σ. It is readily observed that, given the splitting (56), the submanifold

$$\{\sigma = h(x), \ \overline{p}^\lambda_m = 0\} \tag{58}$$

of the Legendre bundle Π over Y is isomorphic to the Legendre bundle Π_h over the restriction Y_h of Y_Σ to $h(X)$.

Let the composite manifold Y be provided with the composite connection (26) determined by connections A_Σ on Y_Σ and Γ on Σ. Relative to the coordinates (57), every Hamiltonian form on the Legendre bundle Π over Y can be given by the expression

$$H = (p^\lambda_i dy^i + p^\lambda_m d\sigma^m) \wedge \omega_\lambda - [\overline{p}^\lambda_i \tilde{A}^i_\lambda + \overline{p}^\lambda_m \Gamma^m_\lambda + \widetilde{\mathcal{H}}(x^\mu, \sigma^m, y^i, \overline{p}^\mu_m, \overline{p}^\mu_i)]\omega. \tag{59}$$

The corresponding Hamilton equations are written

$$\partial_\lambda p^\lambda_i = -p^\lambda_j [\partial_i \tilde{A}^j_\lambda + \partial_i A^j_m(\Gamma^m_\lambda + \partial^m_\lambda \widetilde{\mathcal{H}})] - \partial_i \widetilde{\mathcal{H}}, \tag{60a}$$

$$\partial_\lambda y^i = \tilde{A}^i_\lambda + A^i_m(\Gamma^m_\lambda + \partial^m_\lambda \widetilde{\mathcal{H}}) + \partial^i_\lambda \widetilde{\mathcal{H}}, \tag{60b}$$

$$\partial_\lambda p^\lambda_m = -p^\lambda_i [\partial_m \tilde{A}^i_\lambda + \partial_m A^i_n(\Gamma^n_\lambda + \partial^n_\lambda \widetilde{\mathcal{H}})] - \overline{p}^\lambda_n \partial_m \Gamma^n_\lambda - \partial_m \widetilde{\mathcal{H}}, \tag{60c}$$

$$\partial_\lambda \sigma^m = \Gamma^m_\lambda + \partial^m_\lambda \widetilde{\mathcal{H}}, \tag{60d}$$

plus constraint conditions.

In particular, let the Hamiltonian form (59) be associated with a Lagrangian density (9) which contains the velocities σ^m_μ only in the vertical covariant differential (30). Then, the Hamiltonian density $\widetilde{\mathcal{H}}\omega$ appears independent of the momenta $\overline{p}^\mu_m$ and the Lagrangian constraints read

$$\overline{p}^\mu_m = 0. \tag{61}$$

In this case, the Hamilton equation (60d) comes to the gauge-type condition

$$\partial_\lambda \sigma^m = \Gamma_\lambda^m$$

independent of momenta.

In particular, let us consider a Hamiltonian system in the presence of a background parameter field $h(x)$. After substituting the equation (60d) into the equations (60a) - (60b) and restricting them to the submanifold (58), we obtain the equations

$$\partial_\lambda p_i^\lambda = -p_j^\lambda \partial_i [(\tilde{A} \circ h)_\lambda^j + A_m^j \partial_\lambda h^m] - \partial_i \widetilde{\mathcal{H}},$$
$$\partial_\lambda y^i = (\tilde{A} \circ h)_\lambda^i + A_m^i \partial_\lambda h^m + \partial_i^\lambda \widetilde{\mathcal{H}} \qquad (62)$$

for sections of the fibred Legendre manifold $\Pi_h \to X$ of the bundle Y_h endowed with the connection (27). Equations (62) are the Hamilton equations corresponding to the Hamiltonian form

$$H_h = p_i^\lambda dy^i \wedge \omega_\lambda - [p_i^\lambda A_{h\lambda}^i + \widetilde{\mathcal{H}}(x^\mu, h^m(x), y^i, p_i^\mu, \overline{p}_m^\mu = 0)]\omega$$

on Π_h which is induced by the Hamiltonian form (59) on Π.

8 Gauge gravitation theory

At first, let us consider Dirac fermion fields in the presence of a background tetrad field h. Recall that they are represented by global sections of the spinor bundle S_h (20). Their Lagrangian density is defined on the configuration space $J^1(S_h \oplus S_h^*)$ provided with the adapted coordinates $(x^\mu, y^A, y_A^+, y_\mu^A, y_{A\mu}^+)$. It is the affine Lagrangian density

$$L_D = \{\frac{i}{2}[y_A^+(\gamma^0\gamma^\mu)^A{}_B(y_\mu^B - A^B{}_{C\mu}y^C) - (y_{A\mu}^+ - A^{+C}{}_{A\mu}y_C^+)(\gamma^0\gamma^\mu)^A{}_B y^B]$$
$$-my_A^+(\gamma^0)^A{}_B y^B\}h^{-1}\omega, \qquad \gamma^\mu = h_a^\mu(x)\gamma^a, \qquad h = \det(h_a^\mu), \qquad (63)$$

where

$$A^A{}_{B\mu} = \frac{1}{2}A^{ab}{}_\mu(x)I_{ab}{}^A{}_B$$

is a principal connection on the principal spinor bundle P_h.

The Legendre bundle Π_h over the spinor bundle $S_h \oplus S_h^*$ is coordinatized by

$$(x^\mu, y^A, y_A^+, p_A^\mu, p_+^{\mu A}).$$

Relative to these coordinates, the Legendre morphism associated with the Lagrangian density (63) is written

$$p_A^\mu = \pi_A^\mu = \frac{i}{2}y_B^+(\gamma^0\gamma^\mu)^B{}_A h^{-1},$$

$$p_+^{\mu A} = \pi_+^{\mu A} = -\frac{i}{2}(\gamma^0\gamma^\mu)^A{}_B y^B h^{-1}. \tag{64}$$

It defines the constraint subspace of the Legendre bundle Π_h. Given a soldering form

$$S = S^A{}_{B\mu}(x)y^B dx^\mu \otimes \partial_A$$

on the bundle S_h, let us consider the connection $A + S$ on S_h. The corresponding Hamiltonian form associated with the Lagrangian density (63) reads

$$H_S = (p_A^\mu dy^A + p_+^{\mu A}dy_A^+) \wedge \omega_\mu - \mathcal{H}_S\omega, \tag{65}$$
$$\mathcal{H}_S = p_A^\mu A^A{}_{B\mu}y^B + y_B^+A^{+B}{}_{A\mu}p_+^{\mu A} + my_A^+(\gamma^0)^A{}_B y^B h^{-1} +$$
$$(p_A^\mu - \pi_A^\mu)S^A{}_{B\mu}y^B + y_B^+S^{+B}{}_{A\mu}(p_+^{\mu A} - \pi_+^{\mu A}).$$

The corresponding Hamilton equations for a section r of the fibred Legendre manifold $\Pi_h \to X$ take the form

$$\partial_\mu y_A^+ = y_B^+(A^{+B}{}_{A\mu} + S^{+B}{}_{A\mu}), \tag{66a}$$
$$\partial_\mu p_A^\mu = -p_B^\mu A^B{}_{A\mu} - (p_B^\mu - \pi_B^\mu)S^B{}_{A\mu} -$$
$$[my_B^+(\gamma^0)^B{}_A + \frac{i}{2}y_B^+S^{+B}{}_{C\mu}(\gamma^0\gamma^\mu)^C{}_A]h^{-1} \tag{66b}$$

plus the equations for the components y^A and $p_+^{\mu A}$. The equation (66a) and the similar equation for y^A imply that y is an integral section of the connection $A + S$ on the spinor bundle S_h. It follows that the Hamiltonian forms (65) constitute the complete family. On the constraint space (64), the equation (66b) comes to

$$\partial_\mu \pi_A^\mu = -\pi_B^\mu A^B{}_{A\mu} - (m y_B^+ (\gamma^0)^B{}_A + \frac{i}{2} y_B^+ S^{+B}{}_C{}_\mu (\gamma^0 \gamma^\mu)^C{}_A) h^{-1}. \quad (67)$$

Substituting the equation (66a) into the equation (67), we obtain the familiar Dirac equation for fermion fields in the presence of a tetrad gravitational field h.

We now consider gravity without matter.

In the gauge gravitation theory, dynamic gravitational variables are pairs of tetrad gravitational fields h and gauge gravitational potentials A_h identified with principal connections on P_h. Following the general procedure, one can describe these pairs (h, A_h) by sections of the composite bundle

$$C_L := J^1 LX/L \to J^1 \Sigma \to \Sigma \to X^4.$$

The corresponding configuration space is the jet manifold $J^1 C_L$ of C_L. The Legendre bundle

$$\Pi = \overset{4}{\wedge} T^* X^4 \underset{C_L}{\otimes} TX^4 \underset{C_L}{\otimes} V^* C_L \quad (68)$$

over C_L plays the role of a phase space of the gauge gravitation theory.

The bundle C_L is endowed with the local fibred coordinates

$$\left(x^\mu, \sigma_a^\lambda, k^{ab}{}_\lambda = -k^{ba}{}_\lambda, \sigma_{a\mu}^\lambda \right)$$

where $(x^\mu, \sigma_a^\lambda, \sigma_{a\mu}^\lambda)$ are coordinates of the jet bundle $J^1\Sigma$. The jet manifold $J^1 C_L$ of C_L is provided with the corresponding adapted coordinates

$$\left(x^\mu, \sigma_a^\mu, k^{ab}{}_\lambda = -k^{ba}{}_\lambda, \sigma_{a\lambda}^\mu = \sigma_{a(\lambda)}^\mu, k^{ab}{}_{\mu\lambda}, \sigma_{a\lambda\nu}^\mu \right).$$

The associated coordinates of the Legendre manifold (68) are

$$(x^\mu, \sigma_a^\lambda, k^{ab}{}_\lambda, \sigma_{a\nu}^\lambda, p_\lambda^{a\mu}, p_{ab}{}^{\lambda\mu}, p_\lambda^{a\nu\mu})$$

where $(x^\mu, \sigma_a^\lambda, p_\lambda^{a\mu})$ are coordinates of the Legendre manifold of the bundle Σ.

For the sake of simplicity, we here consider the Hilbert-Einstein Lagrangian density of classical gravity

$$L_{HE} = -\frac{1}{2\kappa} \mathcal{F}^{ab}{}_{\mu\lambda} \sigma_a^\mu \sigma_b^\lambda \sigma^{-1} \omega, \tag{69}$$

$$\mathcal{F}^{ab}{}_{\mu\lambda} = k^{ab}{}_{\lambda\mu} - k^{ab}{}_{\mu\lambda} + k^a{}_{c\mu} k^{cb}{}_\lambda - k^a{}_{c\lambda} k^{cb}{}_\mu,$$

$$\sigma = \det(\sigma_a^\mu).$$

The corresponding Legendre morphism $\widehat{L}_{HE}$ is given by the coordinate expressions

$$p_{ab}{}^{[\lambda\mu]} = \pi_{ab}{}^{[\lambda\mu]} = \frac{-1}{\kappa\sigma} \sigma_a^{[\mu} \sigma_b^{\lambda]}. \tag{70a}$$

$$p_{ab}{}^{(\lambda\mu)} = 0, \qquad p_\lambda^{a\mu} = 0, \qquad p_\lambda^{a\nu\mu} = 0, \tag{70b}$$

We construct the complete family of Hamiltonian forms associated with the affine Lagrangian density (69). Let K be a world connection associated with a principal connection B on the linear frame bundle LX. To minimize the complete family, we consider the following connections on the bundle C_K:

$$\Gamma^\lambda_{a\mu} = B^b{}_{a\mu} \sigma_b^\lambda - K^\lambda{}_{\nu\mu} \sigma_a^\nu,$$

$$\Gamma^\lambda_{a\nu\mu} = \partial_\mu B^d{}_{a\nu} \sigma_d^\lambda - \partial_\mu K^\lambda{}_{\beta\nu} \sigma_a^\beta$$
$$+ B^d{}_{a\mu}(\sigma_{d\nu}^\lambda - \Gamma^\lambda_{d\nu}) - K^\lambda{}_{\beta\mu}(\sigma_{a\nu}^\beta - \Gamma^\beta_{a\nu}) + K^\beta{}_{\nu\mu}(\sigma_{a\beta}^\lambda - \Gamma^\lambda_{a\beta})$$
$$+ B^d{}_{a\nu} \Gamma^\lambda_{d\mu} - K^\lambda{}_{\beta\nu} \Gamma^\beta_{a\mu},$$

$$\Gamma^{ab}{}_{\lambda\mu} = \frac{1}{2}[k^a{}_{c\lambda} k^{cb}{}_\mu - k^a{}_{c\mu} k^{cb}{}_\lambda + \partial_\lambda B^{ab}{}_\mu + \partial_\mu B^{ab}{}_\lambda$$
$$- B^b{}_{c\mu} k^{ac}{}_\lambda - B^b{}_{c\lambda} k^{ac}{}_\mu - B^a{}_{c\mu} k^{cb}{}_\lambda - B^a{}_{c\lambda} k^{cb}{}_\mu]$$
$$+ K^\nu{}_{\lambda\mu} k^{ab}{}_\nu - K^\nu{}_{(\lambda\mu)} B^{ab}{}_\nu - \frac{1}{2} R^{ab}{}_{\lambda\mu},$$

where R is the curvature of the connection B.

The complete family of Hamiltonian forms associated with the Lagrangian density (69) consists of the forms given by the coordinate expressions

$$H_{HE} = (p_{ab}{}^{\lambda\mu}dk^{ab}{}_\lambda + p_\lambda^{a\mu}d\sigma_a^\lambda + p_\lambda^{a\nu\mu}d\sigma_{a\nu}^\lambda) \wedge \omega_\mu - \mathcal{H}_{HE}\omega,$$

$$\mathcal{H}_{HE} = (p_{ab}{}^{\lambda\mu}\Gamma^{ab}{}_{\lambda\mu} + p_\lambda^{a\mu}\Gamma_{a\mu}^\lambda + p_\lambda^{a\nu\mu}\Gamma_{a\nu\mu}^\lambda) + \frac{1}{2}R^{ab}{}_{\lambda\mu}(p_{ab}{}^{[\lambda\mu]} - \pi_{ab}{}^{\lambda\mu}).$$

The Hamilton equations corresponding to such a Hamiltonian form read

$$\mathcal{F}^{ab}{}_{\mu\lambda} = R^{ab}{}_{\mu\lambda}, \tag{71a}$$

$$\partial_\mu k^{ab}{}_\lambda + \partial_\lambda k^{ab}{}_\mu = 2\Gamma^{ab}{}_{(\mu\lambda)}, \tag{71b}$$

$$\partial_\mu \sigma_a^\lambda = \Gamma_{a\mu}^\lambda, \tag{71c}$$

$$\partial_\mu \sigma_{a\nu}^\lambda = \Gamma_{a\nu\mu}^\lambda, \tag{71d}$$

$$\partial_\mu p_{ac}{}^{\lambda\mu} = -\frac{\partial \mathcal{H}_{HE}}{\partial k^{ac}{}_\lambda}, \tag{71e}$$

$$\partial_\mu p_\lambda^{a\mu} = -\frac{\partial \mathcal{H}_{HE}}{\partial \sigma_a^\lambda}, \tag{71f}$$

plus the equations which are reduced to the trivial identities on the constraint space (70a). The equations (71a) - (71d) make the sense of gauge-type conditions. The equation (71d) has the solution

$$\sigma_{a\mu}^\lambda = \partial_\nu \sigma_a^\lambda.$$

The gauge-type condition (71b) has the solution $k = B(x)$. It follows that the forms H_{HE} really constitute the complete family of Hamiltonian forms associated with the Lagrangian density (69).

On the constraint space, the equations (71e) and (71f) are brought into the form

$$\partial_\mu \pi_{ac}{}^{\lambda\mu} = 2k^b{}_{c\mu}\pi_{ab}{}^{\lambda\mu} + \pi_{ac}{}^{\beta\gamma}\Gamma^\lambda{}_{\beta\gamma}, \tag{72a}$$

$$R^{cb}{}_{\beta\mu}\partial_\lambda^a \pi_{cb}{}^{\beta\mu} = 0. \tag{72b}$$

The equation (72a) shows that $k(x)$ is the Levi-Civita connection for the tetrad field $h(x)$. Substitution of the equations (71a) into the equations (72b) leads to the familiar Einstein equations.

Turn now to the fermion matter. Given the L_s-principal lift P_Σ of LX_Σ, let us consider the composite spinor bundle S (2).

Set up the principal connection on the bundle LX_Σ which is given by the local connection form

$$A_\Sigma = (\tilde{A}^{ab}{}_\mu dx^\mu + A^{abc}{}_\mu d\sigma^\mu_c) \otimes I_{ab}, \tag{73}$$

$$\tilde{A}^{ab}{}_\mu = \frac{1}{2} K^\nu{}_{\lambda\mu} \sigma^\lambda_c (\eta^{cb} \sigma^a_\nu - \eta^{ca} \sigma^b_\nu),$$

$$A^{abc}{}_\mu = \frac{1}{2} (\eta^{cb} \sigma^a_\mu - \eta^{ca} \sigma^b_\mu), \tag{74}$$

where K is some symmetric connection on TX and the component (74) corresponds to the canonical left-invariant free-curvature connection on the bundle

$$GL_4 \to GL_4/L.$$

The connection on the spinor bundle S which is associated with A_Σ (73) reads

$$A_\Sigma = dx^\lambda \otimes (\partial_\lambda + \frac{1}{2} \tilde{A}^{ab}{}_\lambda I_{ab}{}^B{}_A y^A \partial_B) + d\sigma^c_\mu \otimes (\partial^\mu_c + \frac{1}{2} A^{abc}{}_\mu I_{ab}{}^B{}_A y^A \partial_B).$$

The total configuration space of the fermion-gravitation complex is the product

$$J^1 S \underset{J^1\Sigma}{\times} J^1 C_L.$$

On this configuration space, the Lagrangian density L_{FG} of the fermion-gravitation complex is the sum of the Hilbert-Einstein Lagrangian density L_{HE} (69) and the modification $L_{\tilde{D}}$ (9) of the Lagrangian density (63) of fermion fields:

$$L_{\tilde{D}} = \{\frac{i}{2}[y^+_A(\gamma^0\gamma^\mu)^A{}_B(y^B_\mu - \frac{1}{2}(k^{ab}{}_\mu - A^{abc}{}_\nu(\sigma^\nu_{c\mu} - \Gamma^\nu_{c\mu}))I_{ab}{}^B{}_C \mu y^C) -$$

$$(y^+_{A\mu} - \frac{1}{2}(k^{ab}_{\ \ \mu} - A^{abc}_{\ \ \ \nu}(\sigma^\nu_{c\mu} - \Gamma^\nu_{c\mu}))I^{+C}_{ab}{}_{A\mu}y^+_C)(\gamma^0\gamma^\mu)^A_{\ B}y^B]$$
$$- my^+_A(\gamma^0)^A_{\ B}y^B\}\sigma^{-1}\omega$$

where

$$\Gamma^\nu_{c\mu} = \frac{1}{2}k^{mn}_{\ \ \ \mu}(\eta_{cn}\delta^d_m - \eta_{cm}\delta^d_n) - K^\nu_{\ \mu}\sigma^\lambda_c,$$
$$\gamma^\mu = \sigma^\mu_a\gamma^a, \qquad \sigma = \det(\sigma^\mu_a).$$

The total phase space Π of the fermion-gravitation complex is coordinatized by

$$(x^\lambda, \sigma^\mu_c, \sigma^\mu_{c\nu}, y^A, y^+_A, k^{ab}_{\ \ \mu}, p^{c\lambda}_\mu, p^{c\nu\lambda}_\mu, p^\lambda_A, p^{A\lambda}_+, p_{ab}{}^{\mu\lambda})$$

and admits the corresponding splitting (56). The Legendre morphism associated with the Lagrangian density L_{FG} defines the constraint subspace of Π given by the relations (64), (70a), the conditions

$$p_{ab}{}^{(\lambda\mu)} = 0, \qquad p^{c\nu\mu}_\lambda = 0$$

and the constraint (61) which takes the form (17).

Hamiltonian forms associated with the Lagrangian density L_{FG} are the sum of the Hamiltonian forms H_{HE} and H_S (65) where

$$A^A_{\ B\mu} = \frac{1}{2}k^{ab}_{\ \ \mu}I_{ab}{}^A_{\ B}y^B. \tag{75}$$

The corresponding Hamilton equations for spinor fields consist with the equations (66a) and (66b) where A is given by the expression (75). The Hamilton equations (71a) - (71d) remain true. The Hamilton equations (71e) and (71f) contain additional matter sources. On the constraint space

$$p^{a\mu}_\lambda = 0$$

the modified equations (71f) would come to the familiar Einstein equations

$$G^{'a}_\mu + T^a_\mu = 0$$

where T denotes the energy-momentum tensor of fermion fields, otherwise on the modified constraint space (17). In the latter case, we have

$$D_\lambda p^{c\lambda}_\mu = G^a_\mu + T^a_\mu \tag{76}$$

where D_λ denotes the covariant derivative with respect to the Levi-Civita connection which acts on the indices $^c_\mu$. Substitution of (17) into (76) leads to the modified Einstein equations for the total system of fermion fields and gravity:

$$-\frac{1}{2}J^\lambda_{ab}D_\lambda A^{abc}_{\mu} = G^c_\mu + T^c_\mu$$

where J is the spin current of the fermion fields.

References

1. J. Cariñena, M. Crampin and L. Ibort, *Diff. Geom. Appl.*, **1**, 345 (1991).

2. G. Giachetta and L. Mangiarotti, *Int. J. Theor. Phys.*, **29**, 789 (1990).

3. M. Gotay, in *Mechanics, Analysis and Geometry: 200 Years after Lagrange*, ed. M.Francaviglia (Elseiver Science Publishers B.V., 1991) p. 203.

4. C. Günther, *J. Diff. Geom.*, **25**, 23 (1987).

5. C. Isham, A. Salam and J. Strathdee, *Ann. of Phys.*, **62**, 98 (1971)

6. D. Ivanenko and G. Sardanashvily, *Phys. Rep.*, **94**, 1 (1983).

7. I. Kolař, P.W. Michor, J. Slovák, *Natural operations in differential geometry*, (Springer-Verlag, Berlin etc. 1993).

8. B. Kupershmidt, *Geometry of Jet Bundles and the Strucuture of Lagrangian and Hamiltonian Formalisms*, Lect. Notes in Math., **775**, 162 (1980).

9. J. Ne'eman and Dj. Šijački, *Ann. of Phys.*, **120**, 292 (1979).

10. V. Ogievetsky and I. Polubarinov, *Sov. Phys. JETP*, **21**, 1093 (1965).

11. R. Percacci, *Geometry of Nonlinear Field Theories* (World Scientific, Singapore, 1986).

12. G. Sardanashvily, *Phys. Lett.*, **75A**, 257 (1980).

13. G. Sardanashvily, *Int. J. Theor. Phys.*, **30**, 721 (1991).

14. G. Sardanashvily, *J. Math. Phys.*, **33**, 1546 (1992).

15. G. Sardanashvily and O. Zakharov, *Gauge Gravitation Theory* (World Scientific, Singapore, 1992).

16. G. Sardanashvily and O. Zakharov, *Diff. Geom. Appl.*, **3**, 245 (1993).

17. G.Sardanashvily, *Gauge Theory in Jet Manifolds* (Hadronic Press, Palm Harbor, 1993)

18. G.Sardanashvily, *J. Math. Phys.* **35**, 6584 (1994).

19. D. Saunders, *The Geometry of Jet Bundles*, (Cambridge Univ. Press, Cambridge, 1989).

20. R. Sulanke and P. Wintgen, *Ddifferetialgeometrie und Faserbündel* (Veb Deutsher Verlag der Wissenschaften, Berlin, 1972).

21. A. Trautman, *Czech. J. of Phys.*, **B29**, 107 (1979).

Gennadi A. Sardanashvily, Editor
New Frontiers in Gravitation
Hadronic Press, Palm Harbor, FL 34682-1577, U.S.A.
ISBN 0–911767–96–7, 1996, Pages 337–344

WHY DO ALL THE CURVATURE INVARIANTS OF A GRAVITATIONAL WAVE VANISH?

Hans - Jürgen Schmidt

Universität Potsdam, Institut für Mathematik
Projektgruppe Kosmologie
D-14415 POTSDAM, PF 601553, Am Neuen Palais 10, Germany

Abstract

We prove the theorem valid for (Pseudo)-Riemannian manifolds V_n: "Let $x \in V_n$ be a fixed point of a homothetic motion which is not an isometry then all curvature invariants vanish at x." and get the Corollary: "All curvature invariants of the plane wave metric .

$$ds^2 = 2\, du\, dv + a^2(u)\, dw^2 + b^2(u)\, dz^2$$

identically vanish."

Analysing the proof we see: The fact that for definite signature flatness can be characterized by the vanishing of a curvature invariant, essentially rests on the compactness of the rotation group $SO(n)$. For Lorentz signature, however, one has the non-compact Lorentz group $SO(3,1)$ instead of it.

A further and independent proof of the corollary uses the fact, that the Geroch limit does not lead to a Hausdorff topology, so a sequence of gravitational waves can converge to the flat space-time, even if each element of the sequence is the same pp-wave.

1   Introduction

The energy of the gravitational field (especially of gravitational waves) within General Relativity was subject of controversies from the very beginning, see [1] and the cited literature. Global considerations - e.g. by considering the far-field of asymptotically flat space-times - soonly led to satisfactory answers. Local considerations became fruitful if a system of reference is prescribed (e.g. by choosing a time-like vector field). If, however, no system of reference is preferred then it is not a priori clear whether one can constructively distinguish flat space-time from a gravitational wave. This is connected with the generally known fact, that for a pp-wave (see e.g. [2] and [3]) all curvature invariants vanish (cf. [4] and [5]) - but on the other hand: in the absence of matter or reference systems - only curvature invariants are locally constructively measurable.

It is the aim of this article to explain the topological origin of this strange property.

2   Preliminaries

Let V_n be a C^∞-(Pseudo)-Riemannian manifold of arbitrary signature with dimension $n > 1$. The metric and the Riemann tensor have components g_{ij} and R_{ijlm} resp. The covariant derivative with respect to the coordinate x^m is denoted by ";m" and is performed with the Christoffel affinity Γ^i_{lm}. We define

Definition: I is called a generalized curvature invariant of order k if it is a scalar with dependence

$$I = I(g_{ij}, R_{ijlm}, \ldots, R_{ijlm;i_1 \ldots i_k}).$$

By specialization we get the usual

Definition: I is called a curvature invariant of order k if it is a generalized curvature invariant of order k which depends continuously on all its arguments. The domain of dependence is requested to contain the flat space, and $I(g_{ij}, 0, \ldots 0) \equiv 0$.

Examples: Let

$$I_0 = sign(\sum_{i,j,l,m=1}^{n} |R_{ijlm}|)$$

I_0 is a generalized curvature invariant of order 0, but it fails to be a curvature invariant. It holds: V_n is flat iff (= if and only if) $I_0 \equiv 0$. Let further $I_1 = R_{ijlm} R^{ijlm}$ which is a curvature invariant of order 0. If the metric has definite signature or if $n = 2$ then it holds: V_n is flat iff $I_1 \equiv 0$.

Proof: For definite signature $I_0 = sign(I_1)$; for $n = 2$, $I_1 \equiv 0$ implies $R \equiv 0$, hence flatness. □

For all other cases, however, the vanishing of I_1 does not imply flatness. Moreover, there does not exist another curvature invariant serving for this purpose:

Proposition: For dimension $n \geq 3$, arbitrary order k and indefinite metric it holds: To each curvature invariant I of order k there exists a non-flat V_n with $I \equiv 0$.

Proof: Let $n = 3$. We use

$$ds^2 = 2\, du\, dv \pm a^2(u)\, dw^2 \qquad (2.1)$$

with a positive non-linear function $a(u)$. The "$\pm$" covers the two possible indefinite signatures for $n = 3$. The Ricci tensor is $R_{ij} = R^m{}_{imj}$ and has $(u = x^1)$

$$R_{11} = -\frac{1}{a} \cdot \frac{d^2 a}{du^2} \qquad (2.2)$$

and therefore, eq. (2.1) represents a non-flat metric. Now let $n > 3$. We use the cartesian product of (2.1) with a flat space of dimension $n - 3$ and arbitrary signature. So we have for each $n \geq 3$ and each indefinite signature an example of a non-flat V_n. It remains to show that for all these examples, all curvature invariants of order k vanish. It suffices to prove that at the origin of the coordinate system, because at all other points it can be shown by translations of all coordinates accompanied by a redefinition of $a(u)$ to $a(u - u_0)$. Let I be a curvature invariant of order k. Independent of the dimension (i.e., how many flat spaces are multiplied to metric (2.1)) one gets for the case considered here that

$$I = I(a^{(0)}(u), a^{(1)}(u), \ldots, a^{(k+2)}(u))$$

where $a^{(0)}(u) = a(u)$, $a^{(m+1)}(u) = \frac{d}{du} a^{(m)}(u)$, and

$$I(a^{(0)}(u), 0, \ldots, 0) = 0.$$

(This is because each $R_{ijlm;i_1 \ldots i_p}$ continuously depends on $a^{(0)}(u)$, $a^{(1)}(u)$, $\ldots$, $a^{(p+2)}(u)$ and on nothing else; and for $a = \text{const.}$, (2.1) represents a flat space.)

Now we apply a coordinate transformation: Let $\epsilon > 0$ be fixed, we replace u by $u \cdot \epsilon$ and v by v/ϵ. This represents a Lorentz boost in the $u - v$–plane. Metric (2.1) remains form-invariant by this rotation, only $a(u)$ has to be replaced by $a(u \cdot \epsilon)$. At $u = 0$ we have

$$I = I(a^{(0)}(0), a^{(1)}(0), \ldots, a^{(k+2)}(0))$$

which must be equal to

$$I_\epsilon = I(a^{(0)}(0), \epsilon \cdot a^{(1)}(0), \ldots, \epsilon^{k+2} \cdot a^{(k+2)}(0))$$

because I is a scalar. By continuity and by the fact that flat space belongs to the domain of dependence of I, we have $\lim_{\epsilon \to 0} I_\epsilon = 0$. All values I_ϵ with $\epsilon > 0$ coincide, and so $I = 0$. $\square$

3 Gravitational waves

A pp-wave (plane-fronted gravitational wave with parallel rays, see [2]) is a non-flat solution of Einstein's vacuum equation $R_{ij} = 0$ possessing a non-vanishing covariantly constant vector; this vector is then automatically a null vector. The simplest type of pp-waves can be represented similar as metric (2.1)

$$ds^2 \;=\; 2\,du\,dv + a^2(u)\,dw^2 + b^2(u)\,dz^2 \tag{3.1}$$

where

$$b \cdot \frac{d^2 a}{du^2} + a \cdot \frac{d^2 b}{du^2} \;=\; 0 \tag{3.2}$$

Metric (3.1) represents flat space-time iff both a and b are linear functions. Using the arguments of sct. 2 one sees that all curvature invariants of metric (3.1) identically vanish. Here we present a second proof of that statement which has the advantage to put the problem into a more general framework and to increase the class of space-times covered, e.g. to the waves

$$ds^2 = dx^2 + dy^2 + 2du\,dv + H(x, y, u)du^2$$

Hall [6] considers fixed points of homothetic motions (which cannot exist in compact space-times) and shows that any plane wave (not only vacuum plane waves) admits, for each x, a homothetic vector field which vanishes at x.

It holds

Theorem: Let $x \in V_n$ be a fixed point of a homothetic motion which is not an isometry then all curvature invariants vanish at x.

Proof: The existence of a homethetic motion which is not an isometry means that V_n is selfsimilar. Let the underlying differentiable manifold be equipped with two metrics g_{ij} and $\tilde{g}_{ij} = e^{2C} g_{ij}$ where C is a non-vanishing constant. The corresponding Riemannian manifolds are denoted by V_n and $\tilde{V}_n$ resp. By assumption, there exists an isometry from V_n to $\tilde{V}_n$ leaving x

fixed. Let I be a curvature invariant. I can be represented as continuous function (which vanishes if all the arguments do) of finitely many of the elementary invariants. The elementary invariants are such products of factors g^{ij} with factors of type $R_{ijlm;i_1\ldots i_p}$ which lead to a scalar, i.e., all indices are traced out. Let J be such an elementary invariant. By construction we have $J(x) = e^{qC} J(x)$ with a non-vanishing natural q (which depends on the type of J). Therefore, $J(x) = 0$. □

Corollary: All curvature invariants of metric (3.1) identically vanish.

Remark: This refers not only to the 14 independent elementary invariants of order 0, see [7] for a list of them, but for arbitrary order.

Proof: We have to show that for each point x, there exists a homothetic motion with fixed point x which is not an isometry. But this is trivially done by suitable linear coordinate transformations of v, w, and z. □

4   Topological properties

Sometimes it is discussed that the properties of space-time which can be locally and constructively (i.e., by rods and clocks) measured are not only the curvature invariants but primarily the projections of the curvature tensor and its covariant derivatives to an orthonormal tetrad (4-bein). (The continuity presumption expresses the fact that a small deformation of space-time should also lead to a correspondingly small change of the result of the measurement.) To prevent a preferred system of reference one can construct curvature invariants like

$$I_2 \;=\; \inf \sum_{i,j,l,m} |R_{ijlm}| \tag{4.1}$$

where the infimum (minimum) is taken over all orthonormal tetrads. From the first glance one could believe that $I_2 \equiv 0$ iff the space is flat. But for indefinite signature this would contradict the proposition of sct. 2. What is the reason ? For definite signature the infimum is to be taken about the rotation group $SO(4)$ (or $O(4)$ if one allows orientation-reversing systems); this group is compact. One knows: A positive continuous function over a compactum possesses a positive infimum. So, if one of the R_{ijlm} differs from zero, then $I_2 > 0$ at that point. For Lorentz signature, however, the infimum is to be taken about the non-compact Lorentz group $SO(3,1)$ and so $R_{ijlm} \neq 0$ does not imply $I_2 \neq 0$.

Another topological argument (which underlies our sct. 2) is connected with the Geroch limit of space-times [8], we use the version of [9]. Theorem 3.1 of the first paper of ref. [9] reads: (1) For local Riemannian manifolds with definite signature, Geroch's limit defines a Hausdorff topology. (2) For indefinite signature this topology is not even T_1. (A topology is Hausdorff if each generalized (= Moore - Smith) sequence possesses at most one limit, and it is T_1 if each constant sequence possesses at most one limit. The main example is a sequence, where each element of the sequence is the same pp-wave, and the sequence possesses two limits: flat space and that pp-wave.) Here the reason is: Only for definite signature, geodetic ϵ-balls form a neighbourhood basis for the topology.

Final remark. The change from Euclidean to Lorentzian signature of a (Pseudo)-Riemannian space is much more than a purely algebraic duality - an impression which is sometimes given by writing an imaginary time coordinate: One looses all the nice properties which follow from the compactness of the rotation group.

Acknowledgements. The author thanks G. Hall, K. Lake and M. Rainer for valuable remarks; K. Lake pointed out that also for the Robinson-Trautman vacuum solutions of Petrov type III all 14 curvature invariants vanish. Financial support from the Wissenschaftler-Integrations-Programm is also gratefully acknowledged.

References

[1] Einstein, A., Sitz.-ber. Preuss. Akad. d. Wiss. Berlin 1914, p. 1030; 1916 p. 688; 1918, p. 154.

[2] Stephani, H., General Relativity, Cambridge University Press 1982, esp. sct. 15. 3. and references cited there.

[3] Ehlers, J., Kundt, W., p. 49 in Witten, L. (Ed.) gravitation, an introduction to current research, Wiley New York 1962.

[4] Hawking, S., Ellis, G. F. R., The large scale structure of space-time, Cambridge Univ. Press 1973, sct. 8.1; at p. 260 they write "R. Penrose has pointed out, in plane-wave solutions the scalar polynomials are all zero but the Riemann tensor does not vanish."

[5] Jordan, P., Ehlers, J., Kundt, W., Abh. Akad. Wiss. Mainz, Math./Nat. 1960, 21. At p. 97 they mention that for a pp-wave all curvature invariants constructed from $R_{ijkl;i_1...i_r}$ by products and traces do vanish.

[6] Hall, G., Gen. Relativ. Grav. **20** (1988) 671; J. Math. Phys. **31** (1990) 1198; Diff. Geom. Appl. (North-Holland Publ.) **1** (1991) 35.

[7] Harvey, A., Class. Quant. Grav. **7** (1990) 715; Lake, K., J. Math. Phys. **34** (1993) 5900 and cited references.

[8] Geroch, R., Commun. Math. Phys. **13** (1969) 180.

[9] Schmidt, H.-J., J. Math. Phys. **28** (1987) 1928; **29** (1988) 1264.

Gennadi A. Sardanashvily, Editor
New Frontiers in Gravitation
Hadronic Press, Palm Harbor, FL 34682-1577, U.S.A.
ISBN 0–911767–96–7, 1996, Pages 345–363

THE UNIVERSAL POINCARE´–SANTILLI ISOSYMMETRY FOR MATTER AND ITS ROLE IN THE UNIFICATION OF GRAVITY AND RELATIVISTIC QUANTUM MECHANICS

J. V. Kadeisvili*
Istituto per la Ricerca di Base
Castello Principe Pignatelli
I–86075 Monteroduni (IS), Italy

Abstract

In a number of contributions, Santilli has constructed the isotopies of the Poincare´ symmetry, today called *Poincare´ –Santilli isosymmetry,* and shown that it constitutes the universal symmetry for all possible (3+1)-dimensional, exterior and interior gravitational metrics, even though being locally isomorphic to the conventional Poincare´ symmetry. In additional contributions, Santilli has identified a novel quantization of gravity, called *quantum-iso-gravity,* which is based on the embedding of gravity in the basic unit of conventional relativistic quantum mechanics, without any need of a Hamiltonian. As such, Santilli's isoquantization is naturally applicable to Einstein's gravitation and permits a particular form of unification of the special and general relativities. In this note we review in a self-sufficient way the essential aspects of these results and show that all of them are a consequence of the universal Poincare´–Santilli isosymmetry.

*) Permanent address: Institute for Basic Research, Box 1577, Palm Harbor, FL 34682, USA, fax +1-813-934 9275, E-mail: ibrrms@pinet.aip.org

The fundamental symmetry of relativistic, classical and quantum mechanics, the *Poincaré symmetry* P(3.1), is well known to describe only systems which are linear, local-differential and potential-Hamiltonian, thus exhibiting manifest limitations, such as a transparent inapplicability to gravitational theories owing to their nonlinear character.

In a series of papers [1–6] and monographs [7–9] Santilli has reached a structural generalization of the Poincaré symmetry which is today called the *Poincaré–Santilli isosymmetry* (see the independent monographs [9–13] and the recent review by this author [14]), and and it is denoted with the symbol $\hat{P}(3.1)$.

The most salient characteristics are: the isosymmetry $\hat{P}(3.1)$ describes well behaved, but otherwise most general possible systems which are linear and nonlinear, local-differential and nonlocal-integral, as well as Hamiltonian and nonhamiltonian; the isosymmetry $\hat{P}(3.1)$ is locally isomorphic to the conventional symmetry, $\hat{P}(3.1) \approx P(3.1)$; and the conventional symmetry P(3.1) is admitted as a simple particular case, thus showing that $\hat{P}(3.1)$ is the *isotopic covering* of the Poincaré symmetry [1–9].

In view of the capability to characterize nonlinear systems, the isosymmetry $\hat{P}(3.1)$ is naturally applicable to gravitation [2,4–6], where it resulted to be *directly universal,* that is, providing the invariance of all infinitely possible, well behaved, (3+1)–dimensional gravitational metrics g(x) (universality), directly in the x-frame of the observer (direct universality).

The operator formulation of the isosymmetry $\hat{P}(3.1)$ and its local isomorphism to the conventional symmetry, $\hat{P}(3.1) \approx P(3.1)$, then imply the additional rather remarkable possibility to unify gravitation and relativistic quantum mechanics [loc. cit.].

In this note we shall review the essential elements of these results in a self-sufficient way and show that they are all derivable from the structural axioms of the covering Poincaré–Santilli isosymmetry which therefore acquires a fundamental role in physics much bigger than that of the conventional symmetry.

To render this note self-sufficient, we recall the main lines of the central methods used by Santilli for the construction of the isosymmetry $\hat{P}(3.1)$, the so-called *isotopies* [7b], which are maps capable of turning any linear, local and Hamiltonian systems into their most general possible nonlinear, nonlocal and nonhamiltonian form, yet capable of reconstructing linearity, locality and canonicity in certain generalized spaces, over suitably generalized fields.

Santilli's fundamental isotopy is the lifting of the conventional (3+1)-dimensional unit matrix $I = \text{diag.} (1, 1, 1, 1)$ of the Minkowskian and Riemannian spaces into a well behaved, nowhere singular, Hermitean and positive-definite 4×4-dimensional matrix $\hat{I} > 0$, while jointly lifting the conventional associative product among generators A×B = AB of an enveloping algebra ξ into the form $A\hat{\times}B$ = A$\hat{T}$B, where $\hat{T}$ is fixed for all elements of ξ. Under the condition $\hat{1} = \hat{T}^{-1}$, $\hat{1}$ results to be the correct (left and right) generalized unit of the new theory, $\hat{1}\hat{\times}A$ = A$\hat{\times}\hat{1} \equiv A$, $\forall\ A \in \xi$, in which case $\hat{1}$ is called the *isounit*, $\hat{T}$ is called the *isotopic element*, and $A\hat{\times}\hat{B}$ is called the *isoassociative product*. The above lifting of ξ, denoted $\hat{\xi}$, is called *isotopic* in the sense that it preserves all original axioms, including associativity, although referred to the new product, $A\hat{\times}(B\hat{\times})C = (A\hat{\times}b)\hat{\times}C$.

Isotopic liftings are mathematically nontrivial because they require the isotopies of the *entire* structure of the original theory into a simple yet unique and unambiguous form admitting of $\hat{1}$ as the new unit. This includes suitable isotopies of: the number theory; functional analysis; differential calculus; vector, metric and Hilbert spaces; Lie algebras, groups and symmetries; Minkowskian, symplectic and Riemannian geometries; etc. [1–9].

The isotopies are also physically non–trivial because, except for the condition of positive-definiteness, $\hat{1}$ possesses an *unrestricted* functional dependence on all needed local quantities, such as space-time coordinates x, wavefunctions ψ and their derivatives, $\hat{1} = \hat{1}(x, \dot{x}, \ddot{x}, \psi, \partial\psi, \partial\partial\psi, ...)$. Such a dependence implies the mapping of linear, local and (first-order) Lagrangian theories into nonlinear, nonlocal and non –first-order)–Lagrangian forms which are however such to reconstruct the linear, local and Lagrangian characters in isospace over isofields (see below).

The most direct way suggested by Santilli to construct the isotopic image of relativistic quantum mechanics (RQM), called *relativistic hadronic mechanics* (RHM) [9] is by submitting RQM to a *nonunitary* transformation on a conventional Hilbert space $\mathcal{3C}$ over a conventional field C of complex numbers. The deviation of the transform from I is assumed to be precisely equal to the isounit of the mapped theory, $U\times U^{\dagger} = \hat{1} = \hat{1}^{\dagger} \neq I$. For the case of the canonical commutation rules we have

$$U\,U^{\dagger} = \hat{1} = \hat{1}^{\dagger} \neq I, \quad \hat{T} = (U\times U^{\dagger})^{-1} = \hat{1}^{-1} = \hat{T}^{\dagger}, \quad \bar{x}_{\mu} = Ux_{\mu}U^{\dagger}, \quad \bar{p}_{\nu} = Up_{\nu}U^{\dagger},$$

$$U\,[\,x_{\mu}, p_{\nu}\,]\,U^{\dagger} = U\,x_{\mu}\,p_{\nu}\,U^{\dagger} - U\,p_{\nu}\,x_{\mu}\,U^{\dagger} =$$

$$= \bar{x}_{\mu}\,\hat{T}\,\bar{p}_{\nu} - \bar{p}_{\nu}\,\hat{T}\,\bar{x}_{\mu} = i\,\eta_{\mu\nu}\,U\,I\,U^{\dagger} = i\,\eta_{\mu\nu}\hat{1}, \tag{1}$$

where one should note that the isounit and the isotopic element have the correct Hermiticity property, and the emerging new commutation rules have exactly the isotopic character of RHM.

However, it is easy to see that the above isotopic theory *is not* form–invariant under an additional nonunitary transform. Moreover, such a theory does not preserve Hermiticity–observability at all times. In fact, the enveloping algebra ξ with unit I, elements A, B, ... and product A×B = AB is mapped under nonunitary transforms into the enveloping isoassociative operator algebra $\hat{\xi}$ with isounit $\hat{1} = U \times U^\dagger$, elements $\bar{A}$, $\bar{B}$, ... and isotopic product $\bar{A} \hat{\times} \bar{B} = \bar{A} \hat{T} \bar{B}$. Starting from the original condition of Hermiticity on $\mathfrak{IC}$, $(< | H^\dagger) | > = < | (H | >)$, $H^\dagger = H$, that under nonunitary transforms *still defined on the original Hilbert space* $\mathfrak{IC}$ becomes

$$(< | T \hat{H}^\dagger) | > = < | (H T | >), \quad \hat{H}^\dagger = \hat{T}^{-1} \hat{H} \hat{T} \neq H^\dagger, \quad T = (U U^\dagger)^{-1}, \quad (2)$$

which, as such, is generally violated because in general H and $\hat{T}$ do not commute.

Santilli resolved the latter problem by constructing the isotopies of the entire structure of RQM. A fundamental point is therefore the occurrence whereby the definition of RHM via the use in part of isotopic structures and in part of conventional structures, is afflicted by rather fundamental inconsistencies which often remain undetected by non–expert in the field, such as: loss of invariance, Hermiticity, etc. In order to be properly defined, RHM must be characterized by the isotopies of the *totality* of the structures of RQM, such as:

A) the lifting of the field F(a,+,×) of real numbers R or complex numbers C with conventional sum a+b and product a×b = ab into the *isofields* $\hat{F}(\hat{a},+,*)$ with *isonumbers* $\hat{a} = a \times \hat{1}$, sum $\hat{a} + \hat{b} = (a+b) \times \hat{1}$, product $\hat{a} * \hat{b} = \hat{a} \times \hat{T} \times \hat{b} = (a \times b) \times \hat{1} = (ab) \hat{1}$, and all generalized operations, including isosquare root $\hat{n}^{\hat{2}} = n^{\hat{2}} \hat{1}^{\hat{2}}$; $\hat{n}/\hat{m} = (\hat{n}/\hat{m}) \hat{1}$, etc. (see [9a] for brevity);

B) the lifting of the conventional Minkowski space M(x,η,R) in the chart x = $\{x^\mu\} = (r, x^4)$, r = (x, y, z), $x^4 = c_0 t$, where c_0 is the speed of light in vacuum, η = diag. (1, 1, 1, −1), with invariant $x^2 = x^t \eta x$ on R(n,+,×) into the *Santilli's isominkowskian space* [1] $\hat{M}(\hat{x},\hat{\eta},\hat{R})$ with coordinates $\hat{x}^\mu = x^\mu$, $\hat{x}_\mu = \hat{\eta}_{\mu\nu} \hat{x}^\nu \neq x_\mu$, *isometric* $\hat{\eta} = \hat{T}(x, \dot{x}, \ddot{x}, \psi, \partial \psi, \partial \partial \psi, ...) \eta$, isotopic element $\hat{T}$, and *isoseparation* on $\hat{R}(\hat{n},+,\hat{x})$ among two points x, y (see ref.[15] for topological aspects)

$$\hat{x}^2 = [(x^1 - y^1) T_{11}(x, ...)(x^1 - y^1) + (x^2 - y^2) T_{22}(x,...)(x^2 - y^2) +$$

$$+ (x^3 - y^3) T_{33}(x,...)(x^3 - y^3) - (x^4 - y^4) T_{44}(x,...)(x^4 - y^4)] \hat{1}, \quad (3)$$

where one should note the necessity of multiplying the isoseparation by $\hat{1}$ in order for the result to be an *isoscalar*, that is, an element of the isofield $\hat{R}$;

C) the lifting of the original Hilbert space $\mathfrak{IC}$ with states $| \psi >$, $| \phi >$, ... and inner product $< \phi | \psi > \in C(c,+,\times)$ into the *isohilbert space* $\hat{\mathfrak{IC}}$ with *isostates* $| \hat{\psi} >$, $| \hat{\phi} >$, ..., *isoinner product*

$$< \hat{\phi} \hat{|} \hat{\psi} > = <\hat{\phi} | \hat{T} | \hat{\psi}>\hat{1} \in \hat{C}(\hat{c},+,\hat{\times}); \qquad (4)$$

D) the lifting of eigenvalue equations $H| \psi > = E_0| \psi >$ into the isotopic form

$$\hat{H}\hat{\times}| \hat{\psi} > = \hat{H}\hat{T}| \hat{\psi} > = \hat{E}\hat{\times}| \hat{\psi} > = \hat{E}\hat{1}\hat{T}| \hat{\psi} > \equiv E| \hat{\psi} >, E \neq E_o , \qquad (5)$$

indicating that the final numbers of the theory are conventional;
   E) the *isodifferential calculus* on $\hat{M}(\hat{x},\hat{\eta},\hat{R})$ which is characterized by the following *isodifferentials, isoderivatives* and related properties

$$\hat{d}\hat{x}^\mu = \hat{1}^\mu_{\ \nu}dx^\nu , \quad \hat{\partial}_\mu = \hat{\partial}/\hat{\partial}x^\mu = \hat{T}_\mu^{\ \nu}\partial_\nu = \hat{T}_\mu^{\ \nu}\partial/\partial x^\nu , \qquad (6)$$

$$\hat{\partial}\hat{x}^\mu/\hat{\partial}\hat{x}^\nu = \delta^\mu_{\ \nu}, \hat{\partial}\hat{x}_\mu/\hat{\partial}\hat{x}^\nu = \hat{\eta}_{\mu\alpha}\hat{\partial}\hat{x}^\alpha/\hat{\partial}\hat{x}^\nu = \hat{\eta}_{\mu\nu}, \hat{\partial}\hat{x}^\mu/\hat{\partial}\hat{x}_\nu = \hat{\eta}^{\mu\alpha}\hat{\partial}\hat{x}_\alpha/\hat{\partial}\hat{x}^\nu = \hat{\eta}^{\mu\nu};$$

   F) the lifting of the operator four-momentum $p_\mu| \psi > = -i \partial_\mu| \psi > (\hbar = 1)$ into the isomomentum with related *fundamental isocommutation rules*

$$p_\mu\hat{\times}| \hat{\psi} > = -i \hat{\partial}_\mu| \hat{\psi} >,$$

$$[\hat{x}_\mu, \hat{p}_\nu\hat{\times}| \hat{\psi} > = (\hat{x}_\mu\hat{T}\hat{p}_\nu - \hat{p}_\nu\hat{T}\hat{x}_\mu)\hat{T}| \hat{\psi} > = i \hat{\eta}_{\mu\nu}| \hat{\psi} >, \qquad (7)$$

   G) the lifting of expectation values $<A> = < \psi | A | \psi >/< \psi | \psi >$ into the *isoexpectation values*

$$\hat{<}A\hat{>} = < \hat{\psi} | \hat{T}A\hat{T} | \hat{\psi} >/< \hat{\psi} | \hat{T} | \hat{\psi} >; \qquad (8)$$

and the compatible liftings of the remaining aspects of RQM [9]. Since $\hat{1} = UU^\dagger$ is Hermitean we can hereon assume it to be positive definite and diagonal.
   The most important properties emerging from the above liftings are the following. First, nonunitary transforms can always be written $U = \hat{U}\hat{T}^{1/2}$, and therefore turned into the *isounitary transforms* on $\hat{\mathcal{H}}$ [9],

$$\hat{U} \hat{\times} \hat{U}^\dagger = \hat{U}^\dagger \hat{\times} \hat{U} = \hat{1}, \qquad (9)$$

under which RHM is form-invariant. In fact, the isounit of the theory is invariant,

$$\hat{1} \rightarrow \hat{1}' = \hat{U} \hat{\times} \hat{1} \hat{\times} \hat{U}^\dagger \equiv \hat{1}, \qquad i \, d\hat{1}/dt = [\hat{1}, H] = \hat{1} \hat{\times} H - H \hat{\times} \hat{1} = H - H \equiv 0; \quad (10)$$

the isoassociative product is invariant, $\hat{0}\hat{\times}(A\hat{\times}B)\hat{\times}\hat{0}^\mathsf{T} = \bar{A}\bar{\times}\bar{B}$; and equally invariant are the fundamental isocommutation rules,

$$\hat{0}\hat{\times}(\hat{\bar{x}}_\mu\hat{\times}\hat{p}_\nu - \hat{p}_\nu\hat{\times}\hat{\bar{x}}_\mu)\hat{\times}\hat{0}^\mathsf{T}\hat{\times}|\bar{\Psi}> = (\bar{x}_\mu\hat{\times}\bar{p}_\nu - \bar{p}_\nu\hat{\times}\bar{x}_\mu)\hat{\times}|\bar{\Psi}> = i\,\hat{\eta}_{\mu\nu}|\bar{\Psi}>,$$

$$|\bar{\Psi}> = \hat{0}\hat{\times}|\bar{\Psi}>, \quad \bar{x}_\mu = \hat{0}\hat{\times}\hat{\bar{x}}_\mu\hat{\times}\hat{0}^\mathsf{T}, \quad \bar{p}_\nu = \hat{0}\hat{\times}\hat{p}_\nu\hat{\times}\hat{0}^\mathsf{T}. \tag{11}$$

Also, *all operators which are initially Hermitean remain so at all times* In fact, the condition of Hermiticity on $\mathfrak{K}$ over $\hat{C}(\hat{c},+,*)$ now reads

$$(< \hat{\Psi}|\uparrow\,\hat{H}^\dagger)|\hat{\Psi}> = < \hat{\Psi}|(\hat{H}\uparrow|\hat{\Psi}>), \qquad \hat{H}^{\hat{\dagger}} \equiv \hat{T}^{-1}\hat{T}\hat{H}^\dagger\hat{T}^{-1}\hat{T} \equiv \hat{H}^\dagger = \hat{H}, \tag{12}$$

and, as such, it *coincides* with the Hermiticity on $\mathfrak{K}$ over $C(c,+,\times)$. All observables of RQM therefore remain observables for RHM.

RHM preserves the linearity, locality and canonicity of RQM in isospaces over isofields. In fact, for evident consistency needs, transformations on $\hat{M}(\hat{x},\hat{\eta},\hat{R})$ must have the isotopic structure $\hat{x}' = \hat{A}\hat{\times}\hat{x}$, from which we have the *isolinearity property* [9]

$$\hat{A}\hat{\times}(\hat{a}\hat{\times}\hat{x} + \hat{b}\hat{\times}\hat{y}) = \hat{a}\hat{\times}\hat{A}\hat{\times}\hat{x} + \hat{b}\hat{\times}\hat{A}\hat{\times}\hat{y}, \quad A \in \hat{\xi}, \quad \hat{a}, \hat{b} \in \hat{R}(\hat{n},+,\hat{\times}), \quad \hat{x}, \hat{y} \in \hat{M}(\hat{x},\hat{\eta},\hat{R}). \tag{13}$$

Also, all theories nonlinear in the wavefunction can be *identically* reformulated in a isolinear form in which all nonlinear terms are embedded in the isotopic element, e.g.,

$$H(x,p,\psi,...)|\psi> \equiv H_0(x, p)\hat{T}(\psi, ...)|\psi> = H_0\hat{\times}|y>. \tag{14}$$

This mathematically elementary reformulations has far reaching physical implications. In fact, the well known problematic aspect of conventionally nonlinear theories is that of *violating the superposition principle.* Even though mathematically impeccable, conventional nonlinear theories therefore have severe limitations in their applicability to actual, nonlinear systems, particularly composite systems. All these problematic aspects are resolved by RHM, trivially, because the superposition principle is fully recovered in isospace thanks to the embedding of the nonlinear terms in the basic invariant of the theory.

Similarly, RHM is *isolocal* in the sense of being everywhere local except at the origin (see [15] for for the emerging new integro–differential topology). Finally, the theory is *isocanonical* in the sense that it is representable via conventional first–order actions, Lagrangians or Hamiltonians although computed in isospace.

Even though evidently not unique, RHM is *directly universal* in the sense of admitting all infinitely possible, well behaved, nonlinear, integro–differential signature–preserving deformations of the Minkowski metric $\hat{\eta} = \hat{T}\eta$ (universality) directly in the frame of the observer (direct universality).

The Poincaré–Santilli isosymmetry is the *universal symmetry of RHM*. The isosymmetry can be easily constructed via the *Lie–Santilli isotheory* [10–14] and consists in the reconstruction of P(3.1) for the generalized unit $\hat{1} = \hat{T}^{-1}$. Since $\hat{1} > 0$, one can see from the inception that $\hat{P}(3.1) \approx P(3.1)$. Under the lifting $P(3.1) \rightarrow \hat{P}(3.1)$ the original generators $X = \{X_k\} = \{M_{\mu\nu}, p_\alpha\}$, $M_{\mu\nu} = x_\mu p_\nu - x_\nu p_\mu$ $k = 1, 2, ..., 10$, $\mu, \nu = 1, 2, 3, 4$, remain unchanged and only require their formulation in isospace, $\hat{X} = \{ \hat{M}_{\mu\nu} = \hat{x}_\mu \hat{p}_\nu - \hat{x}_\nu \hat{p}_\mu, \hat{p}_\alpha \}$ while the original parameters $w = \{w_k\} = \{(\theta,v),a\} \in R$ are lifted into the isoform $\hat{w} = w\hat{1} \in \hat{R}(\hat{n},+,\hat{x})$.

The connected component $\hat{P}_0(3.1) = \hat{SO}(3.1)\hat{x}\hat{T}(3.1)$, where $\hat{SO}(3.1)$ is the connected *Lorentz–Santilli isogroup* first introduced in [1] and $\hat{T}(3.1)$ is the group of *isotranslations* [2], is characterized by the isotransforms on $\hat{M}(\hat{x},\hat{\eta},\hat{R})$,

$$\hat{x}' = \hat{A}(\hat{w})\hat{x}\hat{x} = \hat{A}(\hat{w})\hat{T}\hat{x} = \tilde{A}(w)\hat{x}, \quad \hat{A} = \tilde{A} \times \hat{1}, \tag{15}$$

where the the first form is the mathematically correct one, the last form is used for computational simplicity, the form can be expressed via the *isoexponentiation* in $\hat{\xi}$

$$\hat{A}(\hat{w}) = \hat{e}^{Xw} = \hat{1} + (Xw)/1! + (Xw)\times\cdot(Aw)/2! + ... \tag{16}$$

or via the conventional exponentiation for computational simplicity

$$\hat{A}(\hat{w}) = \hat{e}^{Xw} = \{e^{XTw}\}\hat{1} = \tilde{A}(w)\hat{1} \tag{17}$$

and it is characterized by the *isotopic Poincaré–Birkhoff–Witt Theorem* [7b,9,13,14].

The (connected component of the) *Poincaré–Santilli isogroup* can therefore be written as (or defined by)

$$\hat{P}_0(3.1): \hat{A}(\hat{w}) = \prod_k \hat{e}^{i\,\hat{X}\,\hat{x}\,\hat{w}} = (\prod_k e^{i\,\hat{X}\,\hat{T}\,w})\hat{1} = \tilde{A}(w)\hat{1}, \tag{18}$$

The preservation of the original dimension is ensured by the *isotopic Baker–Campbell–Hausdorff Theorem* [loc. cit.]. It is easy to see that structure (18) forms a connected *Lie–Santilli transformation isogroup* with *isogroup laws*

$$\hat{A}(\hat{w})\hat{x}\hat{A}(\hat{w}') = \hat{A}(\hat{w}')\hat{x}\hat{A}(\hat{w}) = \hat{A}(\hat{w}+\hat{w}'), \hat{A}(\hat{w})\hat{x}\hat{A}(-\hat{w}) = \hat{A}(0) = \hat{1}(x) = [\hat{T}]^{-1}. \tag{19}$$

Note that the use of the original Poincaré transform $x' = A(w)x$ would now violate linearity in isospace, besides not yielding the desired symmetry of invariant (3).

The isotopy of the discrete transforms is elementary [1], and reducible to the forms [1]

$$\hat{\pi}\hat{x}x = \pi x = (-r, x^4), \quad \hat{\tau}\hat{x}x = \tau x = (r, -x^4), \tag{20}$$

where $\hat{\pi} = \pi\hat{1}$, $\hat{\tau} = \tau\hat{1}$, and π, τ are the conventional inversion operators.

To identify the isoalgebra $\hat{p}_o(3.1)$ of $P_o(3.1)$, we use *Santilli's isodifferential calculus* on $\hat{M}$ outlined earlier which yields the *isocommutation rules* [1,3]

$$[\hat{M}_{\mu\nu}\,\hat{,}\,\hat{M}_{\alpha\beta}] = i(\hat{\eta}_{\nu\alpha}\hat{M}_{\mu\beta} - \hat{\eta}_{\mu\alpha}\hat{M}_{\nu\beta} - \hat{\eta}_{\nu\beta}\hat{M}_{\mu\alpha} + \hat{\eta}_{\mu\beta}\hat{M}_{\alpha\nu}),$$

$$[\hat{M}_{\mu\nu}\,\hat{,}\,\hat{P}_\alpha] = i(\hat{\eta}_{\mu\alpha}\hat{P}_\nu - \hat{\eta}_{\nu\alpha}\hat{P}_\mu), \qquad [\hat{P}_\alpha\,\hat{,}\,\hat{P}_\beta] = 0, \tag{21}$$

where $[A\,\hat{,}\,B] = A\hat{T}(x, \psi, ..)B - B\hat{T}(x, \psi, ..)A$ is the *Lie–Santilli product* which does indeed satisfy the Lie axioms in isospace, as one can verify.

The *isocasimir invariants* are then lifted into the forms [1,3]

$$C^{(0)} = \hat{1} = [\hat{T}(x)]^{-1}, \quad C^{(1)} = \hat{p}^2 = \hat{p}_\mu \hat{x} \hat{p}^\mu = \hat{\eta}^{\mu\nu}\hat{p}_\mu \hat{x} \hat{p}_\nu,$$

$$C^{(3)} = \hat{W}_\mu * \hat{W}^\mu, \qquad \hat{W}_\mu = \epsilon_{\mu\alpha\beta\rho}\hat{M}^{\alpha\beta} \hat{x} \hat{p}^\rho. \tag{22}$$

The local isomorphism $\hat{p}_o(3.1) \sim p_o(3.1)$ is ensured by the positive-definiteness of $\hat{T}$. Alternatively, the use of the generators in the form $M^\mu{}_\nu = x^\mu p_\nu - x^\nu p_\mu$ would yield the *conventional* structure constants under a *generalized* Lie product, as one can verify. The above local isomorphism is sufficient, per sé, to guarantee the axiomatic consistency of RHM.

The space components $S\hat{O}(3)$, called *isorotations* [2], can be computed from isoexponentiations (18) and the space components $\hat{T}_{kk}$ of the isotopic element yielding the explicit form in the $(\hat{x}, \hat{y})$–plane

$$\hat{x}' = \hat{x}\cos(\hat{T}_{11}{}^{\frac{1}{2}}\hat{T}_{22}{}^{\frac{1}{2}}\theta_3) - \hat{y}\hat{T}_{11}{}^{-\frac{1}{2}}\hat{T}_{22}{}^{\frac{1}{2}}\sin(\hat{T}_{11}{}^{\frac{1}{2}}\hat{T}_{22}{}^{\frac{1}{2}}\theta_3),$$

$$\hat{y}' = \hat{x}\hat{T}_{11}{}^{\frac{1}{2}}\hat{T}_{22}{}^{-\frac{1}{2}}\sin(\hat{T}_{11}{}^{\frac{1}{2}}\hat{T}_{22}{}^{\frac{1}{2}}\theta_3) + \hat{y}\cos(\hat{T}_{11}{}^{\frac{1}{2}}\hat{T}_{22}{}^{\frac{1}{2}}\theta_3), \tag{23}$$

(see [9b] for general isorotations in all three Euler angles). As one can easily verify, isotransforms (23) leave invariant all infinitely possible ellipsoidical deformations of the sphere $xx + yy + zz = r$ in the Euclidean space $E(r,\delta,R)$, $r = \{x, y, z\}$, $\delta = \text{diag.}$ $(1, 1, 1)$,

$$x\hat{T}_{11}x + y\hat{T}_{22}y + z\hat{T}_{33}z = r , \tag{24}$$

Such ellipsoids become perfect spheres $\hat{r}^2 = (\hat{r}^t \hat{\delta} \hat{r})\hat{1}$, in *Santilli's isoeuclidean spaces* [1]

$$\hat{E}(\hat{r},\hat{\delta},\hat{R}), \hat{r} = \{\hat{r}^k\} = \{r^k\}, \hat{\delta} = \hat{T}_s\hat{\delta}, \hat{T}_s = \text{diag.}\ (\hat{T}_{11}, \hat{T}_{22}, \hat{T}_{33}), \hat{1}_s = \hat{T}_s^{-1}, \tag{25}$$

called *isospheres* [9]. In fact, the deformation of the semiaxes $l_k \to \hat{T}_{kk}$ while the related units are deformed of the *inverse* amounts $l_k \to \hat{T}_{kk}^{-1}$, preserves the perfect sphericity This isosphericity is the geometric origin of the isomorphism $\hat{O}(3) \approx O(3)$, as well as of the preservation of the *rotational* invariance for spheroidal *ellipsoids*.

The connected Lorentz–Santilli isosymmetry $S\hat{O}(3.1)$ is characterized by the isorotations and the *Lorentz–Santilli isoboosts* [1] which can be written explicitly in the (3, 4)–plane

$$\hat{x}^{3\prime} = \hat{x}^3 \sinh (\hat{T}_{33}^{\frac{1}{2}} \hat{T}_{44}^{\frac{1}{2}} v) - \hat{x}^4 \hat{T}_{33}^{-\frac{1}{2}} \hat{T}_{44}^{\frac{1}{2}} \cosh (\hat{T}_{33}^{\frac{1}{2}} \hat{T}_{44}^{\frac{1}{2}} v) =$$

$$= \hat{\gamma}(\hat{x}^3 - \hat{T}_{33}^{-\frac{1}{2}} \hat{T}_{44}^{\frac{1}{2}} \beta \hat{x}^4) ,$$

$$\hat{x}^{4\prime} = -\hat{x}^3 \hat{T}_{33}^{\frac{1}{2}} c_0^{-1} \hat{T}_{44}^{-\frac{1}{2}} \sinh (\hat{T}_{33}^{\frac{1}{2}} \hat{T}_{44}^{\frac{1}{2}} v) + \hat{x}^4 \cosh (\hat{T}_{33}^{\frac{1}{2}} \hat{T}_{44}^{\frac{1}{2}} v) =$$

$$= \hat{\gamma}(\hat{x}^4 - \hat{T}_{33}^{\frac{1}{2}} \hat{T}_{44}^{-\frac{1}{2}} \beta \hat{x}^3) ,$$

$$\beta = v_k \hat{T}_{kk}^{\frac{1}{2}} / c_0 \hat{T}_{44}^{\frac{1}{2}} , \qquad \hat{\gamma} = (1 - \beta^2)^{-1/2}. \tag{26}$$

Note that the above isotransforms are *nonlinear in x*, precisely as expected, and are formally similar to the Lorentz transforms, as also expected from their isotopic character. This proves in a transparent way the local isomorphism $S\hat{O}(3.1) \approx SO(3.1)$.

The Lorentz–Santilli isotransforms characterize the so-called *isolight cone* [3,7], i.e., the perfect cone in isospace $\hat{M}(\hat{x},\hat{\eta},\hat{R})$. In a way similar to the isosphere, we have the deformation of the light cone axes $l_\mu \to \hat{T}_{\mu\mu}$ while the corresponding units are deformed of the *inverse* amount $l_\mu \to \hat{T}_{\mu\mu}^{-1}$, thus preserving the original perfect cone character. Such a preservation is then the geometric foundation of the local isomorphism $S\hat{O}(3.1) \approx SO(3.1)$. The isotopy of the light cone is such that even the characteristic angle of the cone remains the conventional one, i.e., *the maximal causal speed in isospace $\hat{M}(\hat{x},\hat{\eta},\hat{R})$ remains the* *speed of light* c_o *in vacuum* [3,9] (it should be noted that the proof of this property requires, for consistency, the use of the isotrigonometric and isohyperbolic functions we cannot review here for brevity).

The *isotranslations* can be written

$$\hat{x}' = (\hat{e}^{i\hat{p}a}) \hat{\times} \hat{x} = \hat{x} + aA(x, ...), \qquad \hat{p}' = (\hat{e}^{i\hat{p}a}) \hat{\times} \hat{p} = \hat{p},$$

$$A_\mu = \hat{T}_{\mu\mu}^{1/2} + a^\alpha [\hat{T}_{\mu\mu}^{1/2}, \hat{p}_\alpha]/1! + ... \tag{27}$$

The above results imply the following:

Theorem 1 (Santilli's Fundamental Theorem on Isosymmetries [1,2,7]): *The Poincaré–Santilli isosymmetry is the universal invariance of all infinitely possible, well behaved, nonlinear, nonlocal and nonlagrangian/nonhamiltonian isoseparations on the isominkowski space.*

The verification of the above theorem is trivial and can be done by just plotting the isotransforms in isoinvariant (3). Note that *there is nothing to compute,* because Santilli has already provided the solution for the general invariance of the isoseparation for all infinitely possible isometrics in the diagonal form $\hat{\eta} = \hat{T}\eta = $ diag. $(T_{\mu\mu} \eta_{\mu\mu})$. One *merely plots* the isotopic elements $T_{\mu\mu}$ in the isotransforms. The invariance of the isoseparation is then guaranteed by the isotopic methods.

Some of the most salient properties are that RHM and RQM coincide at the abstract level by conception and construction; RHM can approximate RQM as close as desired for $\hat{1} \approx I$); and RQM is contained in RHM as a simple particular case. Thus, RHM is a *covering* of RQM. The preservation of the fundamental symmetry, the Poincaré symmetry, at the abstract level then establish the axiomatic consistency of RHM beyond any possible scientific doubt.

Santilli's constructed the above isotopies to reach an axiomatically correct representation of the so-called *interior dynamical problems,* such as extended-nonspherical–deformable particles and/or electromagnetic waves propagating within physical media, which are representable via a nonlinear, integro-differential dependence of the isounit on coordinates, velocities, etc.

As an example, the assumption for isounit of the quantity $\hat{1} = $ diag. $(\hat{1}_{\mu\mu}) = $ Diag. $(n_1^{-2}, n_2^{-2}, n_3^{-2}, n_4^{-2}) \times F(x, \dot{x}, ...)$, when applied to the isoschrödinger's equation (5) or its classical counterpart [7b]), permits the representation of an extended, nonspherical–ellipsoidical and deformable particle with variables semiaxes $(n_1^{-2}, n_2^{-2}, n_3^{-2})$ moving within a resistive medium with density characterized by n_4^{-2}, which particle experiences resistive, variationally nonselfadjoint, nonlagrangian–nonhamiltonian forces represented by $F(x, \dot{x}, ...)$. It is evident that none of these remarkable representational capabilities can be claimed for the conventional RQM in any credible way.

Similarly, it is known that the central pillar of Einstein's special relativity, the "universal constancy of the speed of light c_0" is a *philosophical* abstraction because in the physical reality the speed of light is a locally varying quantity $c = c_0/n_4$, where n_4 is the local index of refraction with its known functional dependence on the density μ, the temperature τ, the frequency ω, etc., $c = c(x, \mu, \tau, \omega, ...)$. It is also transparent that Einstein's special relativity, while exact for the propagation of electromagnetic waves in vacuum, cannot possible represent in a scientifically credible way the physical reality of locally varying speeds of light (truly incredible inconsistencies emerge for the special relativity if one believes in the contrary, see [7b] for brevity).

Via his isotopies of classical [8] and quantum [9] relativistic formulations, Santilli has achieved a step–by–step isotopic lifting of the special relativity for interior problems today known as *Santilli's classical and operator isospecial relativity* [10–14]. The new relativity permits a direct representation of locally varying speeds of light, that is a representation via the isominkowskian metric itself $\hat{\eta} = \hat{T}\eta = \text{Diag.} (n_1^{-2}, n_2^{-2}, n_3^{-2}, -n_4^{-2})$ where n_4 now assumes precisely the role of index of refraction, and the space counterparts n_k emerge via simple space–time symmetrization. The use of such an isounit in isoseparation (3) then yields the actual speed of light within physical media, $c = c_0/n_4$, as one can see.

The latter isotopies have emerged as having rather precise physical applications, of course, not under Einsteinian conditions, but rather under Santilli's interior conditions, or nonlinear, nonlocal and nonpotential conditions at large. For instance, calculations on gravitational horizons are today done via the use of the light cone, as well known. But the space outside such horizon is far from being empty and the speed of light there is far from being the constant c_0, thus illustrating the mere *approximate* character of current studies on gravitational collapse.

The reconstruction of the exact light cone in isospace for locally varying speeds of light permits more realistic calculations outside gravitational horizon in which the implications of the physical medium is duly taken into account. For these and several other applications of Santilli's isospecial relativity in nuclear physics, particle physics, astrophysics, cosmology, superconductivity, quantum chemistry and other fields, we refer the interested reader to monographs [7]. This completes our very brief review of RHM.

At the *Seventh Marcel Grossmann Meeting on General Relativity* held at Stanford University in July 1994, Santilli ([4], see also the subsequent papers [6,7]) proposed a novel form of quantum gravity, which he called *quantum–iso-*

gravity (QIG), and it is based on the isotopic unification of gravity and RQM, thus naturally resulting in a particular case of RHM. In this note we point out that quantum isogravity can be introduce as the following

Proposition 1 [3,4,9]: *Santilli's quantum–iso–gravity for (well behaved but) arbitrary, (3+1)–dimensional Riemannian metrics g(x) is a particular case of Theorem 1 under the isotopic factorization of the Riemannian into the Minkowskian metric*

$$g(x) = \hat{T}_{gr}(x)\,\eta, \quad \eta = \text{diag.}\,(1, 1, 1, -1), \tag{28}$$

where the "gravitational isotopic element" $\hat{T}_{gr}$ is a 4×4-matrix, and the assumption for isounit of the "gravitational isounit"

$$\hat{1} \equiv \hat{1}_{gr} = [\hat{T}_{gr}(x)]^{-1}. \tag{29}$$

The main idea is the embedding of the component of the Riemannian metric which truly represents gravitation, the gravitational isotopic element $\hat{T}_{gr}$, in the *unit* of RQM. In fact, Santilli [4-6] states that "a consistent operator form of gravity always existed. It did creep in un–noticed because embedded in the unit of the conventional relativistic quantum mechanics."

Alternatively, we have the following:

Proposition 2 [loc. cit.]: *Whenever the isounit assumes the particular value of gravitational isounit (29), relativistic hadronic mechanics constitutes an operator description of gravity .*

This essentially implies that the basic unit of quantum mechanics, Planck's constant is lifted into the gravitational isounit

$$\hbar = 1 \quad \rightarrow \quad \hat{1}_{gr}(x), \tag{30}$$

which preserves all axiomatic properties of $\hbar = 1$, and becomes the fundamental invariant of the theory,

$$\hat{1}_{gr}^{\hat{n}} = \hat{1}_{gr} \hat{\times} \hat{1}_{gr} \hat{\times} ... \hat{\times} \hat{1}_{gr} \equiv \hat{1}_{gr}, \quad \hat{1}_{gr}^{\frac{1}{2}} \equiv \hat{1}_{gr}, \quad \hat{1}_{gr} / \hat{1}_{gr} \equiv \hat{1}_{gr},$$

$$\hat{0} \hat{\times} \hat{1}_{gr} \hat{\times} \hat{0}^{\dagger} \equiv \hat{1}_{gr}, \quad i\,d\hat{1}_{gr}/dt = [\hat{1}_{gr}\,\hat{,}\hat{H}] = H - H \equiv 0. \tag{31}$$

However, the isoexpectation values of the gravitational isounit reproduce Planck's constant $\hbar = 1$ identically,

$$\hat{\Sigma}1_{gr}\hat{\Sigma} = <|\hat{T}_{gr}\hat{T}_{gr}^{-1}\hat{T}_{gr}|>/<|\hat{T}_{gr}|> \equiv \hbar = 1. \qquad (32)$$

This identifies the "hidden" character of gravitation in conventional RQM. In fact, Santilli [9] has presented his QIG as a form of "completion" of RQM much along the celebrated Einstein–Podolsky–Rosen argument. Equivalently, QIG is a special, explicit and concrete realization of the otherwise philosophical "theory of hidden variables" via the isoeigenvalue equation (5). In actuality, Santilli has reached an explicit and concrete realization of a theory of "hidden operators" represented by the isotopic element $\hat{T}$, with "hidden variables" emerging as a simple particular case. Note that von Neumann's theory and Bell's inequality *do not* apply to Santilli's QIG, trivially, because it is a *nonunitary* image of RQM, as indicated earlier (see [7b] for details).

Once the gravitational isounit $\hat{1}_{gr} = \hat{T}_{gr}^{-1}$ is assumed as the fundamental unit of the theory, the *entire* formulation of RHM must be referred to such a unit. This means that the basic numbers of the theory are given by the isonumbers $\hat{n} = n \times \hat{1}_{gr} \in \hat{R}$; all possible associative products AB are lifted to the isotopic form $A\hat{\times}B = A\hat{T}_{gr}B$; the basic isohilbert space is expressed with respect to the *gravitational isoinner product* and related normalization,

$$<\hat{\psi}\hat{|}\ \hat{\phi}> = <\hat{\psi}|\hat{T}_{gr}|\hat{\phi}>\hat{1}_{gr} \in \hat{R}, \quad <\hat{\psi}|\hat{T}_{gr}|\hat{\psi}> = 1; \qquad (33)$$

and the entire Lie–Santilli isotheory is formulated with respect to $\hat{1}_{gr}$.

Note that the Lagrangian or Hamiltonian operators in QIG represent *conventional* interactions, such as weak or electromagnetic interactions, because the gravitational interaction is represented with the basic isounit of the theory. This novel conception of quantum gravity stems from the fact that *the Hamiltonian of Einstein gravitation in vacuum is identically null,* as it is well know. Thus, for evident reasons of consistency, *gravity should be quantized with anything except the Hamiltonian.* Among other conceivable cases, Santilli selects the *unit* for the representation of curvature because of evident geometric advances as well as its primitive character.

Note that the above derivation implies that, by conception, Santilli's QIG is as axiomatically consistent as the ordinary RQM. In fact, any criticism on the axiomatic structure of QIG is a criticism on the axiomatic structure of RQM.

This is not a mere mathematical property because it established, e.g., that Santilli's QIG is one of the few quantum theories of gravity in which *the basic unit of the theory is invariant (thus permitting actual measures), Hermiticity is preserved in time (thus permitting a consistent representation of observables), etc.*

As an illustration of QIG, Santilli has introduced in ref.s [4–6] the following *gravitational isodirac equation*

$$(\hat{\gamma}^\mu \hat{x} \, p_\mu + i \, \hat{m}) \hat{x} | > = [\, \hat{\eta}_{\mu\nu}(x) \, \hat{\gamma}^\mu(x) \, \hat{T}_{gr}(x) \, p^\nu - i \, m \, \hat{1}_{gr}(x)] \, \hat{T}_{gr}(x) \, | > = 0 ,$$

$$\{ \hat{\gamma}^\mu \hat{,} \hat{\gamma}^\nu \} = \hat{\gamma}^\mu \, \hat{T}_{gr} \, \hat{\gamma}^\nu + \hat{\gamma}^\nu \, \hat{T}_{gr} \, \hat{\gamma}^\mu = 2 \, \hat{\eta}^{\mu\nu} \equiv 2 \, g^{\mu\nu},$$

$$\hat{\gamma}^\mu = \hat{T}_{\mu\mu}^{1/2} \, \gamma^\mu \, \hat{1}_{gr} \text{ (no sum)} , \tag{34}$$

where γ^μ are the conventional gammas and $\hat{\gamma}^\mu$ are the *Dirac–Santilli isogamma matrices.* The important point is that at the abstract level the conventional and isogravitational Dirac equations coincide from the topological equivalence of I and $\hat{1}_{gr}$, $(\gamma^\mu p_\mu + im) | > \approx (\hat{\gamma}^\mu \hat{x} p_\mu + i\hat{m}) \hat{x} | >$, $\mathcal{H}$ and $\hat{\mathcal{H}}$, etc. The isolagrangian character is easily illustrated by the derivability of Eq.s (34) from the conventional Lagrangian of Dirac's equation, only written in isospace.

Note that *the anti-isocommutators of the isogamma matrices (34c) yield (twice) the Riemannian metric g(x)*, thus confirming the representation of gravitation in the structure of Dirac's equation. As an example, the *Dirac–Santilli–Schwarzschild equation* is given by Eq.s (34) with

$$\hat{\gamma}_k = (1-2M/r)^{-1/2} \gamma_k \hat{1}_{gr} , \qquad \hat{\gamma}_4 = (1 - 2M/r)^{1/2} \gamma_4 \hat{1}_{gr}. \tag{35}$$

Similarly one can construct the *Dirac–Krasner–Santilli equation* or similar generalization of for the Klein–Gordon, Weyl and any other relativistic field equation [1a].

Next, Santilli's [4–6] notes that the gravitational isotopic element in the Minkowskian factorization $g(x) = \hat{T}_{gr}(x)\eta$ is necessarily positive-definite (because of the locally Minkowskian character of Riemann). We therefore have the following:

Proposition 3 [loc. cit.]: *The universal Poincaré–Santilli isosymmetry of gravitation in (3+1)–dimension is locally isomorphic to the conventional Poincaré symmetry.*

Note the remarkable appearance of the *Riemannian* metric $g_{\mu\nu}(x)$ as the "*structure functions*" $\hat{\eta}_{\mu\nu}$ of the fundamental isoalgebra, a property first identified in [1].

The above property has far reaching implications because it eliminates the historical difference between the special and general relativities whereby the former admits the universal Poincaré symmetry, while the latter does not. Gravitation emerges from QIG as possessing a universal symmetry which turns out to be locally isomorphic to the conventional Poincaré symmetry. The gravitational field on $\hat{M}(x,\hat{\eta},\hat{R})$ must now be isocovariant under $\hat{P}(3.1)$ in essentially the same way as the electromagnetic field on $M(x,\eta,R)$ is covariant under $P(3.1)$ [9b]. We here point out that Santilli's isotopic quantization of gravity is due precisely to the achievement of a universal symmetry for gravitation.

The establishment of a universal symmetry for gravitation is not purely formal, because it carries for gravitation the same implications traditionally exhibited by the Poincaré symmetry for RQM. As one simple, yet remarkable illustration, one should consider the problem of the total conservation laws in general theory of relativity which, besides being truly complex in formulation, is still basically unresolved at this writing (because of apparent lack of compatibility with the relativistic conservation laws).

Both these problems are resolved by the universal Poincaré–Santilli isosymmetry *via a mere inspection* and without any need to do any calculation. In fact, the generators of the isosymmetry are the *conventional* total conserved quantities and their conservation is known to be ensured by the symmetry itself. The compatibility with the special relativity is equally evident and merely occurs for the particular case $\hat{1}_{gr} = I = \text{diag}.. (1, 1, 1, 1)$.

But the implications of Proposition 3 are much deeper than the above. Some of them can be expressed via the following

Proposition 4 [loc. cit.]: *Santilli's quantum–iso–gravity implies the prior structurally novel identification of the special and general relativity at both the classical and quantum levels.*

The foundations of QIG were given by Santilli at the *classical* level (see monographs [6] of 1991 and the original papers quoted therein) and consists of his *isominkowskian reformulation of Riemannian spaces.* Let $\mathcal{R}(x,g,R)$ be a conventional Riemannian space in $(3+1)$–dimension over the reals R. It is well known that $\mathcal{R}$ is *locally Minkowskian,* or, equivalently, we can say that *the conventional Minkowski space* $M(x,\eta,R)$ *is the tangent space to* $\mathcal{R}(x,g,R)$ *at x.* The spaces $\mathcal{R}$ and M however remain non–equivalent, evidently because the former is curved and the latter is flat.

Santilli [1–9] first studied the isotopies of the special relativity for interior dynamical problems with locally varying speed of light, this is *Santilli's isospecial relativity* mentioned earlier, and then introduced a new reformulation of Riemannian spaces $\mathcal{R}(x,g,R)$ in terms of the isominkowski space $M(\hat{x},\hat{\eta},\hat{R})$ under the condition that the isominkowski metric $\hat{\eta}(x, \dot{x}, \ddot{x}, ...)$ coincides with the

Riemannian metric g(x). This yields the isoequivalence

$$\mathfrak{R}(x,g,R) \sim \hat{M}(\hat{x},\hat{\eta},\hat{R}), \quad \hat{x} \equiv x, \quad \hat{\eta} \equiv g(x). \tag{36}$$

The above reformulation with underlying universal symmetry $\hat{P}(3.1)$ evidently establishes that *Santilli's isospecial relativity provides a classical unification of the special and general relativities.* In fact, the latter is formulated for unrestricted isounits $\hat{1}$. As such, it contains the special relativity as a simple particular case for $\hat{1}$ = diag. (1, 1, 1, 1) and the general relativity for $\hat{1} = \hat{1}_{gr}$.

The ultimate foundations of the isotopic unification of the special and general relativities are evidently given by the central notion of all these studies, the universal Poincaré–Santilli isosymmetry. In fact, the unification would not be possible without the reduction of both the special and the general relativity to a single and unique primitive symmetry.

But there is still more. As a necessary condition for isotopy, the lifting $M(x,\eta,R) \rightarrow \hat{M}(\hat{x},\hat{\eta},\hat{R})$ must preserve the original axioms of flatness, although in isospace, a property called by Santilli *isoflatness* [8,9]. In the projection of the isospace $\hat{M}(\hat{x},\hat{\eta},\hat{R})$ in the original space $M(x,\eta,R)$ the full curved character of the space emerges because the isometric $\hat{\eta} = g(x)$ remains unchanged.

This implies that *Santilli's isominkowskian space includes in a symbiotic way both the flat Minkowski space and the curved Riemannian space.* Alternatively, this symbiotic representation is an evident pre-requisite for the unification of the special and general relativities because curvature simply cannot be made to "disappear".

And in fact, the entire machinery of the Riemannian spaces, Christoffel's symbols, curvature tensors, etc., can be applied identically to the isominkowskian space, and only referred to a different unit. We therefore have the following:

Proposition 5 [loc. cit]: *The Riemannian formulation of gravity persists in its entirety in Santilli's quantum-iso-gravity, and, instead of being formulated on a Riemannian space it is formulated in the equivalent isominkowskian space, and instead of being referred to the conventional unit* I = diag. (1, 1, 1, 1) , *it is referred to the gravitational isounit* $\hat{1}_{gr} = \hat{T}_{gr}^{-1}$.

Stated in a nutshell, Santilli managed to unify a flat theory, the special relativity, with a curved theory, the general relativity, because of the isoflatness of his isominkowski space, in which, while conventional axioms of flatness are transparently preserved, the curved character is admitted too because, jointly with a non-null curvature the basic unit is deformed by the inverse amount, thus yielding geometric flatness much similar to the preservation of the perfect sphere in isospace.

The confirmation of the *isoflat* character of QIG is exhibited by the fact that its linear momentum operator *isocommute,* as shown in Eq.s (21b), while conventional curved representations notoriously call for noncommuting linear momenta.

Note the *necessity* of the representation of gravity in *isominkowski* space for the very formulation of its universal isopoincaré symmetry and the consequential achievement of QIG. In fact, no isosymmetry can be constructed in the Riemannian space [7].

We finally note that Santilli proposed his isotopies as particular cases of his more general *Lie–admissible genotopies* for *open–irreversible* conditions [8,9]. In paper [5,6] Santilli also proposed the *Lie–admissible quantum gravity,* or *quantum genogravity* (QGG), which can be constructed from the formalism of this note by merely relaxing the condition that the isotopic element $\hat{T}$ is symmetric, while preserving its nowhere–degeneracy and real–valuedness.

This more general formulation permits a rather natural geometrization of Eddington's "arrow of time" via the use of *genometrics* $\hat{\eta}^> = \hat{T}^>\eta$ for motion forward in time and $^<\eta = \eta^{<}\hat{T}$, for motion backward in time, with related *genounits* $1^> = (\hat{T}^>)^{-1}$ $^<1 = (^<\hat{T})^{-1}$ and inter-relation $(1^>)^t = {^<1}$. It should be noted that QGG is more appropriate than QIG for the geometrization of interior *irreversible* black hole models (see, e.g., [16]) because it is structurally irreversible, i.e., it is irreversible irrespective of whether the Lagrangian is reversible or not.

One should also keep in mind that the applications studied in this note are only *part* of the possibilities of the universal Poincaré–Santilli isosymmetry, because the latter applies for isounits with unrestricted functional dependence, $\hat{1} = \hat{1}(x, \dot{x}, \ddot{x}, \psi, \partial\psi, \partial\partial\psi, \mu, \tau, \omega, ...)$, thus providing the invariance of all possible well behaved systems which have linear and nonlinear, local and nonlocal, Lagrangian and nonlagrangian, classical and quantum, relativistic and gravitational and exterior or interior character.

In summary, the historical open problem in the quantization of Einstein's gravitation is the need, on one side, for RQM to have a meaningful Hamiltonian while, on the other side, Einstein's gravitation in vacuum has a null Hamiltonian. This problem is solved by Santilli by embedding gravity in the unit of RQM and using conventional Hamiltonians for conventional interactions in addition to gravity when present (otherwise H merely represents the kinetic energy).

A second open problem is the achievement of a quantum gravity which is axiomatically consistent as the conventional RQM, i.e., invariant under its own time evolution with physical quantities which are Hermitean–observable at all times, etc. Santilli has achieved this second objective via the systematic application of his isotopies to RQM and then the specialization of the basic unit to the gravitational isounit.

A third open problem of gravity is its need to represent the irreversibility of the interior physical reality, such as that of black holes dynamics [16]. Santilli's achieves this additional objective by showing that RHM is a *nonunitary* image of RQM, as evidently *necessary* for novelty.

A comparison between Santilli's QIG and other models of QG (see, e.g., various papers of these proceedings) is finally in order. The topics reviewed in this note establish that Santilli's QIG, even though possessing an intrinsically *nonunitary* structure, is nevertheless axiomatically correct, that is, the prediction of the theory can be subjected to actual measures because the basic unit is invariant, the theory does indeed admit consistent observables due to the preservation of Hermiticity in time, etc.

By comparison, and this must be stressed because grossly ignored in the literature in the field, *all models of quantum gravity with nonunitary time evolutions, even though mathematically impeccable, cannot be consistently applied to actual physical systems.* In fact, it is easy to see that their basic unit $\hbar = 1$ is not invariant under nonunitary transforms, $UU^\dagger = I$, $U\hbar U^\dagger \neq \hbar$. As a result, no actual measurement is applicable to this class of QG models. Also, the notion of unitarity is not preserved in time, as shown earlier, and such models of QG do not admit any physically meaningful observables. At a deeper analysis, It is easy to see that the data elaboration (e.g. via PP–approximations) of a theory of QG with nonunitary time evolution, even though mathematically correct, have no physical meaning of any nature because their basic unit at a given time $\hbar = 1$ becomes an operator $\hbar' = UU^\dagger$ at later times, thus implying drastically different forms of special functions and transforms [9].

All the above physical problematic aspects of conventional theories of QG occur because they are formulated in a *conventional* Hilbert space over *conventional* fields and, to our best knowledge, all of them are resolved by the use of Santilli's isotopies.

Needless to say, we can only claim at this writing the basic novelty and axiomatic consistency of Santilli's QIG, with the understanding that the theory is at its beginning and so many problems are yet to be addressed.

The entire content of this note is restricted to Santilli's isotopic representation of *matter*. The representation of *antimatter* requires an antiautomorphip map called *isoduality* which implies an appropriate reformulation of the entire content of this note and it is presented in a separate volume of Proceedings of the 1995 Monteroduni meetiings.

Acknowledgments

This author would like to thank Prof. Santilli for suggesting this paper and for making available his computer files. Sincere thanks are due to Dr. G. F. Weiss for editorial control and Mrs. Pamela Fleming for secretarial help.

References

1. R. M. Santilli, Lett. Nuovo Cimento 37, 545 (1983)
2. R. M. Santilli, Hadronic J. 8, 25 and 36 (1984)
3. R. M. Santilli, J. Moscow Phys. Soc. 3, 255 (1993)
4. R. M. Santilli in Proceedings of the Seventh M. Grossmann Meeting on Gravitation, M. Keiser and R. Jantzen, Editors, World Scientific (1996)
5. R. M. Santilli in *Gravitation, Particles and Space-Time*, (Ivanenko Memorial Volume), P. I. Pronin and J. V. Sardanashvily, Editors, World Scientific, (1996)
6. R. M. Santilli, Comm. Theor. Phys. 4, 67 (1996)
7. R. M. Santilli, *Elements of Hadronic Mechanics*, Vol. I (1978) [7a] and II (1983) [7b], Springer-Verlag
8. R. M. Santilli, *Isotopic generalization of galilei and Einstein's Relativities*, Vol.s I [8a] and II [8b], Hadronic Press (1991)
9. R. M. Santilli, *Elements of Hadronic Mechanics*, Vol. I [9a] and II [9b], Second Edition, Ukraine Academy of Sciences (1995)
10. A. K. Aringazin, A. Jannussis, D. F. Lopez, M. Nishioka and B. Veljanoski, *Santilli's Lie-Isotopic Generalization of Galilei's and Einstein's Relativities* (1990), Kostarakis Publisher, Athens, Greece.
11. J. V. Kadeisvili, *Santilli's Isotopies of Contemporary Algebras, Geometries and Relativities*, Hadronic Press, FL (1991), Second Edition, Ukraine Academy of Sciences, Kiev , in print
12. D. S. Sourlas and G. T. Tsagas, *Mathematical Foundations of the Lie-Santilli Theory*, Ukraine Academy of Sciences, Kiev (1993)
13. J. Lôhmus, E. Paal and L. Sorgsepp, *Nonassociative Algebras in Physics*, Hadronic Press, Palm Harbor, FL, USA (1994)
14. J. V. Kadeisvili, An introduction to the Lie-Santilli isotheory, Math. Methods in Applied Sciences, **19**, 362 (1996)
15. G. T. Tsagas and D. S. Sourlas, Algebras, Groups and Geometries **12**, 1 (1995)
16. Ellis, N. E. Mavromatos and D. V. Nanopoulos in *Proceedings of the Erice Summer School, 31st Course: From Superstrings to the Origin of Space-Time*, World Scientific (1996)